Design & technology

For the next generation

A collection of provocative pieces, written by experts in their field,
to stimulate reflection and curriculum innovation

DESIGN & TECHNOLOGY - FOR THE NEXT GENERATION.

Copyright © 2007 Cliffe & Company (Advertising & Marketing) Ltd.
First Edition November 2007.
ISBN-10: 1-901351-00-9 ISBN-13: 978-1-901351-00-2

**Designed, produced & published
by Cliffeco Communications**

cliffeco.com
cliffeco.communications

Steele Grange
Steel Heath
Whitchurch
Shropshire SY13 3LB
England

www.dandt-thebook.com

Editor: David Barlex.
Art editor: Erica Minter.
Designer: Erica Minter.
Picture research: Erica Minter, Nick Cliffe.
Director: Nick Cliffe.

Printed in England by Livesey Limited, Shrewsbury.
The woodpulp for this publication has been sourced
from sustainable forests and bleached using
an Elemental Chlorine Free (ECF) process.

With grateful thanks to all contributors and with particular gratitude to:
Erica Minter for her talent, dedication and resourcefulness;
David Barlex and Nick Baldwin;
Allen Bower, Willy Adam at The Design & Technology Association
and Donna Trebell for additional photography.
Simon Minter, Bronia Perks, Nick Cliffe and Sean Mason for illustrations.

Foreword

Richard Green

Those of us who work in education have come to accept that change is constant - and those of us who work in design & technology education know that change is more regular and rapid than in other subjects. That change is not slowing. In fact in the UK we have already embarked on a series of changes that have significant implications for the subject and the subject community - including new programmes of study, new qualifications, the STEM agenda and a school building and refurbishment programme that will affect every secondary design & technology department over the next few years.

Against this background we have to acknowledge that design & technology is still a relatively young and developing subject which does not yet possess the large hinterland of systematic research and curriculum development accumulated by other, more established subjects. However, that research and critical thinking about the subject does exist and is ongoing but there is little time, particularly on PGCE courses, for trainee teachers to be introduced to it. All teachers, whether they are trainees, new entrants or more experienced, need to be aware of the work of this research community and, more importantly, be encouraged to become part of it. The link between research and practice is critical for the development and growth of the subject and to inform the perceptions of the subject by the subject community, the wider education community as well as the world outside education.

This book is a vital contribution to this process and the Technology Enhancement Programme is to be warmly congratulated on having the vision to produce such an exciting and stimulating publication. It provides those on one year training routes, and those with little time to dedicate to research, with an accessible source of high quality and, in some cases, very provocative opinions about the subject. In doing this it will help readers to develop a subject language they might not otherwise be able to articulate. It also highlights the importance of the subject for developing those creative, problem-solving approaches which are essential components of a 21st century education, rather than the utilitarian ministerial view of a subject aimed at simply developing skills to meet the needs of design, technology, engineering and manufacturing industry. It will help to generate discussion and debate about the subject and the direction in which it is heading. As an Association we aim to facilitate, support and disseminate this process because it is through the engagement of an informed and articulate subject community that the direction and development of design & technology as an essential curriculum subject will be assured.

Richard Green
Chief Executive, Design & Technology Association, October 2007.

About the editor

David Barlex

David Barlex is the editor of "Design & technology - for the next generation".

In 2006 Nick Baldwin of the Technology Enhancement Programme approached David with the idea of a legacy work that celebrated the huge achievement of design & technology in the National Curriculum in England, but put that development in the context of the wide range of research concerning technology education that had been carried out in different parts of the world over the past 20 - 30 years. So the stage was set for writing a collection of provocative pieces that would stimulate reflection and curriculum innovation amongst those entering the profession.

David has directed the Nuffield Design & Technology Project since 1990 and has combined this activity with building a related research portfolio as part of his work at Brunel University where he is a senior lecturer in education. Through this scholarly activity, often in collaboration with others, he has published widely in international academic journals concerned with technology education and attended many conferences in different parts of the world. This has enabled him to build a wide range of contacts with colleagues who are highly regarded and have acknowledged expertise across the emerging discipline of technology education. David was able to call on these colleagues to write the chapters that form this publication.

David is an acknowledged leader in design & technology education, curriculum design and curriculum materials development. He taught science and design & technology in comprehensive schools for 15 years before becoming a teacher educator. In 2002 he won the Design & Technology Association Outstanding Contribution to Design & Technology Education award. David's research activity stems from his conviction that there should be a dynamic and synergic relationship between curriculum development and academic research and include pedagogy that develops design ability and creativity and the professional development of teachers. He currently pursues this activity through partnerships with researchers in the UK, Canada and Sweden. He is cross-appointed as an adjunct associate professor at Queen's University. He is a member of the scientific committee of the Swedish National Graduate School in Science and Technology Education Research, FontD, which advises a consortium of eight Institutes of Higher Education on doctoral studies in science and technology education. Most recently (2007) he has been appointed as the STEM (science, technology, engineering and mathematics) consultant to the Design & Technology Association.

Contents

Introduction   06
David Barlex

Justifying design & technology   08
David Barlex

Philosophical reflections on the nature of design & technology   20
Marc J. de Vries

2020 vision - on the politics of technology   34
Stephen Petrina

Designers on designing   44
Malcolm Welch

The politics of technology curriculum   60
Steve Kierl

The place of sustainability in design & technology education   74
Margarita Pavlova and James Pitt

Vocationalism - friend or foe to design & technology education   90
John Dakers

Developing your own curriculum   108
Nick Baldwin and David Barlex

The pupil as designer   120
Malcolm Welch

Creativity in design & technology   140
Marion Rutland and David Spendlove

Problem-solving in technology education:
the role of strategies, schemes & heuristics   154
Moshe Barak

The role of technical knowledge in design & technology   170
Gwyneth Owen-Jackson and Torben Steeg

The role of making in design & technology   186
Frank Banks and Gwyneth Owen-Jackson

Useful assessment for design & technology:
formative assessment, learning & teaching   198
Stephanie Atkinson and Paul Black

Mind (not) the gap...Take a risk
Interdisciplinary approaches to the science, technology,
engineering & mathematics education agenda   216
Dov Kipperman and Mark Sanders

Gender & pedagogy   236
Patricia Murphy

Implicit theories & pedagogy   252
Wendy Dow

Design & technology: seeing both the wood & the trees   266
Peter Toft

Reference

Hicks, G. (1983, Autumn). 'Another step forward for design and technology'. "Assessment of Performance Unit", 4.

Introduction

David Barlex

This book has been especially written for those at the beginning of their career as teachers of design & technology, although it is likely to be of interest and use to all those involved in teaching the subject, preparing teachers to teach, or providing professional development. George Hicks, writing in 1983, captured the challenge of teaching the subject:

'Teaching facts is one thing, teaching pupils in such a way that they can apply facts is another; but providing learning opportunities which encourage pupils to use information naturally when handling uncertainty, in a manner which results in capability, is a challenge of a different kind'. (p. 1)

One-year post-graduate certificate in education programmes and in-post graduate teaching programmes for design & technology teachers are all too short. Understandably their emphasis is on meeting the immediate and relatively short-term needs of those entering the teaching profession. A particular omission is current research findings that are relevant to classroom practice in design & technology. There is no shortage of high quality and pertinent research but this is spread throughout the academic literature and not easily accessible to busy teachers in the early stages of their career. **"Design & technology - for the next generation"** has been written to fill this gap. Each of the authors is an acknowledged international expert with many years' experience in a relevant field of study. Most of them have been schoolteachers at some stage in their careers. They were commissioned to distil their areas of expertise into readable pieces that were provocative, would stimulate reflection and lead those entering the profession to question current practice and engage in curriculum development. The result is a collection of writing that will serve as the basis for considerable professional development.

It is not a book to be read through from cover to cover in the order prescribed by the text. Rather it is a book to dip into and revisit in response to your needs as a practicing teacher in the early stages of your career.

This book has been written to help bring the teaching and educational research communities for design & technology closer together. Each chapter has a list of books and articles for further reading as well as a list of references so that you can develop your understanding of issues you find of particular interest or relevance. On each page you will find questions to stimulate thought and discussion. You may not agree with the authors but you will not be able to ignore what they have to say. Each chapter has a brief biography of the author accompanied by his or her photograph. So if by some chance you should meet them you will be able to introduce yourself, strike up a conversation and continue the debate.

All curricula are contested and as an arena in a school's curriculum so are the very nature and purpose of design & technology. As a new entrant to the profession your contribution to the discourse that informs the shape and direction of design & technology is essential to avoid ossification, sidelining and irrelevance. It is our hope that this book will empower you to make your mark in the design & technology curriculum.

Justifying design & technology

David Barlex

Dr. David Barlex is a senior lecturer in education at Brunel University in England, director of the Nuffield Design & Technology Project and cross-appointed as an adjunct assistant professor at Queen's University, Ontario, Canada. He is an acknowledged leader in design & technology education, curriculum design and curriculum materials development. David's research activity stems from his conviction that there should be a dynamic and synergistic relationship between curriculum development and academic research.

Justifying design & technology

David Barlex

Introduction

This chapter asks the question why do we teach what we teach in the design & technology curriculum? It traces the emergence of design & technology in the curriculum in England and is in three parts. First it gives a brief account of its precursor - technology education. This is followed by a description of its development within the National Curriculum. The final part discusses some of the issues associated with 'limiting' technology education to design & technology.

Technology education

Education in technology has been seen as important since the time of John Dewey who wrote in 1916:

'Its (technology education) right development will do more to make public education truly democratic than any other agency now under consideration. Its wrong treatment will as surely accentuate all undemocratic tendencies in our present situation, by fostering and strengthening class divisions in school and out… Those who believe the continued existence of what they are pleased to call the 'lower classes' or the 'laboring classes' would naturally rejoice to have schools in which these 'classes' would be segregated. And some employers of labor would doubtless rejoice to have schools, supported by public taxation, supply them with additional food for their mills…(Everyone else) should be united against every proposition, in whatever form advanced, to separate training of employees from training for citizenship, training of intelligence and character from training for narrow, industry efficiency'.

In 1987 Denis Stewart and Christine Ditchfield produced a discussion paper for the Secondary Science Curriculum Review that recommended technology ought to feature strongly in the curriculum and be interdisciplinary in nature. This had been echoed by George Hicks HMI, writing in 1983, who argued that to some extent all subjects contributed to technology education. There were some main players to be sure: craft, design & technology (CDT), art & design, home economics, but science and mathematics could clearly make useful contributions with the humanities and religious education supporting the discussion of value considerations.

The situation was, to put it mildly, confused and confusing with little if any consistency of approach across different schools. In 1985 Paul Black and Geoffrey Harrison had wrestled with this problem by writing the pamphlet **"In Place of Confusion"**. They acknowledged the interdisciplinary nature of technological activity and produced a 'Task-Action-Capability' model for technology education, as shown overleaf.

Underpinning their thinking is the idea that pupils will need to acquire intellectual and practical resources in order to tackle technological tasks and that full technological capability will be achieved through tackling a sequence of these tasks. Paul and Geoffrey were under no illusions as to the fragmented nature of the school curriculum and the difficulty faced by schools in developing a 'Task-Action-Capability' model for technology education. They saw certification on a single subject basis as a major impediment to rewarding achievement in a subject which *'should not be confined to the boundaries of single subjects as at present defined'* (p. 31).

01

02

01 The 'Task-Action-Capability' model for technology education developed by Paul Black and Geoffrey Harrison.
(© Nuffield Chelsea Curriculum Trust.)

02 David Layton, Professor Emeritus at Leeds University. The architect of design & technology in the National Curriculum through his contribution to the "Working Group Interim Report".

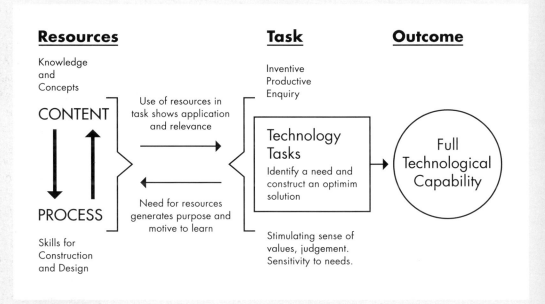

Resources

Knowledge and Concepts

CONTENT

PROCESS

Skills for Construction and Design

Use of resources in task shows application and relevance

Need for resources generates purpose and motive to learn

Task

Inventive Productive Enquiry

Technology Tasks

Identify a need and construct an optimim solution

Stimulating sense of values, judgement. Sensitivity to needs.

Outcome

Full Technological Capability

If you were at school before the introduction of the National Curriculum, cast your mind back to see if you can identify educational experiences that would lead to technological capability. If you experienced National Curriculum design & technology ask yourself to what extent was the teaching you received based on a 'Task-Action-Capability' model?

Design & technology as technology education

In developing a National Curriculum in England the government instituted a range of school subject working parties, each one to consider and identify the unique contribution of their allotted subject to the school curriculum. An intention here was to remove redundancy and overlap so that the school curriculum could be efficient. For the subject technology, which operates across boundaries, this could have been seen as life threatening. However, this did not deter those charged with the daunting task of advising ministers on the school subject which was

to become 'design & technology'. Indeed the naming of the subject was not accidental and the working group's interim report clarified and justified the term design & technology. *'Our understanding is that whereas most, but not all, design activities will generally include technology and most technology activities will include design, there is not always total correspondence. Our use of design & technology as a unitary concept, to be spoken in one breath as it were, does not therefore embody redundancy. It is intended to emphasize the intimate connection between the two activities as well as to imply a concept which is broader than either design or technology individually and the whole of which we believe is educationally important. (Accordingly, we use design & technology as a compound noun taking the singular form of verbs in what follows.)'* (Department for Education and Science and Welsh Office, 1988, p. 2).

The working party had to answer this question. What is at the heart of design & technology, namely the special characteristics which are the ultimate warrant for its inclusion as a foundation subject in the National Curriculum? What is it that pupils learn from design & technological activities which can be learnt in no other way? The answer was elegant and complex. *'In its most general form, the answer to this question is in terms of capability to operate effectively and creatively in the made world. The goal is increased competence in the indeterminate zones of practice'* (Department for Education and Science and Welsh Office, 1988, p. 3).

The report noted the distinction between 'knowing that' and 'knowing how', 'propositional knowledge' and 'action knowledge', 'homo sapiens' and 'homo faber', 'man the understander' and 'man the maker'; pointing out that it is the second of each pair that is indicative of the distinctive nature of education in design & technology. Thus the fundamental nature of design & technology can become its Achilles heel in that it ensures that it is not a subject with venerable roots in the academic tradition, which values particularly the acquisition of knowledge for its own sake. Here again the interim report was clear in its thinking about the place of knowledge in design & technological activities. *'We have argued above that because knowledge is a resource to be used, as a means to an end, it should not be the prime characteristic of attainment targets for design & technology. This is not to devalue knowledge, but rather to locate it in our scheme according to its function. What is crucial here is that knowledge is not possessed only in propositional form ('knowing that'), but that it becomes active by being integrated into the imagining, decision-making, modelling, making, evaluating and other processes which constitute design & technological activity'* (Department for Education and Science and Welsh Office, 1988, p. 29).

To what extent do you think the design & technology lessons you experienced as a pupil or have seen in school are in accord with special characteristic *'to operate effectively and creatively in the made world'*?

Issues of justification

The journey from the publication of the **"Design & Technology Working Group Interim Report"** in 1988 to the current situation has been long and difficult with at least half a dozen revisions of the Statutory Orders along the way. At the moment we have an importance of design & technology statement which reads as follows:
'In design and technology pupils combine practical and technological skills with creative thinking to design and make products and systems that meet human needs. They learn to use current technologies and consider the impact of future technological developments. They learn to think creatively and intervene to improve quality of life, solving problems as individuals and members of a team. Working in stimulating contexts that provide a range of opportunities and draw on the local ethos, community and wider world, pupils identify needs and opportunities. They respond with ideas, products and systems, challenging expectations where appropriate. They combine practical and intellectual skills with an understanding of aesthetic, technical, cultural, health, social, emotional, economic, industrial and environmental issues. As they do so, they evaluate present and past design and technology, and its uses and effects.

Through design and technology pupils develop confidence in using practical skills and become discriminating users of products. They apply their creative thinking and learn to innovate.' (Qualifications and Curriculum Authority, 2007).

The statement centres around pupils' designing and making indicating many areas of understanding that inform the activity including the evaluation of design & technology itself and the impact of its use. It concludes with identifying the role of the subject in developing personal qualities.

In 2001 Richard Kimbell and David Perry revisited and extended the 'Task-Action-Capability' pedagogy when writing **"Design & technology in the knowledge economy"**. They reiterated the distinctive model of teaching and learning that lies at the heart of design & technology:

- *'It is project based and involves learners taking a task from inception to completion within constraints of time, cost, and resources'*;
- *'Students have to unpack the complexity... to enable then to identify and focus on the central issues that need to be addressed'*;
- *'[It reveals] the value issues that inevitably lie inside any claim for "improvement"'*;
- *'[It requires students] to speculate and explore multiple "what ifs"'*;
- *'[It requires students] to acquire and create new, task-related knowledge'*;
- *'[It] involves the active, purposeful deployment of understanding and skills'*.

David and Richard argue that through this approach to teaching and learning design & technology prepares pupils to meet the skills challenge posed by a knowledge economy. *'We have been pursuing and refining these approaches for thirty years and our teachers are in the vanguard of those preparing youngsters for employment in the knowledge economy'* (Kimbell & Perry, 2001 Executive Summary, p. 4).

This clearly gives a broad vocational purpose to design & technology.

To what extent do you think the design & technology lessons you experienced as a pupil or have seen in school mirror the teaching and learning espoused by David Perry and Richard Kimbell? Are they likely to prepare pupils for employment in a knowledge economy?

With its focus on designing and making, the importance statement does echo the idea of capability presented in the interim report *'to operate effectively and creatively in the made world'*. However there are some who consider that technology education has a wider remit than engendering capability. John Dakers, writing in 2006, notes that technology education focuses primarily on

'...the fabrication of artefacts...at the expense of developing critical awareness in young people of the technologically mediated world they inhabit and the way in which their future lives are, and will be, shaped by it'

(Dakers, 2006, p. 1).

He is anxious that

'This unreflectivity...missing literacy...that reduces the concept of technology...to the stuff that we will transform into artifacts that we perceive as necessary for our needs and wants'

(Dakers 2006, p. 2).

If you agree with John that the current design & technology paradigm fails to engage young people with the effect of technology on their lives now and in the future and that this is an important omission then you will need to consider how such an omission might be rectified.

How would you change the balance of teaching and learning activities in a design & technology curriculum dominated by designing and making to ensure that pupils were able to consider the impact of technology on their lives?

David Layton has voiced concern over the way in which evaluation can be limited to considering technical performance and manufacturing proficiency. Writing in 1995 he indicates the folly of limiting evaluation to fitness *for* purpose when in fact the crucial issue is fitness *of* purpose.

'But the ultimate measures of success are essentially pragmatic: is it effective; does it work? Morality, it seemed, had been jettisoned: providing the thumbscrew, the gas chamber, or the bug worked well, we were dealing with high quality D&T.'

(Layton, 1995, p. 108)

If you are in agreement with David that limited nature of evaluation is morally flawed you will need to consider how you might adapt the curriculum to enable pupils to consider fitness of purpose in the products they meet in their everyday lives and those they design & make at school.

How might you change the way pupils are introduced to design briefs in design & technology lessons to meet David's concern over fitness of purpose?

Stephen Petrina, writing in 2000, has suggested that technological literacy should have an explicit political dimension and be critical. Stephen describes much technology education as under the influence of business and industry and hence dedicated to the western capitalist mission of competitive supremacy. He argues that releasing technology education from these malign (as he sees them) influences would empower pupils to collectively organise and agitate to say 'no' to competitive supremacy, ecological destruction, and exploitive practices of globalisation. He is arguing for technology education as a cultural study. This is a long way removed from the acts of designing and making and the general activities of design & technology teachers in workshops, design studios and food technology rooms.

If you agree with Stephen that design & technology education should become politicised and incorporate some elements of cultural study then you will need to consider how this might be achieved.

How would you change the balance of teaching and learning activities in a design & technology curriculum dominated by designing and making to provide pupils with the opportunity to be critical? In what ways could you relate this critical activity to the pupils' designing and making?

Margarita Pavlova, writing in 2005, has described how technology education might respond to issues of social change. She identifies four major processes of social change relevant to technology education.

1. *The shift of emphasis from engaging society members primarily as producers to engaging society members primarily as consumers.* Margarita quotes the arguments of Zygmunt Bauman (1998), a sociologist who believes that work as a duty has been replaced by work as a means to an end. The end in western society is increased consumer power.

2. *The colonisation of cognitive and moral spheres of human life by the aesthetic sphere.* Here Margarita again uses the work of Zygmunt Bauman who has argued that many consumers are guided now by aesthetic interests not ethical ones. This has been described by the designers Richard Seymour and Dick Powell as *'visceral appeal',* a response whereby the consumer desires a product before they know what it is or does.

3. *The integration of people into the technological world.* Here Margarita calls on the thinking of Jurgen Habermas, a philosopher who has described the erosion of the person as an individual and his or her subordination to the performance requirements of the 'technological' system.

4. *The shift from the Welfare state*
to the Competition state.
Here Margarita cites authors who
have described the way in which
educational reform movements across
the world are being colonized
by economic policy imperatives.
She quotes Robert Cowen
writing in 1996:

'*The central goal of the modern education*
system of education, socialisation into
the national culture, is replaced
by the determination to create new patterns
of labour force formation: economic dimension
of education becomes more influential than civic'
(Cowen, 1996, p. 161).

04

05

04 Dick Powell and
Richard Seymour,
co-founders of
product design
agency
Seymourpowell -
product designers
who utlise
aesthetic interests.

05 Zygmunt Bauman,
Emeritus Professor
of Sociology
Leeds University
and expert on
post modern
consumerism.

(Photograph ©
Mariusz Kubik,
Warsaw, 2005.)

Justifying design & technology David Barlex

Margarita, although less strident in tone than Stephen Petrina, is suggesting the politicising of the technology curriculum. She argues that engaging with social change and the role of technology in that change will require radical changes to classroom practice in which pupils take part:

'In democratic debates about the future outlines of technological development, development of their social and ecological sensitivities, avoiding orienting their solutions to the standard of business efficiency and profitability criteria only; helping them to distinguish real needs from desires; discussing the role of designed objects in the life of contemporary society…challenging the way people are manipulated through advertising… and challenging consumer orientated design' (Pavlova, 2005, p. 212).

If you agree with Margarita that technology education should be used to help young people to become aware of social change as it is taking place and challenge this from a critical perspective then you will need to consider how this might be achieved.

Margarita's concerns are rooted in the identity and purpose of individuals within society, and how this is changing, and how this is related to technology. How would you change the balance of teaching and learning activities in a design & technology curriculum dominated in practice by 'narrow' understanding of designing and making to provide pupils with the opportunity to consider the impact of technology on society in the context of social change? To what extent might it be possible to achieve this by orienting design activity, product analysis, and the nature of the projects towards social aspects of technology?

A word of warning

Engaging pupils in designing and making products of worth in ways that develop creativity, problem-solving skills and the ability to collaborate, as part of general education is a demanding task. Widening the remit of design & technology to meet the concerns outlined above places a heavy burden upon the subject. Add to this a vocational obligation and we approach a situation where failure through overload becomes a distinct possibility. David Layton (1995) reminds us of this danger:

'It would be sad if an exciting and radical curriculum innovation, potentially of great significance, should collapse under the weight of the unrealistic responsibilities being placed upon it' (p. 115).

However, Margarita Pavlova (2007) argues that she has evidence from her work in Brisbane which indicates that the key to meeting these demands is in the nature of the projects developed by the teacher.

To what extent do you think the design & technology curriculum is in danger of becoming overloaded with unrealistic responsibilities? How might the load be redistributed or lightened to ensure continued growth and development?

Further reading

Beilharz, P. (Ed). (2001). "The Bauman reader".
Oxford: Blackwell.

Black, P. & Harrison, G. (1985). "In Place of Confusion".
London: Nuffield Chelsea Curriculum Trust.

Layton, D. (1993). "Technology's Challenge to Science
education: Cathedral, Quarry or Company Store?".
Buckingham: Open University Press.

Pavlova, M. (2007). "Empowering Individuals for the Future:
Technology Education and TVET for Sustainable Development".
Netherlands: Springer.

Petrina, S. (2006). "Advanced teaching methods for the
technology classroom". Hershey PA: Information Science
Publishing.

References

Bauman, Z. (1998). "Work, consumerism and the new poor".
Buckingham: Open University Press.

Black, P. & Harrison, G. (1985). "In Place of Confusion".
London: Nuffield Chelsea Curriculum Trust.

Cowen, R. (1996). 'Last Past the Post: Comparative
Education, Modernity and Perhaps Post-Modernity'.
"Comparative Education". 32. (2), 151-170.

Dakers, J. R. (2006). 'Introduction'. In J. R. Dakers, (Ed.),
"Defining Technological Literacy:Towards an Epistemological
Framework". (pp. 1-13). New York: Palgrave Macmillan.

Department for Education and Science and Welsh Office
(1998). "National Curriculum Design and Technology Working
Group Interim Report". London: HMSO.

Dewey, J. (1916). "Democracy and Education".
Full text available at: http://www.ilt.columbia.edu/Publications/
dewey.html accessed on 18.08.07.

Hicks, G. (1983, Autumn). 'Another step forward for design
and technology'. "Assessment of Performance Unit", 4.

Kimbell, R. and Perry, D. (2001). "Design and technology
in a knowledge economy". London: Engineering Council.

Kimbell, R. and Perry, D. (2001). "Executive Summary
Design and technology in a knowledge economy".
London: Engineering Council.

Layton D. (1995). 'Constructing and Reconstructing School
Technology in England and Wales'. "International Journal
of Technology and Design Education". 5, 89-118.

Pavlova, M. (2005). 'Social Change: How Should Technology
Education Respond?'. "International Journal of Technology and
Design Education". 15, 199-215.

Petrina, S. (2000). 'The Politics of Technological Literacy'.
"International Journal of Technology and Design Education".
10, 181-206.

Seymour, R. & Powell, R. (2007). "Emotional ergonomics".
Full text available at: http://www.seymourpowell.com/ideas/
ergonomics.html accessed on 18.08.07.

Qualifications and Curriculum Authority (2007).
"Design and technology programme of study: ks3 The
importance of design and technology". Full text available at:
http://curriculum.qca.org.uk/subjects accessed on 17.10.07.

Stewart, D. & Ditchfield, C. (1987). "Technology and
Science in the Curriculum: some issues and ideas".
London: Secondary Science Curriculum Review.

Philosophical reflections on the nature of design & technology

Marc J. de Vries

Marc J. de Vries is assistant professor in philosophy of technology at the Eindhoven University of Technology and affiliate professor of reformational philosophy at the Delft University of Technology, both in the Netherlands. He recently published a book about philosophy of technology for technology educators ("Teaching About Technology"). Currently he serves as the editor-in-chief of the "International Journal of Technology and Design Education". He also wrote a book on the history of the Philips Research Laboratories, textbooks for technology education at secondary school level, and many articles on philosophy of technology and technology education in academic journals.

Philosophical reflections on the nature of design & technology

Marc J. de Vries

You need not be a Trekkie to know what "**Star Trek**" is. In this popular science fiction television series we see how technology enables people in the future to do all sorts of wonderful things that today we can only dream of. You can satisfy your human curiosity by examining life and cultures on different parts of the universe, travel from one place to the other in seconds by using transporter beams (*'beam me up, Scotty'*), get any kind of food you like instantaneously from the food replicator in your room, or have a great time in one of the holodecs by immersing yourself in a virtual reality that makes you think you are on a Caribbean island. The creator of the original series, Gene Roddenberry, has put all his humanistic convictions into the series to show how technology in the hands of humans will be of great benefit. He was, though, realistic enough to include the use of weapons in his creation as well. Phasers and photon torpedoes feature in almost every episode. Not only the good guys (the crew of Federation starships such as Enterprise, Voyager and Deep Space 9) have them, but the bad guys (such as the Romulans) as well. Evidently, technology can be both blessing and curse, depending on who is involved.

Do you think the question whether technology is a blessing
or a curse is only a matter of users, or do developers
of technology have a role in that too?
Or can they claim that their only concern is to 'make it work'?

In the second "**Star Trek**" series, "**The Next Generation**" (another 'Next Generation', apart from one in the title of this book), a humanoid called Data features, who is 'used' by the series makers to make us think about other aspects of technology as well. Data namely struggles with his artificiality and wants to become human and have feelings. In several episodes he seems to come quite close to it. In the "**Star Trek**" fourth series, called "**Voyager**", there is a hologram, the Doctor, who also displays the desire to be treated as a person, and not as a piece of technology. In one of the last episodes of the series he is even granted copyrights, based on the formal judgement that he ought to be regarded as an author, that is, a person.

Could technology be developed to such a sophisticated
and advanced level that artefacts ('robots') will be able
to experience 'feelings' or 'think'?
Could you give arguments for or against that,
so that your judgement goes beyond an opinion only?

01 "Star Trek" crew
with phasers.

02 'Beam me up,
Scotty'.

03 Data from "Star
Trek - The Next
Generation".

(Images 01 & 02
© MPTV/LFI.
Image 03 © GENE
TRINDL/MPTV/LFI.)

Questions like these (is technology good or bad; can technological products get human characteristics?) make us reflect on what technology is like (and also what humans are like!). Such questions can make us deal with technology in a more conscious way. Most of the time, we do not feel much need to do that; we just take technology as it is and use it when needed (and perhaps also when it is not really needed at all). But when we teach about technology, then maybe it is not appropriate to avoid such reflections. Of course it is possible to confine ourselves to teaching the 'tricks' and 'traps' only, and never let pupils think any deeper. But is that good education? Would it not be good to help pupils get a real understanding of how much an important element technology is in our culture and society? Would it not be necessary as a teacher then first to have thought about such questions yourself?

Ways of thinking about technology

Hopefully you are convinced now that it makes sense for a design & technology teacher to think about what technology is. If not, keep re-reading the introduction until you are too exhausted to defend yourself against this claim. Then continue to read here.

Now a second challenge comes up: Where do I start and how do I continue? When you have never systematically reflected on the nature of technology, it seems like an endless undertaking. Technology is so wide a phenomenon that it is difficult to see how to get grips on what it is. Why do we call some things 'technology' and others not?

Yes, why actually? Can you think of a short definition of your own, or a couple of keywords that characterise technology?

When you try to do this, you will see that it is not easy. Maybe you filled in: 'man-made stuff'. But is all 'man-made stuff' technology? How about paintings and sculptures? Would you call those 'technology'? How about using a stick you found in the wood as a cane? Is that technology, in spite of the fact that it was not man-made? Then, how about certain apes using the same stick to reach the bananas? Do they act technologically? Maybe you wrote: 'application of science'. That certainly holds for a lot of technology, like microchips and lasers, but does it hold for plastic cups and wooden spoons? Or would you say those are not technology?

Fortunately, there are people out there to help you in this troublesome task. They are called 'philosophers'. Now maybe they are not exactly the first type of people that come into your mind for asking about anything that could even remotely be of practical use.

04 | 05
06 | 07 | 08

What is technology?
04 Paintings in a gallery?
05 A stick found in the
   wood as a cane?
06 A stick used by
   an ape as a tool?
   (Photograph by Kabir
   Bakie; http://creative
   commons.org/licenses/
   by-sa/2.5/)
07 A high-tech laser?

08 The answer to the
   big question?

But perhaps you need to revise your ideas about philosophy. Philosophy is not just what you intuitively think it is: seeking the answer to the big *'question of the meaning of life, the universe and everything'*. Thanks to **"The Hitchhikers Guide to the Galaxy"** we know anyway that the answer to that question is: 42.
Still not all philosophers agree on that, but many of them have moved to other questions that may be of equal interest. Philosophers of technology, for instance, have moved on to such questions as: what do we mean by 'technology', by 'technological knowledge' or by 'technological artefacts'? In the past fifty or so years they have found out that there are four different ways of reflecting on the nature of technology. Together those four give you a pretty good impression of what characterises technology.

Those four ways are:
• technology as artefacts;
• technology as knowledge;
• technology as processes;
• technology as a property of humans.

Have you ever thought of how pupils see technology? Try this: ask them to write or give a short definition of technology or just some keywords. Then check how many keywords they use that refer to each of the four ways mentioned above. Anything remarkable?

Let us now look more closely at each of those four.

Technology as artefacts

Artefacts are what we often think of first when reflecting on technology. There are lots of them around us: computers, mobile phones, mp3-players, tables, chairs, but also cars, bikes, houses, bridges, you name it. In design & technology they also get ample attention. They are the outcome of design projects. Sometimes we teach how an existing artefact works. We do not seem to pay much attention, though, to the question of why we call them 'technical' artefacts. We deal with each of them separately, but do we ever think of what they have in common? Let us give it a try.

Write down some keywords that describe what all technical artefacts have in common.

That was by no means a simple question! Artefacts can be so different that you may have thought: do they have anything at all in common? What do a mousepad, an airplane and factory building have in common? Not much in terms of shape or constituting materials. But wait, they do have in common that they have shape and materials. And once you have realised that, you can take the next step and say that their shape and materials are not random, but chosen deliberately to make them fit for doing what they are supposed to do.

There is a somewhat different way of describing the same observation that can be helpful for teaching about artefacts. Let us take an example: a screwdriver.

 Suppose a Klingon visits you from his planet and tells you that he is trying to learn more about earth, and in doing that

09 What do we mean by technology?

...different ways of reflecting on the nature of technology. Technology as:

artefacts

knowledge

a property of humans

processes

came across the term 'screwdriver'. Could you briefly describe what a screwdriver is?

There are different ways of answering that question. Perhaps you have written something like this: it is a long, thin metal device, with a broader, round ending at one side, usually covered with a plastic piece, and the other side ends wedge-shaped. The Klingon, warrior as he is, then may think: *'that sounds like a pretty effective weapon; these Earthlings clearly are not as peaceful as they claim to be in Star Trek'*. This misunderstanding is caused by the fact that the description you gave was not complete. You have described in detail the physical and geometrical properties of the screwdriver, but not what it is for.

10 Technology as an artefact - the Humber bridge.

11 An old-fashioned design of screwdriver.

(Photograph © www.oldtools.co.uk)

12 Is this what a Klingon might imagine a screwdriver is used for?

(Photograph © www.deadbodyguy.com)

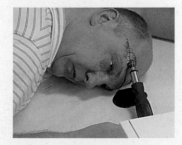

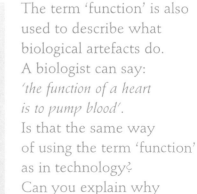

PHYSICAL NATURE

FUNCTIONAL NATURE

13 An artefact can be described in terms of its physical AND functional nature.

14 Proper function.

15 Accidental function.

Alternatively, you may have written that the screwdriver is a device which you can use to insert screws into pieces of wood and also to extract them from the wood if necessary. If you were able to look into the Klingon's thoughts, you may see a weird-looking device, made of a material you have never seen before (probably available on the Klingon's planet only) with a beak-type of ending that probably can turn. Again you have caused a misunderstanding, now emerging from the fact that you have only described what the screwdriver is for. Apparently a full description of what a screwdriver is requires two stories: one about the physical properties of the device, and one about what you can do with it. In other words: the screwdriver can be described in terms of:
• its physical nature; and
• its functional nature.
And so can every other artefact. The physical nature comprises not only physical (hardness, weight, colour etc.), but also chemical (does it rust? does it smell?) and geometrical (size, shape) properties of the artefact.

Let us focus a bit on the functional nature now. The Klingon's idea that a screwdriver is a weapon is not only understandable, but in a way is also true. There is scarcely any doubt that in the past someone has been murdered by someone using a screwdriver. We, humans, have shown great creativity in using all sorts of devices as weapons. Of course that was not what the screwdriver was intended for.

Intended, though, by whom? Well, by the designer of the screwdriver. That designer purposefully selected the physical properties of the screwdriver in such a way that they would make the device suitable in the first place for driving screws. But once in the hands of users, the same physical properties of the screwdriver may appear to make it suitable for other purposes as well. The sharp ending of the screwdriver makes it fit for stabbing in people's chests or stomachs. More moderately, the length of the screwdriver also allows it to be used as a device to open the lid of a tin can.

So while reflecting on the functional nature of artefacts, we found that there are two types of functions:
• proper functions: that is, what the designer had in mind;
• accidental functions: all the other functions that users ascribe to the artefact.

The term 'function' is also used to describe what biological artefacts do. A biologist can say: *'the function of a heart is to pump blood'.* Is that the same way of using the term 'function' as in technology? Can you explain why

16 Catweazle's
'electrickery'.
(Photograph © ITV/
Rex Features).

17 Wash symbols
indicate how a
garment should
be treated.

18 A door handle
to be pushed.
(Photograph ©
NABCO Entrances Inc.).

19 A door handle
to be pulled.

or why not?
How about, for example,
a designer describing
a function?
Might he need to consider
the difference between
proper and accidental
function?

The designer's challenge is to come up
with a physical nature for a new artefact
that fits the desired functional nature.
The user observes the physical nature
of the given artefact and comes up with
a functional nature that is enabled by that
physical nature. In a way, the user also designs
something. We can call that a 'use plan'.
The use plan for a screwdriver is:
take the screwdriver in your hand by gripping
the broad end, then stick the other end
in the ridge of the screw's head, and then
turn the screwdriver, meanwhile turning your
hand clockwise or anticlockwise, depending
on whether you screw in or out.

Sometimes that use plan is difficult to imagine.
The fun of watching **"Catweazle"** on television
is that with his Middle-Age knowledge
he constantly makes mistakes in estimating
how 20th Century devices with *'electrickery'*
like the *'speaking bone'*, should be operated.
Thus it gives us a good laugh when we see
his great disappointment when pulling the
handle of the toilet flush does not switch

on the light in the bathroom. His use plans
are based on wrong assumptions about
the relationship between the physical
nature of the devices he encounters
and their functional nature.

A good designer will also reflect on the
use plan. It would be good to design
the device in such a way that it contains
messages about its use plan. Some door knobs,
for example, seem to shout at you: *'pull me!'*,
while others are clearly meant to be pushed.
Those are examples of how physical
properties are used to suggest what the proper
function is, and with what use plan to realise
it. The designer may also want to reflect
on possible accidental function. An important
reason for that is that not all accidental
functions match with what the physical
nature allows for. Dangerous situations may
occur when users start using the device in
ways that are not allowed for by the physical
properties, or when the device is used under
circumstances that deviate too much from
the ones under which the device ought
to be used (too high temperatures,
for example, or in water instead of air).

Designers may want to prevent those
accidental functions, either by making further
decisions about the physical nature to
disable those functions, or by including
warnings in the manual.

Philosophical reflections on the nature of design & technology Marc J. de Vries

20 Galileo.
21 A 'good' drill?

Technology as knowledge

Now let us move on to the second way of reflecting on technology. Technology is not only artefacts, but it also entails knowledge. It is something you can study. It is something you can be an expert in. Now what is characteristic of knowledge in technology, as compared to other fields in which you can become an expert?

Can you first think of some characteristics yourself? Could you, for example, think of some differences between knowledge in science and knowledge in technology?

Perhaps you wrote that science deals with natural objects and technology deals with technical artefacts. But probably you soon realised that scientists may also study technical artefacts. In order to study falling objects, Galileo used heavy and light artificial balls and not natural objects. Yet he did acquire scientific and not technological knowledge with his experiments. What, then, is a real difference between scientific and technological knowledge? Perhaps the following question can trigger us. Before reading on, try to give your own answer.

Why can an engineer use the term 'good' in knowledge claims, while a scientist can not? For instance, why do we consider it a completely normal knowledge claim when an engineer states that based on expertise she 'knows' that *'this is a good type of drilling machine'* while we consider it absurd when a scientist based on his expertise claims to *'know'* that *'this is a good electron'*?

You might object that a scientist does sometimes use the term 'good' in knowledge claims. For instance, he might state things like: *'I know that this is a good bubble chamber'*. But is that really evidence of scientific knowledge? Is not it a judgment about whether or not the engineers who developed the device have done a good job?

The use of the term 'good' is related to 'fitness for purpose'. And purpose has to do with how we would like things to be rather than how they actually are. Scientists are not interested in how things should be; they focus on how things actually are. They study the behaviour of electrons, falling balls, or drilling machines, but they do not make normative judgements

about those. That is what engineers do. The engineer may say that the electron is 'good' for carrying around energy for use in lightbulbs and other devices with *'electrickery'*.

There is a second feature of engineering knowledge that seems to be different from scientific knowledge. That feature is related again to the fact that engineers deal with how things ought to be rather than how they are. What 'ought to be' is something that is not a matter of discovery, but of agreement. When the engineers as a profession decide that devices based on *'electrickery'* must fulfil certain safety requirements, that is mostly decided after a lot of experimentation, but it is not really something that is a necessary conclusion of the experiment. Experiments show when a dangerous situation occurs; that still leaves it as a matter of choice to decide what safety margin to prescribe in order to avoid such situations. Such decisions require collective acceptance of what then becomes an element in the engineers' knowledge baggage.

So we have seen two characteristics of technological knowledge:
• normativity; and
• collective acceptance.

But is scientific knowledge not also a matter of collective acceptance? In a way it is, but in a different way than for engineers. It is not entirely up to scientists to decide what the laws of nature are. Things are the way they are, and scientists can only agree on whether or not they have followed the correct path to find out how things are. Engineers deal with how things ought to be, and that is really up to them to decide. You may also object that not everything in technology is a matter of decision. Catweazle found that out when he pulled the toilet's handle to switch on the light. Once an artefact exists it is fixed what happens when you exert a certain act on it. That is not a matter of collective agreement. Catweazle can find that out by himself. So at least part of what engineers know is non normative and non-collective.

One more characteristic of technological knowledge wants our attention. You can find that when you try the following.

Write down in a sequence of sentences how to make a text on a computer and store it on a USB-stick. Give it to a young child who never did that before. Do you think that could work? Now write in a sequence of sentences how to ride a bike and give it to a young child who never rode a bike before. Do you think that will work? What then is the difference?

In both cases you have written down what you yourself know to transfer your knowledge to someone else. In one case this works, even though it may require quite a few sentences, but in the other case evidently there is more in your knowledge than you had written down in sentences. In both cases the knowledge concerned the use of a technical artefact. In one case the knowledge could effectively be expressed in sentences, while in the other case it could not. Philosophers use the term 'proposition' to indicate the content of a sentence. In their terms you could say that in technology you can distinguish between:

• knowledge than can be expressed in sentences: propositional knowledge, or knowing-that; and
• knowledge that can not be expressed in sentences, or knowing-how.

Note that both can refer to skills (in one case using a computer and in the other case riding a bike). Apart from that you can also have propositional knowledge in technology about facts (for instance about material properties).

Technology as processes

The third way of reflecting on technology is by seeing it as a way of acting. Technology is about doing things. It is in particular about designing, making and using things. Those three types of processes form the basis of technological innovations. In design & technology traditionally there is a specific

interest in design (which is already expressed in the name of the subject, which in other countries is often called just 'technology'). This interest can be justified by pointing out that the design process is really where the new ideas are born, and that is what triggers all technological innovations. Besides that, the design process is also where you can fully exploit your creativity, and that makes it very appealing as an educational activity.

Write down in what sequence of steps you think a design process normally runs, or even nicer, make it a flowchart that you can use in class.

Well done. Now, throw away the flowchart immediately, because this is not how things work in reality. Irrespective of what sequence you wrote down, it is wrong. There is no such thing as a 'normal design process'. There are at least three wrong assumptions floating around in design & technology classroom practice about design processes: **1.** all design processes are essentially the same; **2.** they are linear; and **3.** they all have problem analysis first and only later concrete ideas for solutions come. Deliberately these three have not been printed as bullets, because there is already so much misunderstanding about this, that readers could easily think they should learn them by heart as proper descriptions of design processes.

24 Designers
working.
(Photograph ©
Gokhan Okur)

Systematic reflection on real design processes has indicated that we need to think about design processes as much more complicated than as the execution of a pre-fixed sequence of actions. In the field of design methodology people have discovered the following about how real designers go about designing (note: bullets now!):

• designers throughout the design process keep learning about both the problem itself and about its possible solutions;

• designers constantly jump from one level in the design to another (from the overall systems level to lower levels of sub-systems and vice versa);

• designers use different strategies for designing different artefacts, and different designers have different design styles.

But, you might object, these are experienced designers. They have learnt to be flexible without making all sorts of mistakes. That does not necessarily hold for novice designers, such as pupils. Okay, granted you are right in that; get back your flowchart from the bin.

How can you adapt your flowchart or description of a sequence of actions, so that it does justice to the findings of design methodology?

In other words, how can you give guidance to novice designers without forcing them into a framework that they need the rest of their lives to be liberated from?

Technology as a property of humans

Finally we have technology as a property of humans to reflect on. Here we can treat this briefly as there is much readable material readily available elsewhere. This is really the 'big question' type of domain you had in mind originally when thinking about 'philosophy'. In the introduction some issues about that have already been raised. Perhaps what is most important to emphasise is that this is where values come in.

Some people say: no explicit values in education! That leads to indoctrination. What do you think about that? Can you imagine proper ways of dealing with values in (design & technology) education?

25 26

25 Immanuel Kant.
26 Waste plastic.
(Photograph ©
Centriforce Products Ltd.)

In technology there are two areas in which values play a vital role: ethics and aesthetics. Ethics deals with questions of 'right or wrong', while aesthetics deals with questions of 'beautiful or ugly'. The philosopher Immanuel Kant wrote about both areas, and his main message was that values can be debated, contrary to the popular saying that they can not because they are just a matter of taste. Of course values are not something you have to accept on the basis of proof. Yet, reasoning does play an important role in ethics and aesthetics. Reasoning can help you investigate what consequences the values you have chosen to hold should have for the way you will appreciate technology. Lots of debates about how technology should develop suffer from all sorts of mistakes in popular argumentation. Let us look at an argument in perhaps its shortest form:

1. plastic bags pollute the environment;
2. you should never pollute the environment;
3. therefore you should never use plastic bags.

Propositions 1 and 2 are called the premises in the argument, and 3 is called the conclusion. Mark that 2 is often left out: plastic bags pollute the environment, so you should never use them. That is striking, because 2 is where the value is. You can tell, because it has an 'ought' in it. It is a normative statement. That makes it different from 1 that states a factual statement. By leaving out 2 it is suggested that you can conclude a normative statement 3 from a factual statement 1. In logic, that is called a natural fallacy.

You find lots of them in newspaper writings about technology. They pollute discussions. Suppose you find it much more important that bags are produced in a cheap way, then you will not conclude 3 from 2. But the nature of your disagreement with the person holding 2 only becomes clear once the two of you have made your values explicit. Doing that can prevent useless debates. Other mistakes in argumentation can be that your factual claim 1 is wrong. In this case that is partially the case. Of course plastic bags put a burden on the environment because they stay around for a long time once thrown away. But many types of plastics can be recycled, and often in easier ways than some other materials. So 1 is true only in a narrow view.

The argument presented above is complex but important.
How might you involve your pupils in understanding the importance of such arguments and become involved in carrying them out for themselves?

In aesthetics similar arguments can be set up. Looking at the impressive height of a Gothic cathedral, you may reason as follows:

27 Interior of Exeter cathedral - Gothic architecture in the UK.

1. Beautiful buildings are those that use space to express certain values;
2. A Gothic cathedral uses height (a spatial aspect of that building) to express the value that its visitors should look upward, to heaven where God is;
3. A Gothic cathedral is a beautiful building.

Note that proposition 1 and 3 are now the normative statements, and 2 is a factual statement. Also note that 1 is stated as if it were a fact. But that is only a matter of language. Do not be misled, because it does express a value. What is beautiful and what is not, depends on your aesthetic convictions. This one is a widely shared one among architects, not only today but throughout the centuries. The fact that such values survive time indicates that not all values are bound to time. Some do seem to be shared by people in all times.

> Now think of a building that you yourself like very much, and try to set up a similar reason through which you can explain why you like it. You might also consider asking your pupils to justify their aesthetic preferences.

Further reading

For those who have now become infected by the 'philosophy of technology' virus, here are some titles that you may want to consider.

Dakers, J. R. (Ed.), (2006). "Defining Technological Literacy: Towards an Epistemological Framework". New York: Palgrave Macmillan.

Kaplan, D. M. (2004). "Readings in the Philosophy of Technology". Oxford: Rowman & Littlefield Publishers.

Mitcham, C. (1994). "Thinking Through Technology". Chicago:University of Chicago Press.

Scharff, R. C. & Dusek, V. (2003). "Philosophy of Technology: The Technological Condition. An Anthology". Malden, MA: Blackwell Publications.

de Vries, M. J. (2005).. "Teaching About Technology". Dordrecht, Netherlands: Springer.

Stephen Petrina

Dr. Stephen Petrina is a professor of technology studies in the Faculty of Education at the University of British Columbia (UBC). His research focuses on the socio-cultural constraints governing how we learn (and teach) technology across the lifespan. He is currently overseeing a large study of cognition and technology. He recently published a book entitled "Advanced Teaching Methods for the Technology Classroom", and is currently publishing books entitled "The Critical Ontology of Technology" and "Technology, Religion, Spirituality and the Sacred".

2020 Vision – on the politics of technology

2020 Vision - on the politics of technology

Stephen Petrina

A dystopian view of 2020 or realistic pessimism?

Like this perhaps…
It's nightfall in 2020 and "The Clash" drones over the central monitors…
'London calling to the faraway towns…now that war is declared and battle come down.'
Smile, you're on 2020 'Tell-Lie-Vision' and every Slim Shady, Jr. you meet looks ominously white
and passes any retinal exam that Scotland Yard and the Omni-Global Surveillance Network
(OGSN) deploy. It is 2020 and we now recognize that they were in our classes and on our
subways all along. How could we know?
'London calling to the underworld…come out of the cupboard, all you boys and girls.'
The fix we made on the future is now the fix we are in.

Will it look as envisaged by Dawid Michalczyk…? (See image 01, overleaf.)

In "**Neuromancer**" William Gibson writes *'Friday night on the Ninsei. He passed yakitori stands
and massage parlours, a franchised coffee shop called Beautiful Girl, the electronic thunder of an arcade.
He stepped out of the way to let a dark suited sarariman by, spotting the Mitsubishi-Genentech logo
tattooed across the back of the man's right hand'*
(Gibson, 1984, p. 10).

In similar vein, *'United States patent number 5,945,577 was vigorously exploited by Advanced Cell
Technologies, Genentech and Syngenta in the early 2010s and Mitsubishi's line of robots were perfectly sized
for the biotech industry. While not entirely the "commercial ownership of humans" scenario projected into the
future during the late 1990s, M-G's property rights claims on 17,000 gene sequences for their cellular
processor implants basically control the fate of this new era of cyborgs"* (Haraway, 1997).

And the results of effective ICT education…
All the pirate cloners, hackers, downloaders and freeloaders are having a field day with the
lawyers and legal counsellors. Every lawsuit, every litigation is an opportunity for the pirates
and a node on which to swarm and propagate crime. 'The Unknown Minor' - remember her
or him? - is still at large and dropped a bombshell in the copyright wars of 2017 by cracking and
releasing the code to "**The Borderliner's Cookbook**". Recall that the automated "**B's Cookbook**"
was rescinded and outlawed in 2014 when the Depression Matrix Squad busted a ring of juveniles
sabotaging master security feeds in Amsterdam, Johannesburg and Sydney.

01 "Suburbs 2100".
(© Dawid Michalczyk,
www.art.eonworks.com)

It is 2020 and the conceptual safety nets we once cherished have all but failed. Rosy as they sounded, they rang hollow...

Should students in design & technology courses be formally involved in futurism and technological forecasting activities? Why or why not? Do the risks of futurism outweigh the benefits?

The recent past may not bode well for future education...

Lifelong learning, the darling of educators for over thirty years, began her demise in October 2001, when the BBC broke the news on the Individual Learning Accounts (ILA) scam, affecting 1.2 million 'students'. Recall that the ringleader, Ferrari Nick, and dozens like him bilked the British government out of the equivalent of $169 million by cashing in on lists of bogus 'students' enrolled in dream courses: Chronic Cats 2001, Creative Writing, Learn to Draw and Paint, National Powerboat Certificate, Exercise to Music, Transcendental Meditation, Summer Glastonbury 2001 and Crystal Healing. As Secretary of State David Blunkett confessed at the time:
'As well as galling, the failure of ILAs struck a devastating blow to' the dream of lifelong learning. It lasted but a generation.

Has a grand fallacy been luring us to our doom?

All these quaint, inflated hopes were hitched onto that grand fiction of sustainable economic growth, which we now realize was bad psychology at best. The neocons, with their **"Project for the New American Century"**, deferred the depression into the future for two decades but then it hit, not suddenly but hard, in 2011. The grind of the economy to that moment was excruciating. We look back with amazement, wondering why we were so gullible and impulsive as we climbed and matched personal debt with national debt, pound for pound, yen for yen, dollar for dollar. Kondratieff (economic cycle) analysts predicted the depression but there was not much anyone wanted to do. There is no one left to blame, as most of the spin-doctors comfortably spun their way out of the mess, retiring to the gated compounds on the islands and in the southwestern United States. Rethinking a collapsed world economy is no small feat and only Africa is in a position to offer anti-capitalist options to global economics. Remarkably, although it is what Rachel Carson (writing **"Silent Spring"** in 1962) anticipated, the environment is recovering and there are reports of the Amazon choking off roads, abandoned timber trucks and backhoes, reminiscent of the jungle's stranglehold on ancient temples in Tibet. It is nevertheless very hot and biohazards threaten corporate food supplies.

PERSONAL GHG EMISSIONS FROM ENERGY USE IN CANADA

Passenger road transportation: 50%
Space heating & cooling: 29%
Water heating: 11%
Appliances: 8%
Lighting: 2%

02 Emissions in Canada.
(Developed with information provided by Environment Canada.)

03 Smog over Toronto.

04 Renewable
- energy
06 technologies.

It is 2020 and the next generation is in the driver's seat. Who are the new teachers and what do they think? What were they thinking back in 2006? And what ever happened to design & technology?

'It's not about the world of design, it's about the design of the world'.
This was the rallying call of the International Council of Societies of Industrial Design (ICSID) in 1997. What does this mean for design and technology educators and students?

On the politics of technology

Here in this moment, someone's 2020 vision is taking us somewhere into the not too distant future. Thatcher's *'Free Enterprise'* and Blair's *'New Labour'* visions directed Britain in two directions toward the future, although many argue that the destinations were the same. Currently, the **"Project for the New American Century"** is failing in the world, but neocon futurists never seem to be short on vision. The politics of technology have never been more important, and it does not matter how you define politics - political party vision, policy, parliamentary procedure, realpolitik, activism, anarchism, libertarianism, authoritarian might, oligopolitical rule, agendas, power, stakes, values, or interests. Take your choice, whatever your definition of technology will be crucial.

With 2010 visions, British and Canadian governments signed the **"Kyoto Accord"**, the international treaty that somewhat binds countries to reduce the amount of greenhouse gases they emit if their neighbours do likewise. Yet CO_2 emissions in both countries have increased since the late 1990s and both governments have failed to stand behind their legislation and policies for reducing greenhouse gases to 2010 targets.
The **"Renewables Obligation"** is aimed at increasing Great Britain's renewable energy production to 10% of the total by 2010. Canada's **"One Tonne Challenge"** called on Canadians to cut greenhouse gas emissions by a tonne per year by taking public transit more often, composting food waste, and adopting energy-saving devices such as programmable thermostats.

The **"Renewables Obligation"** is now the Labour party's agenda for nuclear power, and the **"One Tonne Challenge"** was revoked in April 2006 by the Conservative party.
The United States government did not sign the **"Kyoto Accord"** and its newfound interests in nuclear power are a factor of backlash from dependencies on the Middle East's oil. Global warming policies are great examples of the politics of technology, where politics are understood to be governmental and legislative.

Convenience in design comes at a high price. 'Massive Change' is a movement dedicated to helping us rethink convenience and consumerism.
What is the duty of the designer in today's world? What is the future of the designer? Of design?

Yet, politics extend far into the informalities of education, technology and everyday life. And obviously, no-accounts like Ferrari Nick have their own form of politics that exceed or counter more institutionalized forms of parliamentary politics. Similarly, customers, users and students generate forms of politics to finesse both governmental policies and the Ferrari Nicks of the world. Indeed, for our purposes here, politics are best understood as 'interests', whether the venue is education or technology. Interests in this case refer to connections or commitments to particular causes and outcomes, and the influence necessary to pursue and shape these causes and outcomes. Hence, interests cannot be reduced to 'special interests'. More and more, in the design and use of technology, various interests are colliding. Think of some of our more familiar technology cases where commercial or private, governmental

and public interests collide - greenhouse gas regulation, open source, P2P file sharing, surveillance and security and mobile computing are just a few.

Or think of some common controversial issues in design and technology: acid rain, alternative medicine, artificial life, industrial cancer and risk, CFCs and the ozone, crime and DNA identity checks, deforestation and jobs, disease and treatment, GMOs, habitat preservation, microchip implants, organic farming, privacy and the internet, racing, recycling, rights and new media, SUVs, wildlife management, war, and global warming. The issues are made controversial through competing interests.

Or think about a technology that you will be dealing with in the schools, such as a hammer, microprocessor, plastic tubing, mp3 file, CAD application, or CNC router. Are you prepared to teach both the 'applications' and 'implications' of this technology? Can you demystify it and resensitise your students to its political implications? Are you familiar with the politics of this technology? How will you prepare resources that deal with the politics of these specific small 't' technologies as well as big 'T' Technology? See for example the writings of David Barlex (2006); Steve Keirl (2006); Helen Kennedy (2005); Margarita Pavlova (2005); Kay Stables and Richard Kimbell (2001).

The small-time Ferrari Nicks and big-time neocon visionaries of the world want to make a bigger, easier and faster buck by finessing consumers and markets while governments respond with regulations and policies to govern use, consumption, waste and the flow of commodities. At the same time, the average Joes and Josephines want technologies to work or work differently, easily, ecologically, effectively or equitably. Things get more confusing when our public institutions favour the protection of corporate interests, or commercial interests preclude a consideration of the interests of the average citizen. We are currently witnessing this convergence of the public and the corporate on a grand scale. Corporate governance always refers to governance *in* the corporation and governance *of* the corporate interest, which quite often conflates with the public interest.

What roles are accessible to the average citizen's abilities and desires to participate in technological decision-making, or corporate governance over the public interest? What avenues are available for the average citizen to express their interest in shaping their technological futures? And what nodes of the life cycle of technology ought we to leave open to participation and intervention? Resource acquisition and extraction stages? Design and innovation stages? Diffusion or implementation stages? Recycling and waste disposal stages? At what scale or scope ought participation to be granted? What methods can we deploy to facilitate participation? Is representation or proxy good enough? Is 'consultation' good enough?

Of course, these are the questions we ought to ask of our students' participation in all facets of design and technology.

If particular interests are included and other particular interests are excluded at every node in *forecasting, designing, creating, using, maintaining, managing, regulating, assessing and recycling technologies (information, products, processes and services)*, then it is easy to conclude that, as Langdon Winner (1980) did, *'artefacts have politics'*. Is it the case where someone else's interests are invariably inscribed in these activities? Do my or your interests ever have a chance? To be sure, some artefacts, designs, infrastructures or technologies offer different ways of being in, or interacting with, the world than others do. Bicycle or electric vehicle transport offers a much different relationship to the world than does a petrol-powered 23cc truck. But Winner, a philosopher of technology, reminds us that all artefacts have politics - they are a proxy for someone's interests or delegated to express our interests while we are out and about.

Technology or technologies is/are not politically neutral, although this is what many corporate advocates would have us believe. As if on cue, when Bill Gates, Microsoft's founder and CEO, was recently asked by talk show host Donny Deutsch whether new media were reinforcing crass individuality and anti-social behaviour in young people, Gates (2006) spun the question:

07 Engineer inside
black box.

08 Citizen outside of
black box.

(Illustrations 07 & 08
© Simon Minter.
Adapted from Kline,
1995, p. 181.)

'Technology is just a tool' he answered, *'to let you do what you're interested in… It's an enabler'.* All technologies may not embody a well-defined political agenda, but nor are they neutral instruments of 'progress', or neutral enablers, as Gates would like us to believe. Yet if we open up, disassemble or deconstruct these artefacts, designs, infrastructures or technologies, will we find someone's politics or interests? Winner (1993) says most of these *'black boxes will basically be empty, devoid of any profound democratic interests'.* Artefacts are often called 'black boxes' because most of us do not know how they work or what is inside, which creates a power differential between those who know and those who do not. Other analysts call the entire process of design or technology a 'black box' because we do not typically know how to gain political access to design or innovation processes. This generates power differentials between those with access and those without. The typical criticism is that engineers or designers have access but see only what is going on inside the black box while the rest of us are denied access but have a good idea of what is going on outside the black box. Their interests are included while our interests are excluded. The average citizen does not know how things (artefacts, design, politics, technology etc.) work; we just know that certain things work for some better than others. Does it not seem as though corporate interests are invariably included within the black boxes? What are these corporate interests (e.g., control and expansion

of markets and profits, convergence of services, displacement of labour for capital, mass consumption, planned obsolescence in products and services, proprietary regulations, surveillance of mobility)?

Think of a technology (device, infrastructure, machine, tool, system etc.) that you want to redesign. What advantages accrue through a transparent public design process? What are the limits, if any?

Joel Bakan (2004) argues that when corporate interests dominate our designs in and on the world, the average citizen learns apathy and helplessness while the world travels down the dangerous roads of fascism (Bakan, 2004). In the late 1990s, when Nike products dominated the recreational sports landscape, Phil Jackson, the company's CEO, grew nervous about masses of people saluting what critics called the Nike swooshtika. He also feared brand dilution in a volatile market. The dominance of corporate interests has its costs, some hidden and others visible; some collateral, others deferred. Naomi Klein (2000) has noted that the politics of Nike offer an exemplar of the politics of technology (and see also my own writing, Petrina, 2000). On one hand, Nike influences the politics of design by offering a model for other designers

Price Make-up of a US$100 Sport Shoe
MADE IN INDONESIA

09

09 Inequities in
shoe design
& production.
(© The Clean
Clothes Campaign.)

to emulate (i.e., brand loyalty, cool hunting, fashion ranging, hyper-marketing, sweatshop labour). On the other hand, Nike co-opts its consumers' interests into unsustainable material resource streams and exploitive practices as noted in the poster produced by The Clean Clothes Campaign.

When we kick a football or watch the World Cup we are implicated in a politics of technology extending from the soccer fields of Leeds to the sweatshop factory floors of Thailand, where the football leather is cut and sewn. When we buy a Barbie, two every second across the world, we sanction Mattel's sweatshops in China, where wages are £1.50 per day and conditions are stifling hot. As we involve our students in design, we can also involve them in global movements to monitor, regulate and improve these conditions. The Labour Behind the Label coalition, Clean Clothes Campaign and Maquila Solidarity Network offer political avenues, strategies and instructional materials for contradicting exploitive practices in the world of design. What options do we have?

There is little doubt that designers at the cutting edge of technology produce highly innovative and desirable items. Yet some of these products are manufactured under some of the worst sweatshop conditions in China.
What are the designers' obligations toward ethical production or a more publicly-informed design process?

2020 Vision:
The sources of production

Karl Marx argued that political changes come through controlling the forces of production. Of course, seizing the forces of production - the technologies and materials of production or what Marx called Produktivkräfte - is not so easy. Alternatively, liberals argue that political changes are made by regulating the state, by effectively controlling governmental intervention, which again is never easy. Fascist governments typically invite and accommodate a large amount of corporate control of both the state and the forces of production. This is a lethal combination.

But there is something more profound to control, something that Marx overlooked or could not foresee, and that is the sources of production. And at this moment in time…

A spectre is haunting the matrix - the spectre of open source. Global powers have entered into a desperate alliance to defend markets

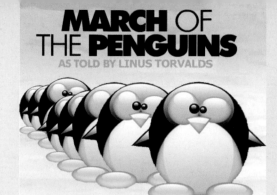

MARCH OF THE PENGUINS
AS TOLD BY LINUS TORVALDS

10 Open Source marches on.
(http://creativecomm
ons.org/licenses/by
/2.0/deed.en_GB)

and property rights from this spectre. The music recording, motion picture and video industry, software giants, big media, corporate commerce and neoconservative politics have converged, once again, to assert control over the forces of production, and by implication social relations and culture. But as the likes of Monsanto are discovering, it is much easier to control the water fountains than the water.

If the forces of production involve your physical labour, the sources of production involve your intellectual labour - your 'intellectual property' or 'intellectual work product' in capitalists' terms, and all the rights and access you may or may not have to this property or work product (Petrina, Volk & Kim, 2004). How much longer can the sources of production be controlled? 2010? 2020? Open source and its counterpart, open access, provide a politics of technology that every design and technology student and teacher can and ought to embrace today. That is as true for this generation as the next, tomorrow, through 2020.

Open source or FLOSS (Free/Libre Open Source Software) is about freedom, and like open access, about sharing. Freedom in this instance means that we have *freedom to* access, change, share and transfer the source code of open source software, *freedom from* the legal and disciplinary constraints of proprietary software, and *freedom to* download and share open source software and other forms of data (e.g., audio, text, video) without financial

exchanges. Open access means that we have *freedom to* access, store, print and share information, be it public or private domain (Willinsky, 2006). The key to both open source and open access is open, universal file formats and open, shared information. Hence, open source and open access fundamentally concern liberties and rights (Petrina, Volk & Kim, 2004).

Linux-based, open source operating systems have been tremendously successful, considering the control that proprietary companies have over the sources of production. Linux-based server operating systems now represent 30% of the global market and Apache web servers have increased to 62%. Microsoft Windows still dominates the desktop systems of the world (93%) but Linux is now cutting into profits and have increased to 4% of the global market. Firefox is also quickly displacing Microsoft Explorer as the most commonly used browser in the world. Corporate control of software is now seriously threatened by FLOSS's **"March of the Penguins"**.

Teachers ought to be interested in adopting open source and open access philosophies and there happen to be very good pragmatic reasons with regards to design and technology software needs. Pragmatically speaking, 2D drawing applications such as Cascade and QCAD, graphics applications such as Inkscape and The Gimp, 3D applications such as Blender, video editing applications such as

Jahshaka, Audacity for audio editing, Moodle for course management, and suites such as Open Office are outstanding open source options for design & technology teachers to adopt. By saying no to proprietary control over the sources of production you say yes to freedom and a democratic politics of technology that is healthy and progressive. And by saying yes to open access and yes to the freedom of information and the free circulation of ideas, you say no to elitist, monopolistic and oligopolistic control of knowledge.

Have you used open source software in your teaching? If not, why not? And if you have, how did it compare with commercially available software?

Every time you make a choice, whether it is over food, football, shoes or software, you are implicated in the politics of technology. The choices this generation makes establish the conditions the next generation faces. Our choices at this moment are necessarily about sources of production and sources of life - choices we will hopefully still have in 2020.

Ocularism aside, what is your 2020 vision for design & technology?

References

Bakan, J. (2004). "The corporation: The pathological pursuit of power". Toronto: Penguin Canada.

Barlex, D. (2006). 'Pedagogy to promote reflection and understanding in school technology courses'. In J. R. Dakers (Ed.), "Defining technological literacy: Towards an epistemological framework". (pp. 179-196), New York: Palgrave MacMillan.

Carson, R. (1962). "The Silent Spring". Now available from Mariner Books, Houghton Mifflin, Boston, MA., USA.

Gates, W. (2006). Interview in "The Big Idea", 9 May.

Gibson, W. (1984). "Neuromancer". New York: Ace Books.

Haraway, D. (1997). "Modest witness @ second millennium: Femaleman meets oncomouse". New York: Routledge.

Keirl, S. (2006). 'Ethical technological literacy as a democratic curriculum keystone'. In J. R. Dakers (Ed.), "Defining technological literacy: Towards an epistemological framework" (pp. 81-102). New York: Palgrave MacMillan.

Kennedy, H. (2005). 'Subjective intersections in the face of the machine: Gender, race, class and PCs in the home'. "European Journal of Women's Studies". 12. (4), 471-487.

Klein, N. (2000). "No logo: Taking aim at brand bullies". Toronto: Knopf.

Kline, S. J. (1995). "Conceptual foundations for multidisciplinary thinking". Stanford: Stanford University Press.

Pavlova, M. (2005). 'Knowledge and values in technology education'. "International Journal of Technology and Design Education". 15. (2), 127-147.

Petrina, S. (2000). 'The political ecology of design and technology education: An inquiry into methods'. "International Journal of Technology and Design Education". 10. (3), 207-237.

Petrina, S., Volk, K. & Kim, S. (2004). 'Technology and rights'. "International Journal of Technology and Design Education". 14. (3), 181-204.

Stables, K. & Kimbell, R. (2001). 'Technology education in South Africa: Evaluating an innovative pilot project'. "Research in Science Education". 31, 71-90.

Willinsky, J. (2006). "Access principle: The case for open access to research and scholarship". Cambridge, MA: MIT Press.

Winner, L. (1980). 'Do artifacts have politics?'. "Daedalus". 109. (1), 121-136.

Winner, L. (1993). 'Upon opening the black box and finding it empty: Social constructivism and the philosophy of technology'. "Science, Technology & Human Values". 18. (3), 362-378.

POSTER

Designers on designing

Malcolm Welch

Malcolm Welch is an associate
professor in the Faculty of Education
at Queen's University, Ontario.
He teaches graduate courses in
research methods and curriculum
design and undergraduate courses in
teaching methods and design &
technology. He has directed several
research projects and has published
widely in academic journals.
Currently, he is principal investigator
on a three-year research study that is
investigating how pupils learn to
make design decisions. He has
worked on major curriculum projects
in England and Canada and has
co-authored eight textbooks.

Designers on designing
Malcolm Welch

The designed world

Hannah Arendt (1958), the social philosopher, wrote that our environment could be divided into two parts: the *'planet'*, which is shaped by natural forces and the *'world'*, which is built up by human effort.

This chapter illustrates the breadth and the beauty of some products that comprise the *'world'* and provides a glimpse into the work and minds of designers who have had a positive impact on the made world.

As you look at the photographs and read about the designers who have created these products, think about the influence your experience and perception of these and similar objects has on your life and the environment in which you live. The designers included in this brief survey all believe the primary purpose of design is to make people's lives better. Few have put this so eloquently as Henry Dreyfus in his now classic book **"Designing for people"** (2003/1955):

'[Designers] bear in mind that the object being worked on is going to be ridden in, sat upon, looked at, talked into, activated, operated, or in some other way used by people individually or en masse. When the point of contact between the product and the people become [sic] a point of friction, then the… designer has failed. On the other hand if people are made safer, more comfortable, more eager to purchase, more efficient - or just plain happier - by contact with the product, then the designer has succeeded.'

There is now a general consensus amongst designers that products should go beyond simply considerations of form and function. Products need to become 'objects of desire'. To achieve this, products must make pleasurable emotional connections with their end-users through the joy of their use and the beauty of their form. To what extent do the products with which you surround yourself bring you joy?

William Morris (1834-1896) was a British craftsman, early Socialist, designer and poet whose designs generated the Arts & Crafts movement in England. He once said: *'have nothing in your house that you do not know to be useful, or believe to be beautiful'*.
To what extent do you agree with this statement?
Are utility and beauty the only criteria for judging the worth of an object?

01 Two sculptural
   arm pieces.
02 Textural
   neckpiece.
03 Neckpieces and
   bangle.
04 Davin Stowell.

(Photograph 04
© Claudia Christen
for Smart Design.)

Angela O'Kelly (1973-)
Jewellery designer

*'[My] inspiration derives from a fascination
with simple shapes, textures and repetition.
It is taken from observing landscapes, boglands,
rock formations and sea life.
Colour is very important, with earthy browns
and greys, and vivid greens, blues and reds
from the sea, featuring throughout my work.'*

Angela O' Kelly is one of Ireland's leading
art and design-led makers.

Angela combines paper with fabric, felt,
silver, gold, cord, recycled plastic and
semi-precious stones using a variety of textile
and jewellery techniques to create wearable
art that crosses boundaries between sculpture,
jewellery and textiles. Texture is her main
consideration, achieved by layering hard
and soft fibres and knotting and sewing
paper cord: *'I produce two ranges: firstly,
large sculptural wearable art pieces; and secondly
smaller neckpieces, brooches and bangles.
Both ranges are bright, tactile, vivacious and subtle.'*

? Is there a place in schools
for collaboration between
the art department and
design & technology?
If so, what would this
collaboration look like?

Which materials, both natural
and synthetic, could you
use with pupils?
How would these be
incorporated into products?

Davin Stowell (1953-)
Designer of Good Grips kitchen aids

'People will pay for safety, ease of use and comfort.'

Sam Farber, an entrepreneur who has
made human-centred design a hallmark
of kitchenware, was in his kitchen one day
and saw how his wife's arthritis was causing
her pain while peeling potatoes with the usual
peeler we are all familiar with; the one made
out of steel with a bent piece of metal
for a handle. Sam's wife struggled and then
turned to him and said, *'can't you make
something that doesn't hurt my hands?'*
Sam, a long-time advocate of human-
centered design, which takes into consideration
the physical, cognitive, social, cultural and
the emotional needs of users, telephoned
Davin Stowell at Smart Design and challenged
him to design a better potato peeler that
was also dishwasher-safe, high quality,
affordable and attractive.

The design team looked at tool handles,
utensil handles, and equipment handles.
In the end, they decided to create a handle
that had a soft, squishy feel that invites

05 'Good Grips'
   peelers & grater.

06 Easily replaced
   peeler blade.

   (Photographs 05 & 06
   © Claudia Christen
   for Smart Design.)

07 Jonathan Ive.

08 Apple's 2006
   ipod family.

   (Photographs 07 & 08
   © Courtesy of Apple.)

you to grab it. And so grab it they did - left hands, right hands, hands with arthritis, small hands, hands with crooked fingers, hands of a mailman, next-door neighbour hands - no hand or handle model went untested. Carving Styrofoam and wood mock-ups produced hundreds of models.

Davin's team also investigated the practice of professional chefs and food preparers. Because blade sharpness is critical for these heavy users, they actually throw out and replace used peelers as often as weekly. They think of peelers like disposable products. So Davin conducted a blind test of twenty peelers, comparing the difference between old, used peeler blades and new ones. He found that new, sharp blades required less force, had wide, even peels and rode over irregular surfaces smoothly. Since a peeler blade, like any knife blade, will dull with use and since you cannot sharpen a peeler blade yourself, Davin designed a blade that is easily and safely replaceable. A spring-loaded blade release was added to the peeler, along with a safety 'peeler blade replacement cartridge'.

? What are the educative benefits of asking pupils to redesign, rather than design, a product or service? What would pupils learn if they were required to identify an object (a toy that broke easily, scissors that hurt the hand or the ugliest lamp ever seen) and redesign it? What questions would you pose to them in order to stimulate their thinking about designing an object?

Jonathan Ive (1967-)
Designer of the iPod and iMac

'It's all about removing the unnecessary.'

The winner of the Design Museum's inaugural Designer of the Year award in 2003, Jonathan Ive is senior vice-president of design at Apple, whose innovations include the iPod and iMac.

'It's all about removing the unnecessary…[and moving toward] the utterly serene' says Jonathan about the ethos that informs his landmark product designs for Apple Computer. Nothing better fulfills Jonathan's ambition to create elegant, intuitive machinery than his revolutionary design for the iPod MP3 player. The iPod is not only a very new product but this ode to minimalism has redefined the way consumers experience technology, to say nothing of music.

09 Philippe Starck.
(Photograph ©
JB Mondino.)

10 Starck's lemon
squeezer, the Juicy
Salif, has become
an icon despite its
impractical design.

11 Philippe Starck's
W.W. stool.

(Photograph © Starck.)

When asked what it is that distinguishes the products that Apple develops, Jonathan replied, *'the decisive factor is fanatical care beyond the obvious stuff: the obsessive attention to details that are often overlooked.'*

Make a list of elegant, whimsical and iconic products that have defined the way that users experience a product group.
How will you introduce this aspect of design to your pupils?

Philippe Starck (1949-)
Architect, interior designer, product designer

'Today, the problem is not to produce more so that you can sell more. The fundamental question is that of the product's right to exist…[An] object must be of good quality…a good product is a product which lasts.'

Philippe Starck, whose work ranges from chic hotels to chairs to lamps to toothbrushes, is one of the best-known contemporary designers in the world. He has not only received public acclaim for his amazing building interior designs but has also proved to be an accomplished architect and product designer.

The items Starck designs become objects of adoration and desire. Although many of them are eventually mass-produced, they often remain akin to artworks in their basic function. Starck has created his own style, which, although not uniform, remains highly recognisable. His designs are sometimes loaded with irony and parody. He has said that, *'my idea is to bring happiness, respect, vision, poetry, surrealism, and magic [to design]… We have to replace beauty, which is a cultural concept, with goodness, which is a humanist concept'*. Philippe Starck wants to bring love and happiness into your life by designing objects, environments, and appliances that will brighten your days.

Philippe Starck has reiterated a design principle first advocated by the Bauhaus: high quality, tasteful industrial design should be available to everyone. Ironically, his lemon squeezer - the Juicy Salif - has become an icon despite its impractical design. To what extent should pupils be given the opportunity to design and make products that are playful, sometimes simply absurd?

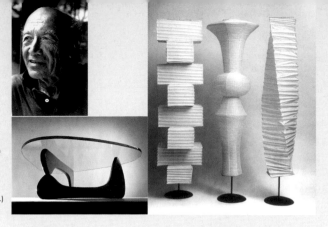

12 Isamu Noguchi.
13 Noguchi coffee
   table.
14 Noguchi Akari
   lighting.
   (Image 12 photograph
   by Jun Miki.
   Images 12 - 14
   © The Isamu Noguchi
   Foundation and Garden
   Museum/ARS, New
   York, 2007.
   Image 13 Photography
   Ezra Stoller © Esto.
   Images 13 & 14
   © DACS, London 2007.)
15 Marcel Breuer.

Isamu Noguchi (1904-1988)
Sculptor and designer

*'New concepts of the physical world and
of psychology may give insights into knowledge,
but the visible world, in human terms, is more
than scientific truths. It enters our consciousness
as emotion as well as knowledge.'*

Trained originally as a sculptor, Isamu
Noguchi brought a sculptural sensibility
to the lighting, furniture, gardens and stage
sets he created.He sought to make sculpture
useful in everyday life, and his furniture
and interior designs display the biomorphic
imagery of his sculpture. After the Second
World War Noguchi moved to the city
of Gifu where he developed new designs
that harnessed the ancient skills of the
Gifu lantern-makers to produce modern
electrified versions of traditional candle-lit
lanterns. The Akari light sculptures,
beautifully shaped and capable of folding
perfectly flat, are still made by hand in Gifu
from the minogami paper that comes from
the bark of mulberry trees.

During the 1950s and 1960s he designed
'organic' furniture in curvily sculpted
wood. He was equally prolific as a landscape
architect. After creating a memorial garden
to his father at Keiō University in 1950,
he recreated the ancient Buddhist stone
gardens he had loved in Kyoto
at several locations.

How will you both
encourage and enable pupils
to identify, understand
and use biomorphic shapes,
that is, shapes derived from
organic or natural forms,
in their design work?

Marcel Breuer (1902-1981)
Architect and furniture designer

*'Objects should be impersonal, standardized,
styleless and timeless. An object's clear and logical
form should be based on rational principles
(economy of means, truth to materials),
determined from the object's primary function
and ergonomic requirements.'*

From 1920 to 1928 Marcel Breuer was
a student and teacher at Germany's
Bauhaus, a school of design where modern
principles, technologies and the application
of new materials were encouraged in both
the industrial and fine arts. During his time
spent there Marcel completed the carpentry
apprenticeship and subsequently became
one of the early 20th century's most
influential furniture designers.

Breuer is best known for his design
of the Wassily Chair No. B23, the first
tubular bent-steel chair, designed in 1925
for Wassily Kandinsky and inspired in part
by the shape and form of bicycle handlebars.

The frame of the chair was made from polished, bent, nickelled tubular steel, which later became chrome plated. The seat came in canvas, fabric or leather. Still in production, the chair can be assembled and disassembled most easily with bicycle tools.

> How will you encourage pupils to use existing products as a stimulus for new ideas? Would attribute analysis be a useful technique to teach pupils?

Charles-Edouard Jeanneret (Le Corbusier) (1887-1965) Architect and furniture designer

'You employ stone, wood and concrete, and with these materials you build houses and palaces: that is construction. Ingenuity is at work. But suddenly you touch my heart, you do me good. I am happy and I say: "This is beautiful". That is Architecture. Art enters in.'

Charles-Edouard Jeanneret, who adopted the pseudonym Le Corbusier in 1920, was a French Swiss-born architect, famous for his contributions to what is now called modernism, or the International Style. He was a pioneer in theoretical studies of modern design and was dedicated to providing better living conditions for the residents of crowded cities.

Le Corbusier placed systems of harmony and proportion at the centre of his design philosophy, and his faith in the mathematical order of the universe was closely bound to the golden section and the Fibonacci series, which he described as *'rhythms apparent to the eye and clear in their relations with one another. And these rhythms are at the very root of human activities.'*

> Mathematical relationships are found throughout the natural world. For example, the spirals of a Norway spruce cone and those in the head of a dahlia are part of a Fibonacci series. How will you both encourage and enable pupils to incorporate the fluid forms found in nature and the precision of mathematics into their designing?

19 Frank Lloyd
   Wright.
20 Frank Lloyd
   Wright's
   Fallingwater house,
   Pennsylvania.

Frank Lloyd Wright (1867-1959)
Architect

'Organic buildings are the strength and lightness of the spiders' spinning, buildings qualified by light, bred by native character to environment, married to the ground.'

Believing that *'the space within [a] building is the reality of that building'*, Frank Lloyd Wright practiced what is known as organic architecture, an architecture that evolves naturally out of a context. Most important for him was the relationship between the site and the building and the needs of the client. From his early Prairie Style homes, to the sculptural curves of the Guggenheim Museum in New York, he defined a North American style of architecture that was rich in emotion and sensitive to its surroundings. As well as creating buildings that were radical in appearance, Wright had a rare ability to integrate them with the landscape - stemming from his deep love and knowledge of nature.

Wright challenged his mentor Louis Sullivan, whose slogan *'form follows function'* became the mantra of modern architecture. Wright changed this phrase to *'form and function are one, joined in a spiritual union'*, using nature as the best example of this integration.

Designers on designing   Malcolm Welch

Richard Seymour and Dick Powell argue that how a product engages with us emotionally is at least as important as how well it performs mechanically. Otherwise, they contend, all our choices would be based strictly on price and functional efficiency rather than emotional resonance and visceral appeal. They call this phenomenon *'emotional ergonomics'* and argue that highly successful products broadcast their appeal on a non-logical wavelength; the potential user feels the attractiveness as an initial response before engaging in any conscious thought about the product. How can you encourage pupils to think about the products they design in terms of emotional ergonomics?

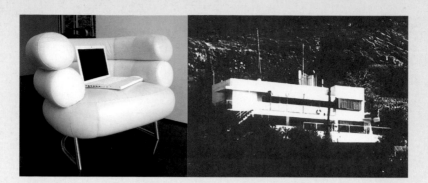

Eileen Gray (1878-1976)
Artist, furniture designer, architect

'To create, one must first question everything'.

Architect and designer of furniture
and ornamental objects, Eileen Gray
grew up in Ireland and moved to London
in 1898 to attend the Slade School of Fine
Arts. After graduating, she moved to Paris
where she studied the process of hand-making
lacquered furniture, folding screens and bowls.
During the late 1920s and early 1930s
Gray designed some of her best-known
furniture and became known as the
'mother of modernism'. A bedside table
from 1926 had a circular top supported
on a stand by a u-shaped base, a form
that she also used for the *'Bibendum'* chair
whose backrest was made from two
stuffed u-shaped pieces. Gray also worked
as an architect, designing several boxy,
modern houses in Paris and near St. Tropez.
The house she designed with Jean Badovici,
Villa E-1027, is the best-documented example
of her work. Neglected for most of her career,
Eileen Gray is now regarded as one
of the most important furniture designers
and architects of the early 20th century
and the most influential woman in those
fields. Her work inspired both modernism
and Art Deco.

Modernism, Art Deco,
Memphis, Bauhaus and
Post-Modernism are names
given to some of the
'movements' in the design
world. Each has attempted
to move design forward
by uniting around a shared
vision and philosophy.
To what extent is it
important for pupils
to examine the development
of design movements
and the works of different
designers from around
the world?
How might this help
them become more
capable designers?

Ebenezer Howard (1850-1928)
Urban planner

*'Town and country must be married, and out
of this joyous union will spring a new hope,
a new life, a new civilisation.'*

Ebenezer Howard thought deeply about social
issues and out of this concern came his book
in 1898 titled "To-Morrow: A Peaceful Path
to Real Reform" (reprinted as "Garden Cities

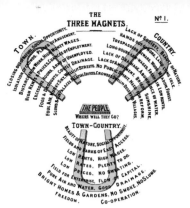

23 Ebenezer Howard.

24 Rushby Mead,
Letchworth.

25 Ebenezer Howard's
"The Three Magnets"
diagram.

(Images 23 - 25 ©
First Garden City
Heritage Museum,
Letchworth Garden
City, UK.)

26 Buckminster Fuller.

of To-Morrow"). His proposal called for the creation of new towns of limited size, planned in advance, and surrounded by a permanent belt of agricultural land. He offered a vision of towns free of slums and enjoying the benefits of both town (opportunity, amusement and high wages) and country (beauty, fresh air and low rents). He illustrated the idea with his famous *Three Magnets* diagram, which addressed the question *'Where will the people go?'*, the choices being 'Town', 'Country' or 'Town-Country' - the Three Magnets. Howard believed that Garden Cities were the perfect blend of city and nature. The towns would be largely independent, and managed and financed by the citizens who had an economic interest in them. His ideas attracted enough attention and financial backing to begin Letchworth Garden City, a suburban garden city north of London.

Christopher Alexander and colleagues at the Center for Environmental Structure at the University of California, Berkeley proposed that people should design for themselves their own houses, streets and communities (Alexander, Ishikawa & Silverstein, 1977).

He observed that most of the wonderful places of the world were not made by architects but by the people. How might a study of vernacular architecture enhance pupils' ability to design?

R. Buckminster Fuller (1895-1983) Inventor, designer, architect, theorist

'Does humanity have a chance to survive lastingly and successfully on planet Earth, and if so, how?'

Philosopher, designer, architect, artist, engineer, entrepreneur, author, mathematician, teacher and inventor; Buckminster Fuller was driven by the design philosophy of *'more for less'*. Convinced that the way the world managed its human and material resources needed to be radically rethought, he sought long-term, technology-led solutions to some of the problems of his time, particularly in the fields of building and transport. He worked simultaneously on plans for houses, cars, boats, games, television transmitters and geodesic domes, all of which were designed to be mass-produced using the simplest and most sustainable means possible.

27 United States
pavilion at Expo
67 by Buckminster
Fuller.
(Photograph © Library
and Archives Canada,
MIKAN No. 3198274.)

28 David Marks &
Julia Barfield.

29 The London Eye.

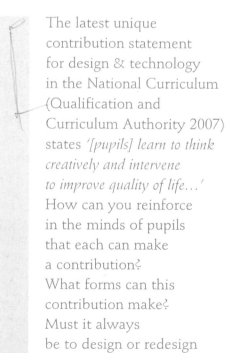

His philosophy evolved to cause him to think in terms of *'four-dimensional, or 4D design'*. He defined this as thinking in time instead of only the three dimensions of space: thinking of consequences for humanity instead of only immediate personal gain. He devoted his life to this question, trying to find out what an individual like him could do to improve humanity's condition that large organizations, governments, or private enterprises inherently could not do.

The latest unique contribution statement for design & technology in the National Curriculum (Qualification and Curriculum Authority 2007) states *'[pupils] learn to think creatively and intervene to improve quality of life...'* How can you reinforce in the minds of pupils that each can make a contribution? What forms can this contribution make? Must it always be to design or redesign a new product?

David Marks and Julia Barfield Architects and designers of the London Eye

'We believe that good design transforms the quality of the environment'.

David Marks and Julia Barfield were winners of Architectural Practice of the Year in 2001 and a Queen's Award for Enterprise in 2003 for designing the London Eye, the largest observation wheel in the world. The wheel carries 32 sealed and air-conditioned passenger capsules attached to its external circumference. It rotates at a rate of 0.26 metres per second or 0.85 feet per second (about 0.9 km/h or 0.5 mph) so that one revolution takes about 30 minutes to complete. The wheel does not usually stop to take on passengers; the rotation rate is so slow that passengers can easily walk on and off the moving capsules at ground level. It is, however, stopped on occasion to allow disabled or elderly passengers time to disembark safely.

This elegant structure has captured the public's imagination. Since its opening in 1999, over twenty million visitors have enjoyed unparalleled views over London, and it has made a significant contribution to the regeneration of the area.

30 Alec Issigonis.
(Photograph ©
British Motor Industry
Heritage Trust.)

31 A Morris Mini-Minor
being delivered
to a family in
Arlington, Texas
in 1959.

The London Eye has become a landmark. Originally, a landmark literally meant a geographic feature, used by explorers and others to find their way back through an area on a return trip. In modern usage, it is anything that is easily recognisable, such as a monument, building, or other structure that might be of interest to tourists due to notable physical features or of historical significance. What would pupils learn about designing if required to list some international cities and their landmarks?

Alec Issigonis (1906-1988)
Automotive designer

'Never, never copy the opposition'.

One of the most original car designers of the modern era, Alec Issigonis is best known as the creator of the Mini, but also designed two more of the five best-selling cars in British motoring history - the Morris Minor and the Austin 1100.

By changing the normal front-to-back location of the Mini's engine to side-to-side, he saved so much space that it was possible to accommodate a four-seater car on a small, easily parked platform. Striving to ensure that as much space as possible was allocated to the passengers, Issigonis squeezed the transverse east/west engine location into so little space that 80% of the three-metre long car was free for the driver and passengers. Launched in 1959, the Mini soon became the best-selling car in Europe and was swiftly hailed as an icon of the early 1960s.

Alec Issigonis was a successful designer because he was able to 'think outside the box', that is, able to look at a problem from a new perspective without preconceptions. Out-of-the-box thinking requires openness to new ways of seeing the world and a willingness to explore. What strategies can be used with pupils to encourage them to think outside the box?

Dean Kamen (1951-)
Inventor of the automatic infusion pump, Ibot Transporter and Segway

*'You have teenagers thinking they're going
to make millions as NBA stars when that's
not realistic for even 1 percent of them.
Becoming a scientist or engineer is'.*

Dean Kamen is well-known as the designer
of the Segway, a self-balancing, battery-
powered two-wheeled transportation device
that can carry one person along pavements
crowded with pedestrians. But Dean is less
well-known for his design of products
that improve the lives of people with certain
types of disease and also disabled people.

While Dean was attending college
in the 1970s, his brother, then a medical
student and now a pediatric oncologist,
complained that there was no reliable way
to give steady doses of drugs to patients.
So Dean invented the AutoSyringe,
an automatic, self-contained, ambulatory
infusion pump designed to free patients
from round-the-clock injections and,
in some cases, from their hospital beds.
The wearable device delivers precise doses
of medication to diabetics and other patients
with a variety of medical conditions.

When Dean watched a man in a wheelchair
try to negotiate a curb in the late '80s,
he wondered whether he could build
a chair that would hop curbs without losing
its balance. After $50 million and eight years
in development, the Ibot Transporter was born
- a six-wheeled robotic *'mobility system'* that
can climb stairs, traverse sandy and rocky
terrain, and raise its user to eye-level
with a standing person.

Each year many people
die from medical errors
in hospitals directly
or indirectly related
to medical device use.
Medical devices can harm
patients, family members,
or healthcare providers as
a result of failure of the
device or the actions
of the user. Human factors
engineering (HFE) is the
science and the methods used
to make devices easier and
safer to use. HFE helps
improve human performance
and reduce the risks
associated with use.
How will you introduce
pupils to human factors
engineering and encourage
them to think about
it when designing?

35 36 37

35 William
McDonough.

36 Brano Meres.

37 Brano Meres'
bamboo bicycle.

(Photograph ©
Brano Meres.)

Sustainable products:
Planet pleasers

*'I believe we can accomplish great and profitable
things within a new conceptual framework -
one that values our legacy, honors diversity,
and feeds ecosystems and societies...It is time
for designs that are creative, abundant, prosperous,
and intelligent from the start.'*
William McDonough, architect and designer.

Sustainable products are those products
providing environmental, social and
economic benefits while protecting public
health, welfare, and environment over their
full commercial cycle, from the extraction
of raw materials to final disposition.

William McDonough's greeting cards
are designed to flow safely through multiple
life cycles. Each card comes with a two-way
return postage-paid envelope that allows
its constituent materials to be safely re-used
rather than discarded. Both the cards
and the envelopes are made from
a Certified Technical Nutrient plastic material.
Cards returned using the self-mailing envelope
are used as raw material for new carpet tiles.

*'I have seen many amazing constructions made
of bamboo and I always wondered why such
[a] light, strong, stiff and elastic material is not
[widely] used for building bicycle frames.'*
Brano Meres, mechanical engineer.

Bamboo is the fastest-growing woody plant.
Several subtropical species can grow 30cm per
day, while others have been documented as
growing over 100cm per day. Brano Meres
has made a prototype bicycle frame from
bamboo rods filled with polyurethane foam
to increase their rigidity. According to Brano,
the frame has better vibration damping than
a carbon fiber frame. Other bamboo frame
makers smoke and heat-treat the bamboo
to prevent splitting.

Jason Iftakhar was struck by the amount
of waste packaging supermarkets generate.
So in response, he developed a forged
steel die cutting tool that enables supermarket
packing machines to turn old cardboard
boxes into simple furniture, allowing
supermarkets to re-use, rather than recycle,
waste product and so save money and,
more importantly, resources.
This upcycling turns a low value item
into a neat new product for the store.
As Jason says: *'My idea is about getting
a big result without wasting a lot of energy.
The materials and the machinery were already
there; it just needed to be harnessed. It's the perfect
environment to take advantage of a system
that's already established'.*

'Industrial ecology' is
a term being used for the
new practice of one industry
using another industry's
dross as raw material

38 Jason Iftakhar's
bench made from
recycled
cardboard.

or redesigning products
to make them easier to
re-use, recycle or incinerate.
Is there dross available
in your community?
If so, how can you acquire
and use it in your classroom?

Endnote

Many professional designers, some
well-known, some not so well-known,
contribute to the made world in which
we all live, work and play.
Charles Owen (2004) has suggested that
*'design is a profession concerned with the creation
of products, systems, communications and services
that satisfy human needs, improve people's lives
and do all of this with respect for the welfare
of the natural environment.'*

From paper clips to airplanes, from clothing
to medical equipment, from packaging
to airports, design means more than styling
or giving shape to an object. Good design
requires a complex process in which various,
often contradictory, requirements have
to be fulfilled so that objects can function
in the desired manner. Design is only
'good' when aesthetics, economics,
durability, function, ecology and comfort
come together to complement
and harmonise with one another.

If this is what designers do, should pupils
learn to design? Is it possible for pupils
to design? What knowledge, skills
and understanding would they need
in order to design?
These are the questions that the chapter,
"The pupil as designer" will address.

Further reading

Caplan, R. (2005). "By design: why there are no locks on the bathroom in the Hotel Louis XIV and other object lessons" (2nd ed.). New York: Fairchild.

Dreyfuss, H. (2003). "Designing for people" (2nd ed.). New York: Allworth.

Fiell, C. & Fiell, P. (Eds.) (2005). "Designing the 21st century". Köln, Germany: Taschen.

Heskett, J. (2002). "Toothpicks and logos: Design in everyday life". Oxford, UK: Oxford University.

Industrial Designers Society of America (2001). "Design secrets: Products - 50 real-life projects uncovered". Gloucester, MA: Rockport.

Linton, H. (2003). "Portfolio design" (3rd ed.). New York: W. W. Norton.

Peto, J (Ed.) (1999). "Design process progress practice". London: The Design Museum.

Rashid, K (n d) "I want to change the world". New York: Universe Publishing.

Rodgers, P. (2004). "Inspiring designers: A sourcebook". London: Black Dog.

Sawyer, R. K. (2006). "Explaining creativity: The science of human innovation". Oxford, UK: Oxford University.

References

Alexander, C., Ishikawa, S. & Silverstein, M. (1977). "A pattern language: Towns, Buildings, Construction". New York: Oxford University Press.

Arendt, H. (1958). "The human condition". Chicago: University of Chicago Press.

Qualifications and Curriculum Authority (2007). "Design and technology programme of study: ks3 The importance of design and technology". Full text available at: http://curriculum.qca.org.uk/subjects accessed on 17.10.07.

Dreyfuss, H. (2003/1955). "Designing for people". New York: Allworth.

Owen, C. (2004). "What is design? Some questions and answers". Full text available at http://www.id.iit.edu/ideas/papers.html accessed on 15.08.07.

Steve Keirl

Currently lecturing in design & technology education at the University of South Australia, Steve has also taught primary and secondary design & technology in England and Australia. He advocates a quality design & technology education - one that is broad, critical and democracy-serving - for every student globally. He has published widely, given keynote addresses at state, national and international conferences and has extensive experience in design & technology curriculum design. His research interests explore 'technological literacy for democratic life'. Steve collects washing-up brushes.

The politics of technology curriculum

Steve Keirl

Teaching is a political act

If you disagree with this statement then we have a debate on our hands. However, the curious thing is that if you *agree* that teaching is a political act, the situation doesn't change - we still have a debate on our hands.

Education is both a tool for, and a reflection of, the State. In an espoused democracy we educate both to maintain the democracy and to do so in democratic ways. As Pat White said *'There is at least one policy which must be in the public interest in a democracy. This is, an appropriate education for a democracy.'* (White, 1973, p. 237). A democratic education isn't desirable to a dictatorship - what happens there is more likely to be indoctrination.

So, there is a nuanced interplay of State-public (citizens') interests. Ideally, they are similar. In practice, the nuances amount to competing values positions which have to be contested, debated, advocated and defended. Contestation is key to democratic life and the idea that what constitutes teaching, or education, or curriculum is somehow 'obvious' or a 'given' cannot be presumed. The contestation of competing values is politics and your own values have varying degrees of compatibility with those of your students, colleagues, policy developers and government.

The big picture

The politics of design & technology curriculum doesn't happen in a vacuum - we have to consider the context of it all. We can look at the global situation and quickly identify the matters that are of concern to people globally - peace, justice and environment, for example. We are also drawn to the term globalisation - of which there are many interpretations, from enlightened to aggressive.

We are led to believe that we operate in a *'market economy'* (the benign name for capitalism [J.K Galbraith, 2005]) and that these are the days of the 'knowledge society'. Such terms are created (designed) to convey a meaning for their time. Cycles of change happen continuously and the big picture of one decade is not that of another. Of late there has been a deliberate blurring of the boundaries between democracy (and its education) and economy. As Michael Apple (2001) says *'For neoliberals, the world in essence is a vast supermarket...(E)ducation is seen as simply one more product...Rather than democracy being a political concept, it is transformed into a wholly economic concept.'* In this world, he suggests, the term 'consumers' is preferred to 'citizens'. (p. 39)

"Rather than democracy being a political concept, it is transformed into a wholly economic concept"

This is the ideology of now and it may or may not last. Ideology tests democracy. If one has an ideology to deliver, having critical, debating, questioning citizens isn't what you want. This last point obviously applies to dictatorships but it can also apply to those who want everyone to see democracy 'their way'. Thus, they create a *climate* of suppression, control and derision of criticism to subvert opposition. Anti-democratic actions then erode democracy.

The politics of technology itself is the very background of the big picture and its interplay with design & technology curriculum is at once subtle, powerful and undeniable. A milestone research project on design & technology was David Layton's (1994) international study which showed some of the many and competing, political interests in shaping our field. While the *economic instrumentalists* may hold sway for now, he documents a range of (still significant) players - professional technologists (e.g. engineering bodies who would have us working to produce more and better engineers - apply this rationale to myriad other professions/trades); *sustainable developers*; *girls and women*; *defenders of participatory democracy*; and *liberal educators*. We can take any one of these groups and imagine re-designing design and technology curricula to serve their needs exclusively. Layton (1994) expresses matters well: *'...the politics of technological literacy -*

who creates and controls the meanings of the phrase, how the imposition of meaning is being attempted - is a central concern of technology education today.' (p. 13)

How is curriculum shaped? Who has influence and how is it exerted? Where are you - the teacher - in shaping curriculum?

We can look another way at the big picture and that is at the (mistaken) orthodoxies that are held - often by those beyond, but sometimes within, our profession. These are the ideas that technology is about the *new*, that it's *I-tech/hi-tech*, that it's *things*, that it's *neutral*, it's *applied science*, it's *inevitable* (progress/ beyond control), or that, as a result of all these, it's *incomprehensible*. If these are the perspectives of technology promoted to, and held by, the public, do we have an educational role to play? Are we *educating* everyone - society - about the multiple ways of understanding technologies and the designed world?

Finally another bigger picture that we can view is education jurisdictions beyond our own. There is much design & technology practice internationally which offers models for discussion (written about in journals such as **"Design and Technology Education: An International Journal"** and the

02 "Design and
Technology
Education:
An International
Journal".

03 "International
Journal of
Technology and
Design
Education".

(Volume 16, No. 2,
2006. With kind
permission of
Springer Science
and Business
Media.)

"International Journal of Technology
and Design Education"). We are fortunate
in having a range of technology curricula
around the world. It is interesting to see,
for example, how much professional freedom
for curriculum interpretation some
colleagues have compared with others.

Curriculum

It's useful to draw on the root of 'curriculum'
(Latin - currere) and think of it as the running/
current - as the fluid, and (ambiguously) the
now. You no doubt theorised 'curriculum' at
university but now you're in it!

Policymakers might 'hand down' curriculum
but then multiple mediations kick in. It's not
a religious (though some might see it so) edict,
binding and inflexible. Nor is curriculum the
sum of a set of syllabuses. It includes
syllabuses, pedagogies, knowledges, learnings -
all plural, all contested, many valid yet fighting
for validity. Curriculum is not a tidy package
but is problematic, changing, open to
subversion, and is State-driven if not also
ideologically driven. At its most democratic,
it is openly critiqued.

Think of all the 'ingredients'
which make up the totality
of curriculum.
How much influence
do you have over
each ingredient?
Which have you most
influence over -
and which least?

To take just one (very powerful) aspect
of curriculum as politics, try assessment.
Consider assessment as a political sieve -
a rationer of educational opportunities.
Consider 'standards' and basic skills tests.
Consider how your teaching and the ethos
of your school is shaped by these. To probe
curriculum critically is to probe the motives
of its architects and to ask whose interests
are served and how.

'Why design & technology education?'

To really interrogate educational practice
it is helpful to step back every now and
then and question one's own assumptions.
Thus: *'Why design & technology education?'*
What's your answer? Because it's there -
a tradition? Because you did it at school?
Has it a defensible place in schools? How did
it get to where it is? Because of policy?
Teacher action? Modelling on other curricula?
What formulation does it take 'officially'
and in the minds of you and your colleagues?
In what ways can it serve society
and *each* student?

Is it merely passive-technical or is it contributing to the development of critical-thinking citizens? To critique the status quo further what's in the name? Why is it called 'Technology Education' in this project? Why not Technacy (Seemann, 2003) or Design & Technology or Technological Literacy? All subjects have an archaeology and a politics of naming. They also have a yet-to-be-determined future.

You and design & technology

Given you are now a design & technology practitioner, what has been your own journey and why are you travelling it? Are you the navigator or are you following a prescribed path? What are your perceptions of you in design & technology now, compared with university, compared with school? What fulfils you and what frustrates you?

> Where are you on a spectrum between dutifully doing the government's (or system's) bidding and operating as an autonomous professional deciding on the best for your students?

Addressing such questions requires us to unpack the multiple values interests that shape education. To engage with all the values interests at play in education - not least, the students' - is to be an attuned professional. You find yourself in a position of weighing up competing values as well as having to resolve them through how you teach, assess and act. This is no easy matter but it does matter.

Teacher identity - what positions us?

Of course, the play of the politics of curriculum is also about power and the differential power arrangements between government, unions, professional associations, managers, teachers and students. Such things shape our identity as teachers and we tend to forget that we are teachers first and design & technology teachers second. Equally, we can feel that we carry the weight of many issues. When politicians and media almost compete to say what schools should be doing to cure society's ills, or to perpetuate the now 20-year myth of 'failing schools', it is easy to forget the real good we can achieve when left to our professional self-determination.

Michael Apple (2001), Andy Hargreaves (2003) and Judith Sachs (2003) all present cogent and topical analyses of how teachers are currently *positioned* by systems to replicate the systems' intentions. In climates of standardisation, teaching to the test, meeting targets, stifled pedagogical creativity (see Keirl, 2004 re creativity, innovation and design & technology curriculum) and in isolation of any democratic social mission, as Hargreaves (2003) documents, *'…it (is) almost impossible for many teachers to teach either **for** the knowledge society or **beyond it** as part of a broader social mission.'* (p. 162, emphasis added). In such climates it is easy to become professionally isolated. A huge challenge is to open our collective selves to public scrutiny and to be critiqued - in sum, to challenge our personal-professional and public-professional identities.

What do you think it means to have a personal-professional identity?
What do you think it means to have a public-professional identity?
Discuss the risks and gains that could result from taking our professional curriculum decision-making into the public arena.

Part of our identity is also about collegial self-knowledge, understanding that we are part of the big picture too and to respond accordingly - as Michael Bottery (cited in Judith Sachs, 2003) says: *'…to see that (we) do not necessarily occupy the centre of any occupational universe, but are part of a much more complex ecology of occupations'* (p. 15).

Put another way, we need to know ourselves well in order to be active professionally beyond our workplaces.

What of design & technology's identity?

Does design & technology really have a valid and defensible place in a democratic education of *every* student? To know our own curriculum considerations and arguments well is to be able to advance the design and technology case. To know others' curriculum arguments well is better still. Curriculum is continuous contestation and design & technology will only have its place so long as it can present its case.

Let's hypothesise. Why not dismantle design & technology and cast it to the curriculum winds - crafty bits to the arts, skilling bits to vocational training (it cannot be education - see Richard Peters, 1973), theory bits to science and values bits to social studies? The problem of design & technology's challenges resolved! Now consider design & technology (the name wouldn't actually work now) as just one of these 'bits' and imagine the kind of subject and pedagogy in each case. None of these alone could embrace *in a holistic and meaningful way* all of design, enterprise, innovation, making, communication, creativity, thinking, critique, etc., in the way that design & technology can. But to do this is to

04 Doctor Kurt
Seemann.

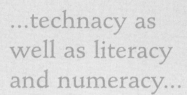

...technacy as
well as literacy
and numeracy...

conceive of design & technology holistically and to serve a democratic future and not any narrow, current ideology. It is to embrace critique, change and challenge and to see all technologies for what they are - essentially controversial and problematic.

Technological literacy?

This term can only be given brief comments here but I believe it offers a place for debate and discussion. The absence of 'design' in the name is problematic and just as we can conceive of 'design literacy', other conceptual possibilities have been offered. For example, Kurt Seemann, seeking to redress the attention given to 'numeracy' and 'literacy' in the curriculum, has developed the term *'technacy'* (Seemann, 2003). A comprehensive collection of writings around technological literacy has been assembled by John Dakers (2006) and a key discussion of the politics of technological literacy was presented by Stephen Petrina (Petrina, 2000b).

When we are weighing up all the competing variables of design & technology's own 'design', using a term like technological literacy can be helpful. It also helps articulate design and technology's richness to those people beyond the field (our managers come to mind) who haven't received the benefit of a quality design and technology education. Recalling David Layton's words on

technological literacy we can explore the relationship between how the term is constructed and who controls the curriculum. Some would say that *skilled* people are technologically literate but this is not enough.

We could say that someone who *understands the social effects and uses of technologies* was technologically literate but this is not enough either. Further, we could say that someone who had *a critical disposition to see themselves as a being in relation to technologies and to choose to act autonomously with regard to them* was technologically literate. Would this satisfy technological literacy's meaning?

I would argue that there is a case for shaping design & technology in ways that are: holistic - multiple dimensions interplay; critical - questioning and discomfort with regard to technologies are valid; and dynamic - all aspects are subject to change and modification. Clearly, this is not a content- (knowledge-) based model for a school subject but it is a lot closer to the world of designed technologies. If we are to embrace the politics of technologies, of environment and of government, then (as with assessment in design & technology) atomised and reductionist approaches just don't work. For example, Stephen Petrina (2000a), argues against technocentric approaches to design & technology in favour of a 'political ecology' approach while my own focus has been on ethics-democracy-technological literacy interplay (Keirl, 2006).

(Re)visioning the profession

When you reflect (alone or with colleagues)
on design & technology curriculum,
what disquiets you? Could we be in a
different place - strategically, professionally,
in how it looks, in what it does? Democracy,
education, curriculum, design & technology
are *all* in some sense ideals - cases of perpetual
searches for the goals they espouse.
They are never arrived at. That is their lot.
But they are about determination and change.

There is an important dimension here
and it is the concern of many curriculum
theorists today. It is about professional *vision*,
and considering ways of boosting our personal
and collective efficacy. It legitimately embraces
such non-material values as hope and
optimism and belief in change for the (global)
better - not just the 'more-is-good' mantra
of progress cast as economic growth.
In this vein, Hargreaves (2003) talks
of the *'...need for social ingenuity and moral
integrity...(and it being) time to redefine our vision
and reassert some values.'* (pp. 161-162).

? Do you think there
is value in the idea
of having 'professional
vision'?
How can it be both
idealistic yet practical?

Metaphors and descriptors for teachers

You've probably played the metaphor game
at some time - teacher as lion-tamer, as juggler,
shepherd and so on - and it's a useful exercise
to pursue. After years of pressure for teachers
to perform better, to maintain standards
and to be more and more efficient, it seems
fitting to see the teacher as a cog in the
machine. Better, perhaps, we can elevate
our status to technician, proud to do the job
well but not expected to apply any
professional judgement at all. Is this
acceptable? There are plenty of teachers
who would just say *'Give me the syllabus
and I'll teach it the best I can with the resources
you give me'* (teachers always say something
about resources). This is the sausage factory
model - no visionary or social thinking,
no professional judgement, no input to the
curriculum. You produce, you're paid,
your output is measured (and your
productivity is recalibrated next time round).

But what of change, vision and action?
We can turn to teacher as curriculum
designer/builder; as professional; as activist;
as ethical agent; as reflective practitioner;
as enquirer; as researcher; as political actor
and so on. Each of these metaphors
or descriptors is worth collegial exploration
and each can be theorised as a possibility
or, better, drawn upon and blended into
your own vision of professional.

"Professional
development
apartheid"
- something
to be resisted

05 Professor Andy
Hargreaves.

But the key question is - how do we get to a better professional position within, and for, design & technology? Not from complacency, whingeing or leaving it to others to act. Professional determination is called for.

An exercise that can be fun yet serious too is that of discussing apt metaphors for you as teacher.
Is there a metaphor which doesn't apply at present but might be worth working towards?

Professional action - new determinations

It seems to me that determination can have several senses. First, it is anti-determinist - it rejects ideas that 'progress' and 'fate' are forces immune to our intervention. Second, it avows our efficacy - our faith in ourselves and our can-do as a profession that *can* effect change for the better. Thus, third, when we determine choices, we *apply* our reasoned decision-making capabilities to come up with the best possible option at that time. It is one thing *to know that we have the power* to determine futures and it is another *to choose to act* - to use that power for good.

If we are sincere about professional action then we need new determinations -

ones which are ethically grounded so they are defensible as actions within and for democratic practice and life. They also need to be political - i.e., strategic in intent and guided by the expression of collegial values - the professional ethic. If democracy is the most ethically defensible way of co-existing then the education system, those it serves (citizens singly and collectively) and those who serve it (us) need ethically defensible arguments. Defending our educational values in public will only happen if those values promote the common good.

If collegiality and collectivism are ways forward, then we need to celebrate debate and critique - with all colleagues within and beyond design & technology and in the public arena. We can re-cast ourselves in ways that see us as moral visionary (Hargreaves, 2003) with re-established social status and dignity. If a sophisticated society needs sophisticated educators, then a visionary society needs visionary educators. Both Mihaly Csikszentmihalyi (1996) and Richard Florida (2003) adopt this approach when they write about creativity.

When Florida portrays the kinds of occupational classes he sees in society (creative, working, service, agriculture) he subdivides the first of these into a 'super-creative core' and 'creative professionals' (Florida, 2003, p. 328). And there are we - teachers and educators - members of the super-creative core!

Professional learning communities	Performance training sects
Transform knowledge	Transfer knowledge
Shared inquiry	Imposed requirements
Evidence informed	Results driven
Situated certainty	False certainty
Local solutions	Standardized scripts
Joint responsibility	Deference to authority
Continuous learning	Intensive training
Communities of practice	Sects of performance

06

06 Professional learning communities and performance training sects

(Based on an original article by Andy Hargreaves).

Professional breathing

But to take visionary action we need room for professional breathing. Here, of course is one of the many conundrums we face. When we are kept so busy (intentionally, it can be argued) with our day-to-day work, one challenge is simply to find the time to spend with colleagues to discuss matters of mutual professional interest. How do we build our collegiality? There are several options - particularly through one's professional association - reading about the practice of others, reporting your own best practice and attending seminars and conferences.

It is interesting to look at the work that has been done in studying teacher renewal - the idea that we need continuously to refresh and to re-orient (even re-determine) our values and aims throughout our careers. While we might be reflective practitioners on a daily basis, what are the opportunities to renew collegially? While what is known as professional development can provide this, it might just be worth looking at the form that this takes. (I'm reminded of one Dean of Education who refuses to take her staff on annual 'retreats', preferring more frequent 'advances'.)

Discussing professional growth, Andy Hargreaves (2003) presents two broad approaches evident from his team's research. He compares 'professional learning communities' (PLCs) with 'performance training sects' (PTSs). The contrasting language in the naming is illuminating though they are not an opposing binary. Let's consider the summary attributes of each in the table above.

To unmask the politics of these approaches one has only to consider how power is distributed for each of the listed criteria. For example: Who's in? Who's out? Who decides? Who benefits? So we find that, while both of these approaches may have their place in education, the PTS positions us as *dependent* whereas the PLC empowers us as *autonomous professionals*. Hargreaves argues that it is the latter to which we should aspire - what do you think? He also shows how the PTS is used by systems for the majority of schools (including those deemed to be 'failing') while the PLC is reserved for the few 'high-flyer' schools. Such segregation and distribution is nothing if it is not political. Hargreaves calls it 'professional development apartheid'.

Politicking design & technology

Judyth Sachs (2003) discusses *'old professionalism'* and *'transformative professionalism'*. The former she describes as being characterised by *'exclusive membership; conservative practices; self-interest; external regulation; (being) slow to change; and, (being)*

07 Professor Judyth Sachs.

"An activist teaching profession is an educated and politically astute one"

reactive' (Sachs, 2003, pp. 11-12).
The latter is the focus of her text which finishes with:
'...a call to action. An activist teaching profession is an educated and politically astute one. The will to achieve this is lying dormant in many of us, and now is the time to work towards its development and realization in systematic and collective ways' (Sachs, 2003, p. 154).

For many years the design & technology community has carried more of a curriculum development burden than most subjects - especially those born with their silver spoons (English, maths, science) who have historical precedent, unchallenged status, and assured resources on their side. The changes that have brought about what we now know as design & technology are the result of many actions - not least excellent and innovative teaching. But it is also a matter of being political, always with well supported argument, and this is a matter of combining theory, practice, research, thinking, big picture, local innovation, staffroom push and political lobbying.

What has been achieved over the last three to four decades is quite remarkable for one subject. Yet things remain insecure. New fashions and trends come along. Governments get new ideas, act with little heed to what the profession might think, and 'sell' the idea through the media. To have significant influence over the agenda calls for strong and articulate

professionals and professionalism. It calls for 'action beyond' and 'thinking beyond'.

Such action and thinking begs political perspectives and I would suggest that there are five ways that we can look at design & technology curriculum politically:

1. **The global.**
   Design & technology's relationship to design(ing) and technology/ies 'out there' as human practices. Are we just playing curriculum-catch-up all the time - trying to mimic the technological world with skills and knowledge for industry and economies? Or are we thinking of other worlds too - of the enlightened kind?

2. **The would-be stakeholders.**
   Can we effect a balance? Who are we really serving in our educational work? Do certain curriculum alliances and funding sources really help our cause and design & technology's integrity?

3. **Society.**
   How and what we contribute to the general education of all students as citizens. That is, to create a society with design intelligence as part of its culture, to show how technologies behave in democratic and anti-democratic ways, and to help citizens engage more in technological decision-making (Keirl, 2001; Baynes, 2005).

4. Students as fulfilled persons.
How we defend design & technology
education for all students as persons -
helping their critical thinking, designerly
dispositions, a host of skills, communication
and information abilities, their creativity
as a means of empowerment,
and their problem-overcoming capability.

5. Curriculum dynamics.
Advocating and defending our legitimate
place in a 21st Century curriculum.
This calls for a/our capacity to articulate
comprehensive (not partial) educational
arguments with all those with whom
we interact and who have
curriculum influence.

? Consider each of these
five perspectives and
discuss the extent to which
you act on them in your
professional work.
For each of them,
what are the implications
of your not acting
on them?

Political act-ing

There is no field so educationally stimulating,
challenging and worthwhile as design
& technology. *We* know that! But nice rosy
statements aren't enough.
We are not a curriculum island.

Paulo Freire (1972) wrote the much
referred-to political critique of education
and literacy **"Pedagogy of the Oppressed"**
and he saw curriculum as a dialogue
to be created and re-created. We might
see it as a building that we can modify
and change for its dwellers. That is the way
of things, to design and to redesign
as an articulate professional group.

The key, for me, is our efficacy - our ability
to engage, deliver and be heard within
and beyond the profession.

This calls for our (respected) professional
judgement, which will be the consideration
of all the factors discussed here.
That judgement will, ultimately,
need to be ethically defensible - to serve
each student, the whole of society,
and humanity. Enlightened globalisation
shows us the interconnectedness
of these three.

But the judgements are nothing without
action - that other sense of determination -
the awakening of the 'dormant will'.

The question *'How should we act?'*
is both ethical and political. Having
come to a reasoned ethical position,
alone or with others, means little if we
don't act - by taking our values 'out there'.
Ultimately, we could ask *'What is our vision
for education through design & technology?'*
and having our vision, *'How will we go about
achieving it?'*

References

Apple, M. W. (2001). "Educating the 'Right' Way: markets, standards, God and inequality". New York: Routledge Falmer.

Baynes, K. (2005). "Design and democracy: speculations on the radical potential of design, design practice and design education". Wellesbourne, UK: The Design and Technology Association.

Bottery, M. (1996). 'The challenge to professionals from the new public management: implications for the teaching profession'. "Oxford Review of Education". 22. (2), 179-197.

Csikszentmihalyi, M. (1997). "Creativity: Flow and the psychology of discovery and invention". London: Harper Perennial.

Dakers, J. R. (Ed.) (2006). "Defining Technological Literacy: Towards an Epistemological Framework". New York: Palgrave Macmillan.

Florida, R. (2003). "The Rise of the Creative Class: and how it's transforming work, leisure, community and everyday life". North Melbourne, Australia: Pluto Press.

Freire, P. (1972). "Pedagogy of the Oppressed". London: Penguin.

Galbraith, J. K. (2004). "The Economics of Innocent Fraud". London: Penguin.

Hargreaves, A. (2003). "Teaching in the Knowledge Society: Education in the age of insecurity". Maidenhead, UK: Open University Press. (Also available from Teachers College Press, New York, 2003.)

Keirl, S. (2001). 'As if Democracy Mattered... design, technology and citizenship or "Living with the temperamental elephant"'. In E. W. L. Norman & P. H. Roberts, (Eds.). "Design and Technology Educational Research and Curriculum Development: The emerging international research agenda". (pp. 70-89). Loughborough, UK: Loughborough University.

Keirl, S. (2004). 'Creativity, Innovation and life in the lily-pond: nurturing the Design and Technology family while keeping the alligators fed. "Journal of Design and Technology Education". 9. (3), 145-160.

Keirl, S. (2006). 'Ethical technological literacy as democratic curriculum keystone'. In J. R. Dakers, (Ed.), (2006), "Defining Technological Literacy: Towards an Epistemological Framework". (pp. 81-104), New York: Palgrave Macmillan.

Layton, D. (Ed.) (1994). "Innovations in Science and Technology Education". Vol. V. Paris: UNESCO.

Peters, R. S. (Ed.). (1973). "The Philosophy of Education". London: Oxford University Press.

Petrina, S. (2000a). 'The Political Ecology of Design and Technology Education: An inquiry into methods'. "International Journal of Technology and Design Education". 10, 207-237.

Petrina, S. (2000b). 'The Politics of Technological Literacy'. "International Journal of Technology and Design Education". 10, 181-206.

Sachs, J. (2003). "The Activist Teaching Profession". Buckingham, UK: Open University Press.

Seemann, K. (2003). 'Basic principles in holistic technology education'. "Journal of Technology Education". 14. (2), available at http://scholar.lib.vt.edu/ejournals/JTE/v14n2/seemann.html.

Seemann, K. W. & Talbot, R. (1995). 'Technacy: Towards a holistic understanding of technology teaching and learning among Aboriginal Australians'. "Prospect, UNESCO Quarterly Review of Comparative Education". 25. (4), 761-775.

White, P. A. (1973). 'Education, Democracy, and the Public Interest'. In R. S. Peters, (Ed.). "The Philosophy of Education". London: Oxford University Press.

The place of sustainability in design & technology education

Margarita Pavlova

Margarita Pavlova currently works in the Faculty of Education at Griffith University, Australia. She has two PhDs: from Russia and Australia. She works as a researcher and consultant with international, national and state agencies, including the World Bank; UNESCO; the Russian Ministry of Education, and Education Queensland. Her main research interests include conceptualisations of technology education through philosophical, sociological and comparative studies. Her current research projects are in the area of education for sustainability. Margarita is the author/co-author of seven books.

James Pitt

A design & technology teacher by background, James is now senior research fellow in education at the University of York. He has published extensively in the area of education for sustainable development (ESD) and runs an MA by Research with an ESD focus. His other interests include the relationship between science and technology learning in schools, the emerging school engineering agenda and competency-oriented learning. He has worked extensively in all these areas overseas and especially in Russia, where he is a professor at Komsomol'sk-na-Amure State Pedagogical University.

The place of sustainability in design & technology education

Margarita Pavlova and James Pitt

Introduction

The need to address sustainability has suddenly appeared in agendas for educational policy around the globe. The emergence of the issue has been motivated by a number of reports that suggest that humankind is living beyond the carrying capacity of planet earth. Footprinting studies (a way of measuring the environmental impacts of different lifestyles) such as the **"Living Planet Report"** (WWF, 2006) indicate that we globally began to live beyond the Earth's carrying capacity in 1987 (see image overleaf).

Recent studies by WWF (2006) and Jerrard Pierce (2005) demonstrate that industrialised countries have the greatest impact on this process. Jerrard Pierce's cartogram (2005) shows graphically the relative contributions of different countries to global ecological footprints.

The "Ecological footprint by region…" graph (overleaf) gives comparable data by region for 2003. The overall area of the rectangle indicates the impact. Thus relatively few people in North America living at a high level of consumption have an impact significantly higher than the whole population of Africa. The charts for energy footprints and water withdrawal paint similar pictures - that people in the wealthy countries consume a disproportionate amount of resources (WWF, 2006).

The UK can be taken to represent the industrialised world. If everyone in the world were to live at the same level of consumption as people in the UK, there would be a need for three planets.

> If people emerge from poverty and aspire to western lifestyles, can the planet earth sustain it? But what are the alternatives - continued poverty, huge reductions in population, or some other way of limiting damage to the planet?

Clearly the present trends are unsustainable. Almost every scientific academy in the world now says that there is a causal connection between high levels of consumption, greenhouse gases and climate change, which is already having a disproportionate impact on poorer people. Image 03 (overleaf) presents the model of the world by the 2050s where global warming and climate change has a disproportionate impact in the poorer countries. People in the industrialised world need to radically rethink how we live - our buildings, travel, diet, use of energy and in particular the type of technologies we use. Without a rethink of lifestyle a forecast for the wellbeing of the earth is not optimistic.

In October 2006 the government published the "Stern Review on the Economics of Climate Change". This report made clear that the situation facing the world is very serious. Here are some quotes from the executive summary.

- *'The scientific evidence is now overwhelming: climate change is a serious global threat, and it demands an urgent global response'.*
- *'Climate change could have very serious effects on growth and development'.*
- *'The costs of stabilising the climate are significant but manageable; delay would be dangerous and much more costly'.*
- *'Action on climate change is required across all countries, and it need not cap the aspirations for growth of rich or poor countries'.*
- *'A range of options exists to cut emissions (of greenhouse gases); strong, deliberate policy action is required to motivate their take-up'.*

01 Humanity's world ecological footprint over time.
(© 2006, WWF (panda.org). Some rights reserved.)

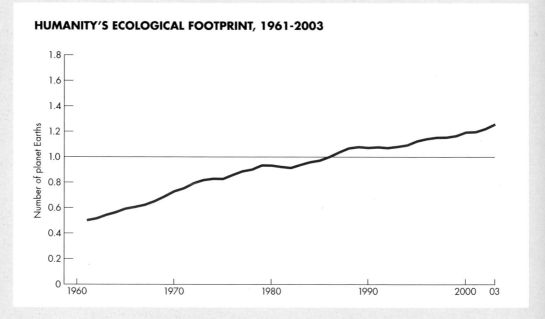

HUMANITY'S ECOLOGICAL FOOTPRINT, 1961-2003

- *'Climate change demands an international response, based on a shared understanding of long-term goals and agreement on frameworks for action'.*

You can find out more about the Stern Review at this website: http://www.hm-treasury.gov.uk/independent_reviews/stern_review_economics_climate_change/sternreview_index.cfm

The Stern Review's findings have been emphasised by the recent report of the Intergovernmental Panel on Climate Change (2007). It seems obvious that the way forward is through sustainable development but this is not straightforward as there is no one broadly accepted definition of the concept of sustainable development.

02 Ecological footprint by region.

03 Prospective relative impacts of climate change assuming 'business as normal'.

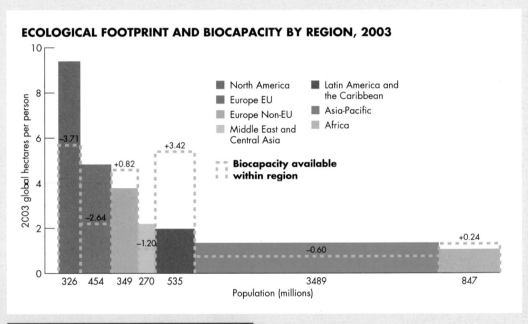

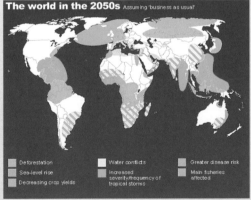

To what extent do you think it is possible for design & technology lessons to provide space for students to rethink what is desirable and to challenge assumptions about what is needed?

What is meant by 'sustainable development'?

A widely used definition comes from the World Commission on Environment and Development (1987), in what is generally known as the "Bruntland Report". Sustainable development is defined as *'development that meets the needs of the present without compromising the ability of future generations to meet their own needs'.* This has led to a well-known approach for analysing sustainability that includes social, economic and environmental dimensions without any prioritising. Although widely accepted, this approach has been recently criticised. "Forum for the Future" argues that in this form this approach is invalid.
'A popular way of understanding sustainability is the concept of the triple bottom line of economic, environmental and social accountability. This idea proposes that an organisation's licence to operate in society comes not just from satisfying stakeholders through improved profits (the economic bottom line), but by improving its environmental and social performance…

Whilst this concept is useful, we feel it is limited by giving equal weighting to each of the three bottom lines. We believe that environmental sustainability is pre-conditional, because without it the other bottom lines can't exist!'
(Forum for the Future, 2006)

People in many developing countries might give greater emphasis to economic or social aspects of development. For Western societies, however, it is important to give the environmental bottom line particular significance. The model of sustainable development described here presupposes that the carrying capacity of the ecosystem (environmental limits) defines and envelops the extent of human action. The economy is tailored to work within this ecosystem's capacity. The needs of communities to develop and maintain eco-efficient and sustainable technologies or ways of doing things have to work within the limits of natural ecosystems.

Sustainable development can be seen as change for the better in which social, cultural and economic needs are met without plundering non-renewable resources nor threatening eco-systems. Forum of the Future defines sustainable development as:
'A dynamic process which enables all people to realise their potential and improve their quality of life in ways which simultaneously protect and enhance the Earth's life support systems'.
(Forum for the Future, 2006)

Working within an essentially capitalist model of society, they extend the concept of capital to include natural, human, social, manufactured and financial capital and say: *'Sustainable development is the best way to manage these capital assets in the long-term. It is a dynamic process through which organisations can begin to achieve a balance between their environmental, social and economic activities…*

In the sustainable society, four conditions must apply…The system conditions mean that nature is not subject to systematically increasing

1. *concentrations of substances extracted from the earth's crust - such as heavy metals.*
2. *concentrations of substances produced by society - such as plastic waste.*
3. *degradation by physical means - such as rising sea levels or desertification.*

And, in that society…

4. *human needs are met worldwide…'*

This thinking is expanded by Jonathan Porritt (2005) in his book **"Capitalism as if the earth matters"**. He argues that (a) we have to live sustainably on Planet Earth, and that if we do not we are faced with ecological disaster; (b) that since capitalism will remain the dominant economic system for the time being, we have to work towards sustainability through a capitalist economy.

This view is challenged by other thinkers such as Arne Naess (1990), the author of the **"Deep Ecology"** concept which proposes a radical critique of capitalism. Two points made by Naess are:

1. All life has value in itself, independent of its usefulness to humans.
2. Basic ideological, political, economic and technological structures must change.

To what extent do you believe that 'All life has value in itself, independent of its usefulness to humans'? What are the implications for designing and making?

However sustainable development is conceptualised, everyone agrees that education plays an essential role as we move towards more just and sustainable relationships and hence world order. In this chapter we are considering the contribution of design & technology towards education for sustainable development, which is usually called just ESD.

Recent developments in ESD

As governments, industry, NGOs and policy makers generally have become more aware of the urgency of sustainable development, educators have increasingly seen that there is a vital role in both formal and non-formal teaching and learning towards sustainability. UNESCO (2004) has dedicated 2005- 2014 as the **"Decade of Education for Sustainable Development"**.

Doorway	2. Energy and water
Curriculum	Schools can use the curriculum to cultivate the knowledge, values and skills needed to address energy and water stewardship - both at a local and a global level.
Campus	Schools can review their use of energy and water and establish policies for monitoring and reducing their use through good management and the deployment of appropriate technologies.
Community	Schools can use their communications, services, contracts and partnerships to promote awareness of sustainable energy and water use among their stakeholders.
Target	By 2020, the Government would like all schools to have minimised their carbon emissions by becoming good examples of energy efficiency, showcasing wind, solar, bio-fuel and other appropriate energy sources in their communities. Within the same time frame, the Government would like to see all schools minimising their use of freshwater by becoming good examples of sustainable water management, demonstrating freshwater conservation, rainwater use, and other water-saving measures in their communities.

04

04 Recommendations for the energy and water 'doorway'.

Back in 1999 Faye Benedict developed a model of a systematic approach to sustainable environmental education. She proposed that for change to occur, teaching as an activity should take place in a multilevel system: teacher-student level, classroom level, school level, school system level, political level and outside world. She argued that teachers should consciously act at a range of levels, putting their efforts into a broad perspective. This is supported by focus group studies in England conducted by Cai Cheadle, Gillian Simmons and James Pitt in 2004. The Department for Education and Science in England acknowledged this need for multi-level intervention in 2006 when they published their sustainable schools policy as a framework for planning. The centrepiece of this approach is to think in terms of 'doorways'. Rather than impose yet another 'you ought to do this…' onto browbeaten teachers and school administrators, schools are being invited to examine all the different ways they can engage in more sustainable behaviour, under the headings of curriculum, campus and community.

There are 8 doorways into becoming a more sustainable school:
1. food and drink;
2. energy and water;
3. travel and traffic;
4. purchasing and waste;
5. buildings and grounds;
6. inclusion and participation;
7. local well-being;
8. global citizenship.

For each doorway there are recommendations for how the school should behave (campus) and how this can link to teaching and learning (curriculum). Schools can develop or use their relationships in the local community to become champions and living examples of sustainable development (community). The fifth row specifies targets.

The thinking is that it does not matter which doorway is emphasised within a school, as sooner or later they all link up. The energy and water doorway is reproduced above.

The strength of this approach is that it links teaching and learning to school policy and practice. There are huge opportunities in the first five themes for design & technology teachers.

What might go into the curriculum, campus, community and targets for
• food and drink?
• travel and traffic?
• purchasing and waste?
• buildings and grounds?

You can check out your answers against the

05

05 Where the Sakha people live.

framework provided by the government at this url: http://www.teachernet.gov.uk/sustainableschools/framework/framework_detail.cfm

The relationship between humanity, technology and nature

Throughout history the relationship between humanity and nature has been among the most important existential and philosophical issues. In traditional, rural cultures the unity of humanity and nature was part of the overall perception of the world and up until now some indigenous cultures have preserved this view. For example the people of Sakha, one of the nations of the Far North of Russia, have a number of 'rules' related to respect and protection of spirits and nature:

'Don't spoil fire.
Don't pollute water; keep it clean.
Don't dig up the earth.
Keep air clean.
Don't break stones into pieces.
Do not trample down the green grass.
Do not damage a tree.
Protect animals and birds'.
(Shamaeva M.I, Semenova V.D & Sitnikova N.V, 1995, p. 69)

As humankind has developed, this holistic understanding of the world in terms of the relationships between humanity and nature has changed, particularly in the West. The accumulation of technological knowledge has been aimed mainly towards the effective control of the physical world in terms of the exploitation of nature and its resources. The conceptual split between humans and nature that philosophers refer to as a 'Cartesian dualism' has established a dualism that is fundamental to the Western worldview: *'One key legacy is that we still separate or disassociate things that are related... Separation and fragmentation extended to almost everything including science, art, ecology and economics, people and nature. It is essentially a materialist worldview, which isolates and diminishes spiritual and sacred aspects of reality'* (Stephen Sterling, 1993, p. 75).

A strong belief that science and technology can expand human power has been predicated on an unaccountable use of natural resources. People saw this scientific-technological progress as an independent source of profit creation, on which economic growth depends. In the view of Jurgen Habermas the process of the *'scientization of technology'* has gone hand in hand with research under government contracts in the military sector, at least since the end of the 19th century (Habermas, J. 1968/ 1971, p. 104). Thus, technological development and an increase of the technocratic ideology with its strong belief in the unlimited development of technology have greatly contributed to environmental and social problems. This in turn has impacted on the way that sustainable development is conceptualised.

> What is your view on the extent to which technology can contribute towards the resolution of social problems that will lead to sustainable development? How might students be encouraged to go beyond the environmental dimensions of sustainable design, so that they also consider the social and economic impacts of a new product or technology?

Education for sustainable development as a 'frame of mind'

In reviewing different approaches to ESD, John Huckle (2005) distinguishes between two broad trends: (a) ESD as *policy*, and (b) ESD as a *frame of mind*.

(a) ESD as policy

One approach to design & technology might look like this. As teachers we inform students about resource depletion, use and abuse of energy, pollution, poverty and so on. We invite them to make design decisions (in their projects) that have the minimum negative impact on the environment, economy or social relations. We encourage them to weigh up the three dimensions of sustainable development (social, environmental and economic) and to justify their design decisions by demonstrating an overall improvement when comparing what they have designed with the product it is replacing or need that it is meeting.

In each year or key stage we will ensure that there is a project which lends itself to raising issues of sustainability across the whole lifecycle of a product. We hope that what they learn in this project can be extrapolated and applied to other projects. We further hope that once their eyes are opened as to how things can be made better through design and technology, students will make 'better' choices as designers and consumers, in their lives outside and beyond school. As teachers and curriculum developers we aim to *'develop "positive" attitudes among our students, to realise sustainability indicators and deliver "relevant" knowledge as set down in policy documents'* (John Huckle, 2005).

> To what extent does this describe what you have seen in school?

John Huckle questions this whole approach. Sustainability can be viewed as a policy designed to achieve a certain state of affairs, whilst covertly failing to question the 'attitude of mind that sanctions the continued exploitation and oppression of human and non-human nature'. Huckle implies that the viewing of sustainability as policy, and ESD as one aspect of this policy, does not and will not work. It is not enough to know that burning fossil fuels causes climate change. We have known this for a long time and we are still increasing the use of fossil fuels. We know that air travel is unsustainable and yet the UK government will not tax aviation fuel. New cheap airfares and routes are appearing all the time. We know that over 25% of traffic on motorways is generated by shifting food around the country yet we continue to buy from supermarkets rather than farmers' markets - and so on. We are shocked by images of poverty and exploitation yet continue to buy clothes without questioning their provenance. The question is, why do we not change our behaviour?

Many bodies view ESD as an aspect of overall sustainable development policy, one which is *designed to close "value-action" gaps between people's knowledge and concern for sustainability issues and their lack of relevant action and support for relevant policy'* (John Huckle, 2005). Put the facts in front of people (this thinking goes) and they will change their behaviour.

Huckle argues that this is a simplistic view based on assumptions of cause and effect that simply do not hold true. The so-called 'facts' are not agreed, or at the very least are open to very different interpretations or meanings.

We are not always rational in our decision-making. Our value systems (seldom made explicit) influence the way we perceive the world and think. There is no consensus about what needs to be done. And treating ESD as one aspect of policy allows teachers and schools to compartmentalise it in a way that dissociates anything that children might learn from what they actually do.

(b) ESD as a 'frame of mind'
An alternative approach is to think about sustainability and hence ESD as a frame of mind starting from very different assumptions:
- There is no consensus as to what is meant by 'sustainable development'.
- Different people have different views and interpretations about the bio-physical world and social relations. These both inform and are influenced by each person's underlying values and beliefs.
- These values and beliefs need to be made explicit as we explore the concept of sustainability as a way of relating to nature.
- Therefore both the content of what we teach and the way in which we teach should be informed by these different views.

John Huckle (2005) quotes Michael Bonnett (2002):
'If we are to enable pupils to address the issues raised by sustainable development rather than preoccupy them with what are essentially symptoms masquerading as causes, we must engage them in those kinds of enquiry which reveal the underlying dominant motives that are in play in society;

motives which are inherent in our most fundamental ways of thinking about ourselves and the world. That such a metaphysical investigation will be discomforting for many seems unavoidable, but it promises to be more productive in the long term than proceeding on the basis of easy assumptions about the goals of sustainable development as though it were a policy whose chief problems are of implementation rather than meaning'.

To what extent do you think it is the role of design & technology alone in the curriculum to engage in ESD? Discuss with colleagues who teach geography and science what their views are and find out to what extent they adopt a frame of mind approach.

Implications of ESD for teaching and learning in design & technology

In order to consider how ESD might influence teaching and learning in design & technology we must first position design & technology within the overall education endeavour. The recent QCA initiative to review the secondary curriculum states that the aim of the curriculum is for all young people to become:

• *'Successful learners who enjoy learning,*
make progress and achieve'
• *'Confident individuals who are able to live safe, healthy and fulfilling lives'*
• *'Responsible citizens who make a positive contribution to society'*

See http://curriculum.qca.org.uk/subjects (accessed on 17.10.07) for more detail.

This looks uncontentious until particular phrases are unpacked. For example, what is meant by making *'a positive contribution to society'*? If this is seen solely in terms of making an economic contribution, then the role of design & technology becomes the narrow one of fitting young people for employment within occupations that require the particular knowledge, understanding and skill that can be learned in a vocational manifestation of the subject. The place of ESD here is limited at best and will probably not involve a frame of mind approach. If, however, making a positive contribution to society is seen in much wider terms as developing an ecologically-oriented and critical world outlook, then design & technology is well positioned to respond to ESD with the opportunity to adopt a frame of mind approach.

For the two views of making a positive contribution to society put in order of priority the following statements about the purpose of design & technology education:

1. It should prepare students with technical skills so that they can get jobs;
2. It should enable students to uncover and analyse the moral decisions that underlie the development and production of a product;
3. It should be a central part of helping students to see what changes need to be made if they are to live more sustainably;
4. It should give students generic competencies such as thinking, problem-solving and team-working;
5. It should prepare students with life skills such as cooking and making things so that they are technically competent as adults.

Product life cycle analysis is a key concept in discerning the impact of a product or technology on the environment and, with the use of appropriate tools, the wider impact on society and economic activity. It can be used to good effect in the curriculum as part of a frame of mind approach to ESD. Product life cycle analysis is sometimes referred to as cradle-to-grave analysis. For any given product this analysis requires a consideration of the following:

- The raw materials and their sources;
- How these materials are processed;
- How the processed materials are manufactured to give rise to the product;
- How the product is distributed and sold;
- How the product is used;
- What happens to the product at the end of its useful life.

At most stages there will be transport involved. Sometimes the materials, manufacture and disposal will have the biggest impact, as in the case of a battery-powered torch. By contrast the impact of an electric kettle will be largely in its use: the oil or gas burned and resulting CO_2 emissions in electricity generation will have an impact some thousands of times higher than that of bringing the product into being and disposing of it.

So pupils can be taught to use product life cycle analysis when considering existing products, in speculating on the impact of the products they design and make should they be put into production and also those products that they develop to the 'concept only' stage. If done regularly, the sophistication with which the process is carried out can lead to the unpacking of different views and

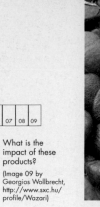

06 - 09 What is the impact of these products?

(Image 09 by Georgios Wollbrecht, http://www.sxc.hu/profile/Wazari)

interpretations of the relationships between nature and humanity. In this way the gradual movement from ESD as policy to ESD as a frame of mind can occur.

The approach can be extended by considering winners and losers at each stage of the product's life. In the development, use and disposal of any product there will be those who benefit and those who become worse off. The winning and losing can take place at individual and community level and involve both economic and social impacts. In many cases these impacts are related. For example, the building of nuclear power stations in England has massive environmental implications stretching far into the future, but for the communities of coal miners who became unemployed because nuclear power was the government's preferred option to coal-fired generation of electricity, the result was economic decline and social malaise through the disintegration of their communities.

Choose one or more of the following products and carry out product life cycle analysis. Use this analysis to identify the environmental impact of the product.

• Fair trade coffee from Africa.
• Scissors manufactured in China.
• A computer manufactured in Taiwan.
• Clothing manufactured in India.

Use a winners and losers analysis for some of the stages in the cycle to extend this analysis to include social and economic impacts.

To what extent do you think it possible to engage pupils in design & technology classes with this approach?

You can find out more about a structured approach to winners and losers at this url: http://www.secondarydandt.org/resources/ks3/frk3_0000000013.asp

Analysis undertaken by Margarita Pavlova (2006a, 2005) demonstrates that to deal with ESD via design & technology is a very complex task. Two popular approaches identified in the literature towards SD - 'technological fix' and 'value change' (Robinson, 2004) were analysed by Margarita to explore which one might work better for design & technology. After she conducted the analysis of both approaches using philosophy of technology and sociology of consumerism, she concluded that neither approach would work on its own.

To appreciate the value of the *'technological fix'* approach Margarita has critically analysed the concept of technology within the broader philosophy of technology. Margarita Pavlova (2006b) demonstrates that technology on its own cannot fix all the problems of the modern world and concludes that it is even dangerous to believe that. She raises the question as to whether it is always possible to use technology ethically. For example cloning technologies provide a lot of possibilities, but legislation in some countries prevents scientists from carrying out any experiments on humans due to a number of ethical issues. However, some scientists have been using this technology on human cells. Although most technologies have positive features that can be used for sustainable development of the world, their major aim is the optimal performance. Henry Skolimowski (1966, p. 375) describes this as:

'…maximizing output (the information or modifications obtained) and minimizing input (the energy expended in the process). Thus, these are the main aims for developing technology. The nature of technology could be described as "to produce more and more diversified objects with more and more interesting features, in a more and more efficient way"'.

 To what extent do you agree with Margarita Pavlova that a technological fix could not be seen as the only way to achieve sustainability?

Margarita Pavlova (2005) uses the sociology of consumerism to analyse how a *value change* approach to ESD could be positioned in a consumer society, the society where aesthetics, not ethics, is the prevailing paradigm. People, Margarita argues, are preoccupied with the appearance of the products. In particular aesthetics plays an increasingly important role in influencing youth's identity. At the same time ethics has a diminishing role, even though ESD is thought of as an ethically-based approach to education. Similar to the *'technological fix'* approach, a *'value change'* approach cannot be seen as the only one to be used in the classroom. However, another important aspect emerged from this analysis - the importance of aesthetics. If we accept this, an important role for aesthetics should be design for sustainability, or to put it the other way, education for sustainability should pay more attention to aesthetics. There is a need to understand the relationships of interdependence of the ethical and aesthetical components of sustainability, as well as the relationships with social and economic aspects of product design.

It is important to note that aesthetics today is conceived in broad terms. As Ralph Alan Smith and Alan Simpson (1991, p. 18) express it, aesthetics *'…tends not to concentrate exclusively on the concept of beauty; aesthetics is the attempt to understand our experiences of and the concepts we use to talk about objects that we find perceptually interesting and attractive'.*

Fruit from a local farm, picked and put on display at a farmers market is unlikely to look as uniform or unblemished as fruit on display at a supermarket. It is also unlikely to be available in such a wide variety, being restricted to what can be grown seasonally in the locality. But the range of choice and blemish-free uniformity comes at a price, air miles and a process of selection with the rejected fruit probably going to waste. Appreciating the beauty of the locally grown requires underpinning of more than a little life cycle analysis! This close relationship between aesthetics and ethics can be used for the development and use of the concept of aesthetics for sustainability with students. Through their product design they can influence consumer choices in modern society in a positive way.

There is a danger, however, that students (many of whom are products of a materialistic, individualistic, hedonistic, high-consumption-and-bugger-the-consequences, instant gratification society) will be bored out of their heads by overt moralising. The key (following John Huckle) is to see ESD as discourse analysis. Let us examine what people are actually thinking and feeling and saying to each other about design decisions and ask, why do they think that? What are their (and our) presuppositions and preconceptions? Let teachers confess their own duplicity and share this with their students in dialogue. Perhaps one consequence of adopting a frame of mind approach is that teachers must be prepared to deal with conflict - not comfortable, but possible.

To what extent do you think it will be possible to educate pupils in an aesthetics of sustainability? Try to develop some useful examples.

Conclusions

We believe that in the teaching and learning of design & technology it is vital to avoid the implicit suggestion that sustainability is just another thing to think about.

Further reading

Fuad-Luke, A. (2005). "The Eco-Design Handbook - a complete sourcebook for the home and office". London: Thames and Hudson.

Huckel, J. & Sterling S. (Eds.)(1996). "Education for Sustainability". London: Earthscan Publications.

Oldfield, J. D. & Shaw, D. J. B. (2002). 'Revisiting sustainable development: Russian cultural and scientific traditions and the concept of sustainable development'. "Area". 34. (4), 391-400.

Piqueras, M. (1998). 'Meeting the Biospheres: on the translations of Vernadsky's work'. "International Microbiology". 1. (2), 165-170.

Wheeler, K. A. & Bijur, A. P (2000). "Education for a Sustainable future: A paradigm of hope for the 21st century". New York, Boston: Kluwer Academic/Plenum Publishers.

"Teaching and Learning for sustainable future: A multimedia teacher education programme". Available at http://www.unesco.org/education/tlsf.

Useful websites

For a fuller elaboration of different approaches to the concept of sustainable development, useful starting points are:

http://www.biothinking.com/

UNECE: http://www.unece.org/env/esd/events.htm

UNESCO: http://portal.unesco.org/education/en/ev.php-URL_ID=19648&URL_DO=DO_TOPIC&URL_SECTION=201.html

UNESCO-UNEVOC:
http://portal.unesco.org/education/en/ev.php-URL_ID=31336&URL_DO=DO_TOPIC&URL_SECTION=201.html

http://en.wikipedia.org/wiki/Sustainable_development

http://www.gdrc.org/sustdev/definitions.html

http://www.forumforthefuture.org.uk/aboutus/sd_page170.aspx. Go to 'Tools for Sustainable Development' for more detail.

References

Benedict, F. (1999). 'A Systematic Approach to Sustainable Environmental Education'. "Cambridge Journal of Education". 29. (3), 433- 446.

Forum for the Future (2006). Available at http://www.forumforthefuture.org.uk/aboutus/sd_page170.aspx

Habermas (1971). "Toward a Rational Society" (Trans. J. J. Shapiro.). London: Heinemann. (Original work published 1968).

Huckle, J. (2005). "Education for Sustainable Development: a briefing paper for the Teacher Training Agency". Available at http://john.huckle.org.uk/publications_downloads.jsp

"Intergovernmental Panel on Climate Change" (2007). Reports available at http://www.ipcc.ch/

Naess, A. (1990). "Ecology, Community and Lifestyle: Outline of an Ecosophy" (Trans. D. Rothenberg). Cambridge: Cambridge University Press.

Pavlova, M. (2005). 'Social Change: How Should Technology Education Respond?'. "International Journal of Technology and Design Education". 15 (3), 199-215.

Pavlova, M. (2006a). 'Education for sustainable development: the nature of the issue in the multicultural world'. In P. Ruohotie & R. Maclean (Eds.). "Communication and learning in the multicultural world". (pp. 377-397). Hameenlinna: University of Tampere Press.

Pavlova, M. (2006b). 'Education for Sustainability through Design and Technology education: some issues for a research agenda'. Presented at "2nd European Fair on Education for Sustainable Development". Hamburg, Germany 13 -15 September, 2006.

Pierce J. (2005). Available at http://pthbb.org/natural/footprint/img/cartogram.gif

Porritt, J. (2005). "Capitalism as if the World Matters". London: Earthscan Publications.

Robinson, J. (2004). 'Squaring the circle? Some thoughts on the idea of sustainable development'. "Ecological Economics". 48, 369-384.

Shamaeva, M. I., Semenova, V. D. & Sitnikova, N. V. (1995). Didakticheskii material - "Natsional'no - regionalnuj component na urokah anglijskogo jazuka" [Teaching materials - "National - regional component for English lessons"]. Yakutsk: Bitchik.

Skolimowski, H. (1966). 'The structure of thinking in technology'. "Technology and Culture". 7, 371-383.

Smith, R. A., Simpson, A. & Ralph, A. (1991). "Aesthetics and Arts Education". Illinois: Illinois Press.

Sterling, S. (1993). 'Environmental education and sustainability: a view from holistic ethics'. In Fien, J. & Trainer, T. (Eds). "Environmental education: a pathway to sustainability". (pp. 69-98). Geelong, Australia: Deakin University.

UNESCO (2004) "Decade of Education for Sustainable Development". Available at http://www.unesco.org.uk/Education_for_Sustainable_Development.htm

World Commission on Environment and Development (the Brundtland Comission) (1987). "Our Common Future". Oxford: Oxford University Press.

WWF (2006) Living Planet Report 2006. Available at http://www.panda.org/news_facts/publications/living_planet_report/index.cfm

vocationalism -
friend or foe to design
& technology education

John Dakers

John Dakers lectures in the
department of Educational Studies
in the Faculty of Education at the
University of Glasgow.
His particular research interests
are in the philosophy of technology
and the philosophy of education.
He recently acted as a consultant
to the European Commission on
matters relating to increasing
recruitment to technology related
disciplines. His most recent book,
"Defining Technological Literacy:
Towards an Epistemological
Framework" was published by
Palgrave MacMillan in New York.

Vocationalism - friend or foe to design & technology education

John Dakers

Introduction

The question mooted in the title of this chapter is not an easy one to answer. Trying to define what we mean by vocational education in the form of design & technology education is, as we shall see later, highly complex. However, we can define what it is not. It is not specific job training in the traditional apprenticeship sense. Thus, we might conclude that it exists primarily for the student rather than for the world of work. So design & technology occupies a unique position in schooling as it is about a different way of learning than is offered by either an academic curriculum or as training for a specific occupation. Whether this is a good thing or bad is open to debate, but in my view, design & technology education is often perceived to be a curriculum for those who are less intellectually capable of following an academic curriculum. These judgements are difficult to change in well-established cultural systems which have long valued academic qualifications as being, in some way, superior to vocational ones.

Before we take this debate any further however, it might be worth considering what your own views are on this right now, and, importantly, why you think that you hold those views. It is certainly the will of the Government that you should support the notion of vocationally based education. They are promoting the establishment of National Skills Academies which are, in their own words, to be:

'Focused on vocational education and skills training, delivering to young people (16-19 years old)…[and] located in geographical areas of real disadvantage, and challenge the culture of educational under-attainment'
Read at: http://www.dfes.gov.uk/publications/nsaprospectus/

Moreover, the current emphasis is on construction, financial services, food and drink and manufacturing, four areas considered by the Government to be major sectors of the economy. Do you support the Government on this? Do you think that children who are perceived to under-attain should follow a vocational curriculum which is guided by the needs of the economy? What might be the cause of under-attainment?

 Given that the Government considers the sectors of construction, financial services, food and drink and manufacturing, to be important in terms of economic development, should the school curriculum be changed in line with this thinking?

Ancient philosophers who considered knowledgeable activity.

01 Socrates.
02 Plato.
03 Aristotle.

Suppose, for example, that a mother of two teenage brothers tells you that John is good with his hands but does not like reading, whereas Jack is clumsy, but has always got his head in a book. Does this suggest that John would be better to follow a vocationally orientated curriculum and Jack an academic one? Is John more academic than Jack? What indeed do we mean when we talk about vocational education and academic education? What is the purpose of such a distinction and should such distinctions even be made? These are the kinds of questions that I hope we can explore in this chapter.

I will start by considering what the perceived differences between academic and vocational education actually are. I will then look to history for some answers to the same set of questions. Finally, I will ask you, the reader, to consider what your own perceptions are in relation to design & technology education as a vocational subject, and whether they have changed in any way after having read this chapter.

The brains or brawn argument

If you look it up in a dictionary you will find that 'vocational education' has quite different meaning from the term 'vocation'. Vocation is usually defined as a sort of calling, usually in the religious, teaching or healing domains, whereas vocational education is usually defined as training for some practical activity, usually related to industry, and having a stronger emphasis on the use of the body and hands than the use of the mind. This, I will argue, is especially the case when we consider design & technology education as taught in schools. Virtually everyone that I have ever spoken to about this contends that design & technology education is 'vocational', whereas the subject of English for example, is 'academic'. Interestingly, I always get lots of variation about what they mean by 'vocational education' when I ask! Moreover, I would also suggest that perceptions about the vocational education domain at school are more often associated with 'less able' children than with 'more able'. What do you think? And why do you think this should be the case? These perceptions have great potency.

 What are the differences, if any, between vocational education and occupational education?

If you look at the personal qualities and skills required for various occupations in job advertisements, the language used tends to situate brains with one type of occupation and brawn with the other. For trades such as carpentry, plumbing or bricklaying, for example, we see the requirements for qualities and skills as:
• being physically fit;
• able to work with your hands;

- having a head for heights;
- having a good eye.

Whereas for what we might refer to as the professions, the qualities and skills are seen as:
- having an ability to solve (design) problems;
- having a logical mind;
- creative and artistic abilities;
- having a lively and enquiring mind.

It is clear that the former relate to the body and the latter to the mind. Moreover, the former are also associated with the vocational curriculum and the latter with the academic curriculum. Ironically, when vocational education is seen to take place within an academic base such as architecture, engineering or medicine, it is held in much higher esteem.

This is by no means a new debate. Socrates (470-399 BCE), his student Plato (428-347 BCE), and his student, in turn, Aristotle (384-322 BCE) all held the notion that there were two types of knowledgeable activity: *'Techné'*, which related more to the skills associated with the mechanical arts and fabrication, and *'Phronesis'* which characterises a person who knows how to live a virtuous life. It is acquired and deployed not in the making of any product separate from oneself, but rather in one's actions with one's fellow human beings. In Aristotle's own words: *'whilst making has an end other than itself, action cannot, for good action itself is its end'*.

John Dewey, drawing from Aristotle, wrote:
'While training for the profession of learning is regarded as a type of culture, as a liberal education, that of a mechanic, a musician, a lawyer, a doctor, a farmer, a merchant, or railroad manager is regarded as purely technical and professional. The result is that which we see about us everywhere - the division into "cultured" people and "workers", the separation of theory and practice'.
Can design & technology education engage in issues relating to culture?

Is it these guys therefore who started this debate? Are they responsible for the academic versus vocational divide? Plato certainly advocated a tripartite form of society which comprised first, those who were workers like labourers, carpenters and plumbers etc. Second came the warriors. They were adventurous, strong and brave and would protect society by belonging to what we now refer to as the armed forces. Finally, there were those who governed or ruled. These were much fewer in number and had to be intelligent, rational and self-controlled.

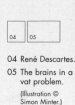

04 René Descartes.
05 The brains in a vat problem.
(Illustration © Simon Minter.)

They mostly came from the aristocracy or wealthy families. Already we can begin to see a distinction emerging between Plato's first two classes whose members followed more practical activities with an emphasis on using the body and an elite ruling class whose members used their minds in order to cultivate society.

Whilst this distinction between the mind and body has been a subject of debate ever since Plato, it is the French philosopher René Descartes who, in the seventeenth century, gave us the famous *'cogito ergo sum' - 'I think therefore I am'*. Essentially, Descartes made the claim that the mind was actually separate from the body. They were, for him, two distinct entities. Whilst a great number of modern philosophers now dispute this claim, the jury is still out for a significant number of others. One modern American philosopher called Hilary Putnam has offered an interesting scenario to explore this notion which I have adapted for this chapter. It is called the brains in a vat problem. It assumes that the mind resides in the brain.

Let us suppose that technology has advanced to the stage where we have discovered a completely safe way to remove a human brain from its skull, and, by using the latest micro technology, we can use the equivalent of 'blue tooth' technology to allow the brain to communicate with the body, and in turn, the body to communicate with the brain whilst both are actually separated.

This enables the body to move around as it did before the separation, whilst the brain is stored in a vat containing nutrients which are able to keep it alive and functioning. Essentially, nothing has changed except that the brain is now connected to the central nervous system and vice versa, remotely, by radio waves. This is literally separating the mind, or at least the brain, which might be considered to be the operating system for the mind, from the body, as Descartes argued. This techno-fantasy allows us to consider the duality argument in interesting ways. For example, if we are also able to communicate with the brain in the vat through the use of a computer system, without the body being present in the same place, could we teach the brain alone? Could we teach it 'academic' subjects like English or mathematics without the involvement of the body? Could we teach it the practical skills required for the fabrication of an artefact without the body being present? Conversely could we teach the body practical skills or activities without the involvement of the brain? If not, what are the implications for the vocational versus academic education debate?

The answer to this argument is that one cannot function without the other. The mind cannot actually operate without the body and vice versa. The mind needs the body's sense perceptors to engage with the world and the body needs the mind to interpret those senses. This is the way that our perception of the

06 Are you able to
- distinguish by
10 looking alone if
they are
'vocationally'
or 'academically'
orientated?

(Image 08 ©
Jimena Allasia.)

world works. We sense the world through our bodies (seeing, hearing, touching etc.) and then we interpret what we sense. Interestingly the personal qualities and skills required by employers as mentioned before, like being good with your hands, or physically fit (body emphasis), as distinct from having a logical mind or being creative (brain emphasis), are beginning to be combined to some extent, with more emphasis being given, by organisations such as the CITB (Construction Industry Training Board) and CBI (Confederation of British Industry), for a combination of mind and body requirements such as:

• interpersonal skills;
• communication skills;
• entrepreneurial skills;
• flexibility of learning;
• problem-solving skills;
• critical abilities.

These qualities and skills are more generic and can be developed equally across the academic/vocational, mind/body divide.

Another reason that I have discussed this mind/body argument is that whilst I believe there to be a widely held perception that 'bright' children will predominantly follow academic subjects where the emphasis is on the development of the mind, and less able children will orientate towards 'vocational education' where the emphasis is on practical activity, I also contend that there may be a correlation between those children perceived

to be academic and their social status. In your experience, how many children from privileged middle-class backgrounds aspire to become carpenters or plumbers or sheet metal workers? How many from less privileged backgrounds aspire to become lawyers or doctors or architects? Why do you think this is? Let's see if looking again at history can shed any more light on this.

Look at the photographs of children. Are you able to distinguish by looking alone if they are 'vocationally' or 'academically' orientated? What other information would you need to make this kind of judgement?

Some histories of education

In the time of the hunter gatherers

It was about 2.6 million years ago that hunter gatherers roamed the world in search of food and shelter. Our technological heritage starts around this time. There were no distinct vocations or occupations at that time. Boys tended to follow their fathers and girls their mothers, in terms of work. The economy was based upon small communities working together. Interestingly the Sami people in northern Scandinavia, also known as the Lapps, had, until fairly recently, a similar nomadic existence where they carved out

10 Medieval tradesfolk, David Gentle's Charing Cross underground station mural.

(Photograph by Michael Greifeneder, http://creative commons.org/ licenses/by-sa/2.0/)

a living from fishing, hunting and reindeer herding. They lived and existed in a natural economy which changed very little over the years. Survival in these types of communities was based upon skills being handed down from father to son, mother to daughter. This type of existence had no formal education, academic or vocational. There was thus no academic/vocational divide.

In medieval times

The long transition from hunter gatherers to city states and modernism, however, sees the emergence, in England, of formal schooling occurring in the medieval period. The medieval period covers a very long time which may be seen as starting at the end of the Roman occupation, and finishing around the beginning of the Renaissance. It was the influence of the Romans that shaped the curriculum which had essentially three components: elementary learning (reading, writing and arithmetic), grammar (correct composition of literary texts), and rhetoric (the theory and practice of oratory). Most, if not all of the texts during the first half of the medieval period were in Latin. Schools were mostly fee-paying and so elitist. The lower classes, peasants and the like, were not encouraged to go to school. Records indicate that in 1391, a petition was put forward to the House of Commons, by an assembly of the gentry and prosperous burgesses, asking the King to forbid serfs from putting their children in school. They felt that it would breach the traditional social order. They did not want the lower orders to rise to wealth by means of education.

Attendance at school was based upon the available resources (schools, teachers, texts etc.) and personal ambition. If you wanted to follow a certain trade or business that required literacy and numeracy (vocational education), elementary education followed by a couple of years of grammar would be sufficient. However, if you wanted to take holy orders, or attend university or undertake a legal education in London (academic education), a much longer period studying grammar and rhetoric was required.

Given that education was elitist, poverty had an impact on progression. Schooling was not always a continuous process and was often interrupted by poverty. Records indicate, for example, one William Green who was the son of a 'husbandman', or peasant, in Lincolnshire who, during the 1510s, spent two years at the free grammar school at Wainfleet, before leaving to work with his father for five or six years as a farmer and sawyer (someone who saws wood for a living). Later he managed to attend Boston school for two more years by living with his aunt and doing part-time work. However, when he finally got to Cambridge University he found it almost impossible to survive on a combination of study, work, and poor relief. School education in this period then was clearly academic in delivery and formed the basis of our grammar schools today.

11 Children at work.
&
12

Education for trades-based occupations was not the remit of schools but tended to be in the form of apprenticeships and it is during the later medieval period that we see the formation of trades Guilds.

The medieval grammar school curriculum did have a practical or vocational element, but this was restricted to the crafts or trades that involved writing, reading and record-keeping such as required for example by clerks. Skills for trades involving bodily effort, such as for masons, wheelwrights or blacksmiths were not taught at school. In 1402 for example, Sir John Depeden left twenty pounds for the education of a boy with the proviso that when he could read or write, he should be sent to London to train as a fishmonger, grocer or mercer. The academic bit was done at school whilst the vocational bit was carried out on the job.

In medieval times, education for the trades was not taught at school. Trades were learned on the job, so to speak. This follows the rationale for modern apprenticeships.
Should vocational education be learned on the job, or can it be taught in subjects like design & technology?

In response to the industrial revolution

Following on from the medieval period we enter the period most associated with the beginnings of mass production: the industrial revolution. This heralded the beginning of a state-funded educational system for the working classes. In order to operate the new factory machinery, it was deemed necessary to educate workers in the basics of reading, writing and arithmetic to enable them to understand the instructions for operating the new and emerging machinery. Private schools continued to teach an academically orientated curriculum while the new state funded schools continued to have a curriculum more geared to serving the needs of industry.

The Industrial Revolution saw a clear and distinct division of labour where children from poor families were used as cheap labour for the factories. Do you agree that in today's society, schools should accommodate a similar division, based upon a young person's ability to pass examinations?

In the first half of the 20th century

A great number of changes in UK systems of education took place between the period

13 James Callaghan.
(Photograph ©
Ron Coverson.)

of the Industrial Revolution and the second world war. Compulsory education took hold, segregated schools were introduced, and, in 1944, the Butler Education Act made secondary education free for all pupils. However, it also introduced the '11 plus' examination. This determined what schools in the new 'tripartite' system pupils would attend. Depending upon their performance in the '11 plus' examination, taken in the last year of primary school, pupils would either attend a Grammar school, a Technical school or a Secondary Modern school. I failed the Scottish equivalent to the '11 plus' and attended a Secondary Modern school where the emphasis was on practical subjects. I distinctly remember having to stand on the opposite side of the road from my long time primary school friend each morning. He had passed his '11 plus' and had to get a bus to the equivalent of a Grammar school in Hamilton. I had to get the bus to Uddingston where the secondary modern was, literally and symbolically, in the opposite direction.

However, in the post war period, state-funded school education, which was now the right of all children, began to follow a more prescriptive and standardised curriculum which did not, as it was later discovered, meet all children's needs.

In the second half of the 20th century

A major change in thinking came about in 1963 when a chap called Newsom was commissioned to prepare a report entitled **"Half our Future"**. The report recommended that the school curriculum should be made more relevant to the needs of pupils of differing abilities. Newsom argued that: *'...all schools should provide a choice of programmes, including a range of courses broadly related to occupational interests, for pupils in the fourth and fifth years of a five year course'.* In particular, students in the lower streams (again in the main from the working classes) were seen to require 'non-academic' courses to help prepare them for their life outside school - this 'need' being seen by Newsom as reflecting the 'reality' of working-class adult life. Does this constitute 'vocational' education, and, is [was] design & technology the perfect subject domain for its delivery? Indeed, what, if anything, has changed since 1963 (or 300 BCE for that matter)?

The link between the 'less able' or 'lower order' students and the needs of industry was further reinforced in 1976 when the 'Great Debate' took place at Ruskin College. The then Prime Minister, James Callaghan argued: *'It is vital to Britain's economic recovery and standard of living that the performance of the manufacturing industry is improved and that the whole range of government policies, **including education**, contribute as much as possible to improving industrial performance and thereby increasing national wealth'.*

14 Antonio Gramsci.

15 John Dewey.

(Image from Special Collections Research Center, Morris Library, Southern Illinois University Carbondale.)

16 Paulo Freire.

(Image from Paulo Freire Cooperation in Europe.)

Join in the Great Debate. Do you agree with Callaghan? How can school education contribute to national wealth today?

The Great Debate followed on from a period which saw the introduction, and in 1965, the beginning of a Government dictate, that Local Authorities should be compelled to start the conversion towards a universal comprehensive education system. This was due, in the main, to dissatisfaction with the tripartite system based upon academic ability, which was clearly not working in a lot of areas around England, particularly less affluent areas. Significantly, it was when Margaret Thatcher became Secretary of State for Education in 1970, that she ended the compulsion for Local Authorities to convert to Comprehensive systems although a great many schools were comprehensive by that time. However, it was the introduction of the comprehensive system that influenced Callaghan in his 'Great Debate' to argue for, amongst other things, a core curriculum and the use of more informal teaching methods (a lot of teachers for example, in all sectors, were still wearing gowns, the practice of which was more associated with Grammar schools).

This thinking tended to coincide with, or possibly initiate, the new liberal principles of progressive child-centred education which concentrated upon education for citizenship rather than for the needs of industry which had dominated since the post war period (and before). These principles were commonly held to be the root cause of the breakdown in discipline in schools which resulted in, amongst other things, a lack of basic skill procurement. This period therefore helped pave the way for what was to become known as 'new vocationalism', which was developed in the 1980s and which can partly be seen as a reaction against liberal and progressive education.

Modern critics of technology education as skill production in the interests of industry, such as Antonio Gramsci, Paulo Freire and John Dewey, also opposed the separation of 'academic' and 'vocational' education, based upon differentiation on the basis of 'merit'. These arguments, which continue to the present day, are made on the grounds that the whole process is, in effect, still one of selection based upon class. This model, it is argued, jeopardises a child's future as a result of early and narrow professional or trades specialisation which instructs for a specific occupation, and which is lacking in 'general ideas', a 'general culture' and a 'soul', while being in possession only of an 'infallible eye' and a 'firm hand' (the emphasis on body over mind). These concerns, about narrow vocational specialisation at an early age in fact anticipate much of the contemporary criticism of the 'new vocationalism'.

Notwithstanding, however, the general trend appears to have been economically driven. Since Callaghan's 'Great Debate' in the 70s, the trend towards vocationalism, particularly in the area of design & technology education, appears to have gained momentum.

The introduction of the National Curriculum

The 1988 Education Reform Act legislated for the following:

'For the first time the Government laid down a National Curriculum which required pupils to study mathematics, English, science, history, geography, technology, music, art and physical education, plus a foreign language for 11-16 year old pupils. This was intended to ensure that pupils concentrated on what the Government saw as key subject areas'.

Why do you think the government decided on subjects as the organising principle for the National Curriculum? What other organising principle might be used?

This act encouraged the establishment of what were to become 'City Technology Colleges', inner city institutions which would have a specialisation in technology education for the 11-18 age range. Significantly, they were to be sponsored by private industry and not by state funding. Moreover, they would be independent of local Education Authorities and would compete with existing state schools for pupils.

To what extent would an industry-dictated curriculum be in the best interests of pupils?

A number of other initiatives occurred around the same time. The Technical and Vocational Education Initiative (TVEI) for example started as a pilot scheme in 1983. This was designed to run alongside the conventional curriculum for 14-18 year olds and had to include work experience. It was rolled out to all schools in 1986 and later extended to include sixth form and tertiary education. The rationale behind this initiative was to give a more formal and direct understanding of the workplace and the economy in order to produce pupils who would be more likely to get jobs.

In 1985 a similar initiative to TVEI was instituted for those over 16 who were uncertain about what they wanted to do after school. The Certificate for Pre-Vocational Education (CPVE) taught practical skills and, whilst open to all, tended to be taken by those who were considered to be less 'academically' able. Whilst it was not considered to be a great success it was the precursor to other vocationally orientated qualifications such as GNVQs and NVQs.

It was in 1986 that the National Council for Vocational Qualifications was set up to introduce standardised vocational qualifications which were specifically orientated to particular occupations. About 170 National Vocational Qualifications (NVQs) were in place by 1990 and more were being added every year. These NVQs were designed to reward particular achievement through the demonstration of 'competencies'. They had four levels ranging from level 1, roughly equivalent to GCSEs, to level 4, roughly equivalent to postgraduate level of study. In 1994 the NVQs were replaced by General National Vocational Qualifications (GNVQs) which were intended to offer alternative routes from the 'academic' routes associated with 'A' levels.

The academic versus vocational divide saw another significant change which was introduced into the school curriculum in 1988. It combined the 'O' levels, which were considered to be more orientated towards the academically gifted, and the Certificate of Secondary Education which was for students judged to be less academically able. These merged to become a single General Certificate of Secondary Education (GCSEs).

And the situation today

Former Prime Minister Tony Blair has been consistent in his support for vocational education. He believed that school education should be divided into vocational and academic. In his last Labour Party Conference (2006) he stated his desire for:

'A society where we put the same commitment to quality vocational skills as we do academic education, with new vocational courses at school'. Taken from his speech at the conference and read at: http://news.bbc.co.uk/1/hi/uk_politics/3697434.stm

This clearly indicates an education model orientated towards the economic needs of the State and industry.

The most recent innovations include the introduction of specialised diploma development partnerships (DDPs) which consist of representatives from employer groups, further and higher education institutions, awarding bodies and schools. These diplomas have a very clear link with industry as described by the Sector Skills Development Agency who describe the four key goals of this initiative are:
- to reduce skills gaps and shortages;
- to improve productivity, business and public service performance;
- to increase opportunities to boost the skills and productivity of everyone in the sector's workforce;
- to improve learning supply including apprenticeships, higher education and National Occupational Standards (NOS).

You can find more details of the specialised diplomas at http://www.qca.org.uk/qca_10325.aspxf

Once again it becomes apparent that the Government is making a clear link between school-based vocational education and industry. Moreover, the emphasis is on the needs of industry at the time. These diplomas form the bulwark of the new Skills Academies mentioned earlier in this chapter.

Under this model, design & technology education is seen to be largely concerned with promoting economic growth through concentrating on improving skills and the workforce rather than being about the promotion of equality and opportunity.

Aldous Huxley, just over 75 years ago, painted a rather dystopian view of a 'brave new world' in his seminal work of the same title. He suggested then, that Big Government was able to genetically standardise large sectors of the population into workers, soldiers etc. To what extent do you think that the vocationalisation of the curriculum as described above is a psychological, as distinct from a genetically-modified version of the same thing?

In other words, to what extent is Government obliged to continually supply industry with a standardised workforce in the interests of the economy?

Implications for design & technology education

If schools are able to provide diplomas which have a clear and distinct relationship with the needs of industry, in other words dedicated vocational, or more correctly stated, occupational qualifications, what then are the implications for design & technology education? If you believe that design & technology education is vocational, then to what specific vocations or occupations is it allied? What subjects will pupils who are not considered 'academic' choose given these new options and why might they be motivated to do so? Their choices include:

• taking a specialised diploma leading to a specific career which has been identified as belonging to a skills gap shortage, so a good chance of employment;
• attending a skills academy which gives the same, or possibly more benefits as described above;
• choosing to study design & technology.

If we continue to argue that design & technology is vocational, and cannot demonstrate a clear and obvious link with specific industries, pupils will be more inclined, I would argue, to choose the new occupational skills routes. They clearly offer pupils a more obvious pathway to a job at the end of the day. We need then, to follow one of two routes. If we believe that design & technology education is vocational, we need to establish clear and obvious links with specific industries, and these links should be more appealing than the ones offered by the skills academies if design & technology is making a claim on their ground.

The former view situates education, and particularly vocational education, as serving the interests of the economy and so not about Aristotle's notion of education as *'Phronesis',* the development of the virtuous citizen, which would constitute the second view. John Dewey, almost one hundred years ago, argued against the former view on the grounds that school education should not, under any circumstances, be vocational. I reproduce a quote in this respect. It is a long quote but a most significant one which is worthy of reproduction.

'Its (technology education) right development will do more to make public education truly democratic than any other agency now under consideration. Its wrong treatment will as surely accentuate all undemocratic tendencies in our present situation, by fostering and strengthening class divisions in school and out…Those who believe the continued existence of what they are pleased to call the "lower classes" or the "laboring classes" would naturally rejoice to have schools in which these "classes" would be segregated. And some employers of labor would doubtless rejoice to have schools, supported by public taxation, supply them with additional food for their mills…(Everyone else) should be united against every proposition, in whatever form advanced, to separate training of employees from training for citizenship, training of intelligence and character from training for narrow, industry efficiency'.

The recent revision of the secondary curriculum is interesting as it has more than a hint of Phronesis. The aims of the curriculum are for all young people to become:

- Successful learners who enjoy learning, make progress and achieve;
- Confident individuals who are able to live safe, healthy and fulfilling lives;
- Responsible citizens who make a positive contribution to society.

To what extent do you think design & technology can contribute to these broad aims?
You can visit this url to find out more: http://curriculum.qca.org.uk/subjects (accessed on 17.10.07)

Reflecting upon your own views

Cast your mind back to when you were at school. I accept that this may be an easier exercise for some than for others. Nevertheless, try to transport yourself back to when you started secondary school. Did you have aspirations about what you wanted to do when you left school? If so, did you fulfil them? If not, why not? Who influenced your decision either way? My point is this: Did you favour some school subjects more than others? I suspect you did - why?

Let us now try this thought experiment in reverse. You are now a beginning teacher of design & technology education - why? Have you come into this straight from school and university? Have you come into this as a mature student? What influenced you to do this? Was it taking design & technology at school?

When you were at school and you reached the stage when you were asked to choose the subjects you wanted to study, list the subjects that you actually did choose, and of those, highlight which ones you consider(ed) to be vocational. Now create another list indicating the various (or only) occupation(s) you have held. (Becoming a design & technology teacher might be your first occupation). Consider the two lists and try to remember whether you chose the 'vocational' subjects on your list because these subjects reflected most closely the occupation that you wanted to pursue. This is difficult because there will have been a multitude of other factors involved. Try to filter these out, however, and concentrate only on the correlation between the 'vocational' school subject(s) chosen and your occupational aspirations at the time. Remember, this is not necessarily what you ended up actually doing, it is what you wanted to end up doing (a train driver, admiral or astronaut springs to mind for me).

I think that, for most of us, the task above will prove to be difficult, if not impossible. If I am honest in my own reflections, I cannot remember, at that time, having the slightest clue as to what occupation I wanted to pursue, but you may have different more specific recollections regarding your occupational aspirations.

This now opens up a number of pathways to consider in this reflection. If like me, you did not have much of a clue about what you wanted to 'be' when you left school, why did you choose the 'vocational' subjects that you did? Conversely, if you were clear about what you wanted to 'be', what were the defining aspects about the 'vocational' subject(s) that correlated with your chosen career path? Or, and for this reflection we need to slide down the snake all the way back to the beginning of our reasoning, it may be that you did not choose a 'vocational' subject at all!

Conclusion

As a beginning design & technology teacher you should consider the reasons that you want your students to choose the subject. You should also think about the kind of student you might expect to choose your subject. This will affect the way that you perceive the subject and, in turn, the way you teach it.

For me, design & technology education is not vocational. To label it so only serves to confuse the participants who, for the most part, perceive vocational education as the passing on of manual skills from one generation to the next, where most people are educated 'on the job' in particular by experiencing some sort of formal or informal apprenticeship. Moreover, they are traditionally viewed in class terms. Design & technology is a school subject like any other school subject. It has academic components, it has practical components, experiential components and, one other particular, and in some senses ironic (considering the arguments presented in this paper) advantage over most other subjects in the curriculum: it actually has a relationship with the 'real' world outside school, a relationship which serves to *introduce* young people to the world of commerce and industry, but it must do this from a critical perspective, not a subservient one. This resonates with Dewey's notion of *'Democracy in Education'* where he distinguishes between education *through* the various industries as against education *for* the various industries. This is crucially important. Students cannot be critical when they are completely immersed in it under the guise of vocationalism. I believe that design & technology education should be perceived in terms of a paradigm shift. That is, it is not some poor cousin to academic education which seeks to offer an alternative, less rich learning experience designed for the less able. It is rather, a rich and experiential way to learn which does not separate or categorise different forms of learning with different ability groups. It combines, cerebral *with* practical, mind *with* body, design *with* technology.

Further reading

Huxley, A. (1932). "Brave New World".
New York: Harper Collins.

Dewey, J. (1961). "Democracy and Education". Full text available at: http://www.ilt.columbia.edu/Publications/dewey.html

Carr, D. (1995). "The Dichotomy of Liberal Versus Vocational Education: Some Basic Conceptual Geography". Available at: http://www.ed.uiuc.edu/EPS/PES-Yearbook/95_docs/carr.html

Pitt, J. & Pavlova, M. (2001). 'Pedagogy in Transition: from Labour Training to Humanistic Technology Education in Russia'. In S. Webber & I. Liikanen, (Eds.). "Education and civic culture in post-communist countries". (pp. 231-247). Hampshire, UK: Palgrave.

Dakers, J. R. (2006). 'Towards a Philosophy for Technology Education' in J. R. Dakers, (Ed.), "Defining Technological Literacy: Towards an Epistemological Framework". (pp. 145-158). New York: Palgrave Macmillan.

Related articles

"Journal of Career and Technical Education" (Formerly the "Journal of Vocational and Technical Education"). Available at http://scholar.lib.vt.edu/ejournals/JCTE/

"Journal of Industrial Teacher Education". Available at http://scholar.lib.vt.edu/ejournals/JITE/

"Career and Technical Education Research" (Formerly the "Journal of Vocational Educational Research"). Available at http://scholar.lib.vt.edu/ejournals/CTER/

References

BOOKS

References to medieval schools are taken from:
Orme, N. (2006). "Medieval Schools: From Roman Britain to Renaissance England". USA, CT: Yale University Press.

References to several issues relating to post war vocational education are taken from:
Haralambos, M. & Holborn, M. (1995). "Sociology: Themes and Perspectives". (Fourth Edition), London: Collins Educational.

WEBSITES

Education and skills:
http://www.dfes.gov.uk/publications/nsaprospectus/

Tony Blair's speech:
http://news.bbc.co.uk/1/hi/uk_politics/3697434.stm

Sector Skills Development Agency:
http://www.ssda.org.uk/ssda/Default.aspx?page=2861

Nick Baldwin

Nick Baldwin is director of TEP, based at Middlesex University. A Loughborough graduate, he has a wide breadth of school management experience and is a Marconi trainer and visiting lecturer supporting ITE programmes and CPD across the UK. He devised the Millenium Schools Project, while principal research fellow at the University of Warwick. Nick manages various training and research projects across the UK and edits "News and Views". His responsibilities include engineering, electronics education and broadening and securing industry-education partnerships.

David Barlex

Dr. David Barlex is a senior lecturer in education at Brunel University in England, director of the Nuffield Design & Technology Project and cross-appointed as an adjunct assistant professor at Queen's University, Ontario, Canada. He is an acknowledged leader in design & technology education, curriculum design and curriculum materials development. David's research activity stems from his conviction that there should be a dynamic and synergistic relationship between curriculum development and academic research.

Developing your own curriculum

Nick Baldwin and David Barlex

This chapter will explore the processes by which a newly qualified teacher can make a contribution to the design & technology curriculum. It is in six parts. First the chapter will consider the classroom conditions a teacher must create if his or her teaching is to be successful. Second we will explore four key features that determine the success of a subject in the curriculum. Third we will investigate how a newly qualified teacher might develop and articulate their vision for the subject. Fourth we will consider the importance of working with colleagues as part of the design & technology team in a school. Fifth we will discuss the areas in which you might make a contribution to developing the curriculum. Finally we will consider how you can become a reflective and effective practitioner through curriculum development.

Establishing yourself as a teacher

There are four conditions that a teacher needs to meet if his or her teaching of design & technology is to be successful.

Firstly the teacher should have the expectation that pupils will be capable. This means that it will be perfectly acceptable for pupils to make decisions and take action based on those decisions. In some cases the actions will require teacher approval but in many cases they will be autonomous.

Secondly the teacher needs to facilitate pupil capability by organising and maintaining an appropriate environment. This means that pupils will have open access to materials, components, tools and equipment. In most cases they will be able to collect what they need, as they need it, use it and return it. In some cases particularly scarce resources may need to be booked in advance. But it is essential that decisions, once taken, can be acted upon if pupils are not to become dispirited and de-motivated.

Thirdly the teacher will need to provide the resources for capability by teaching the technical knowledge and understanding, aesthetics, design strategies, making and manufacturing skill and values needed for successful designing and making.

Fourthly the teacher should maintain the motivation for capability through insight into pupils' motivations ensuring that activities are relevant, urgent, important and attractive.

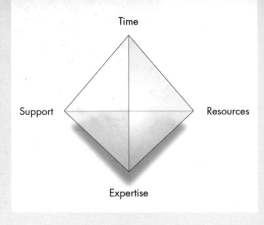

01 A busy classroom scene.

02 The four key features tetrahedron.

Once these conditions are established in your classroom you will be in a strong position to suggest changes to your school's established curriculum. Meeting these conditions will give you credibility with both pupils and fellow colleagues. This credibility is a pre-requisite to your ideas being given serious consideration.

To what extent do you think that the conditions for success are realistic? What are the pros and cons for each condition? What action could you take to turn the cons into pros?

Understanding four key features

Four features need to be in place for a subject to maintain a robust position in the school curriculum. These are effective use of time, availability of resources, development of expertise and accessing professional support. They can be represented as occupying the vertices of tetrahedron as shown above. If any of these vertices fails then the tetrahedron will instantly collapse. This analogy of sudden structural collapse with the fate of a subject in the school curriculum is perhaps not entirely valid but the lack of any one of these features seriously weakens a school subject and whilst this might not cause sudden catastrophic failure

it will prevent the subject fulfilling its potential and meeting legitimate aspirations. A general lack of engagement with the features can contribute to the lingering demise of a subject.

Effective use of time

It is of course important that a subject has a reasonable amount of time in the school timetable but it is well worth considering how this time is distributed. Many secondary schools adopt a highly fragmented use of time. The unit of planning, e.g. a 30 or 40 minute lesson, becomes the building block and it is rare for pupils in the 11 - 16 age group to experience on a regular basis any more than a double block of units. This is not the situation in many primary schools where head teachers are organising immersive experiences for pupils that last two or three whole days in succession. Margaret Lynn, a head teacher of a primary school in Formby is convinced that this is a powerful way forward. In 2001 she wrote:

'I decided that a radical approach was needed; one in which the children and their teachers had enough time to become intensely involved in designing and making and to have this experience often enough for the children to make progress. So I chose to suspend the timetable for 3 consecutive days each term and dedicate those days to design & technology.

From the first 3 days we learned three important lessons; avoid being over ambitious, target parent help where it is most needed, take care to ensure all resources are in place. The second 3 day event went very much as planned with the children eagerly

03 Margaret Lynn, a primary head teacher who is enthusiastic about immersion education.

anticipating more designing and making. Staff took the third 3 day event in their stride and it was particularly pleasing to see that the children had made significant progress over the year; drawings of design intentions were matching made outcomes, manual dexterity had improved, constructive evaluation of design decisions was becoming the norm.'

It is undoubtedly easier for a primary school to adopt an immersive approach to teaching a subject than it is a secondary school. But it is important that secondary schools give serious thought to how this might be achieved. Many secondary schools run activity weeks at the end of the summer term in which practically based subjects flourish. It requires an imaginative approach to organising time to transfer this to the mainstream curriculum.

Availability of resources

There is now a wide range of 'intellectual' resources available to support design & technology. Curriculum development projects such as Nuffield Design & Technology and TEP, the Design & Technology Association and the Qualifications and Curriculum Authority all provide examples of schemes of work, pupil activities, and high quality information relevant to design & technology. In some cases these resources are available free of charge so all schools can access these at relatively little expense. However design & technology requires significant capital funding to set up and maintain the tools, equipment and working environment needed for pupils

to tackle designing and making. Similarly it is important to have access to a significant consumable expenditure budget to provide pupils with the materials and components they need to model and make their design ideas. In a nutshell resourcing design & technology is an expensive affair. Governors and senior managers will need to be convinced that the expense is worthwhile. Marketing the subject and its imperatives internally with the school is crucial. Providing a showcase of pupil experience and work exemplars or adopting a governor into departments is an ideal strategy. Examination performance is one indicator of success and a department that performs poorly here is likely to find their expenditure strongly scrutinised. It is also important for you and your colleagues to move the senior management team beyond the examination performance criteria and share with them your vision for the subject and its impact on the self esteem and aspirations of pupils whatever their career intention.

Development of expertise

Design & technology in the world outside school is a rapidly expanding field. New and emerging technologies are becoming part of everyday life at an ever-increasing rate. Who would have dreamed ten years ago that the laser cutter, thermochromic materials and the PIC chip would be a part of many schools design & technology provision? Approaches to designing and the assessment of designing are also developing. The e-scape project (2007) is currently exploring ways of using digital technology in both these areas. And educational research is developing new insights into the way we learn. Recently Steve Higgins, Viv Baumfield and Elaine Hall published a fascinating report entitled **"Learning Skills and the development of learning capabilities"**. It will be important for you and other members of the design & technology department to maintain and extend your expertise in areas that are changing. Individually you cannot be experts in all fields but collectively you can build and maintain a portfolio of expertise that keeps your department at the forefront of developments. Where possible it makes sense to plan student and pupil experiences so that knowledge can be accessed and skills acquired on a just-in-time rather than a just-in-case basis.

Accessing professional support

Collaborating with and learning from others in your department is an important part of your professional life. However you are part of a wider professional community and it is important that you and your colleagues access the collective wisdom of this wider community. A first step here is to join the professional association for design & technology teachers, the Design & Technology Association. Through its hard copy publications and website it keeps its members informed of developments and the opportunities

for professional development. It is also important to work with local networks relevant to design & technology. Your local SETPOINT and Science Learning Centre are charged with supporting STEM (science, technology, engineering and mathematics) activities in the curriculum so it is well worth staying in regular contact. Often risk-taking ideas and curriculum projects can start in after school clubs and extracurricular activities. This allows the teacher to grow and trial new ideas at low risk.

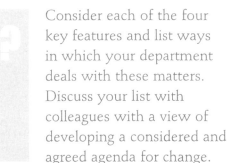

Consider each of the four key features and list ways in which your department deals with these matters. Discuss your list with colleagues with a view of developing a considered and agreed agenda for change.

Articulating your vision for the subject

Curriculum development should not be a random process of knee jerk response to the latest fashionable notion. Any curriculum development of worth requires underpinning by specific and clearly articulated drivers. To discern these drivers you will need to explore your fundamental beliefs about design & technology and why it makes an important contribution to the curriculum. Without this

04 05 06 07

04 What drives your
- passion for design
07 & technology?
Read other
chapters in this
reader to help
you find out.

underpinning the development is likely to be flawed and even if worthwhile liable to 'run out of steam' before fruition. You will find it useful to read the chapter on implicit beliefs and pedagogy by Wendy Dow (pages 252 - 265) in this reader.

There are a number of different aspects of the subject that might fire your imagination and act as drivers to fuel your vision for the subject. Of course the drivers that inspire you may not be those that enthuse your colleagues. They are not necessarily mutually exclusive although some may make for uneasy bedfellows!

You may feel that design & technology is best justified by appeals to its role in the general education for all pupils whatever eventual career path they choose. You might frame this as the role that designing plays in cognitive development. On the other hand you may believe that it is appeals to its vocational potential that lie at the root of its worth. You may consider that the role design & technology can play in education for sustainable development is sufficient to justify its place in the curriculum and that this should be the main thrust of its educational effort. You may believe that design & technology provides pupils with the capacity for active citizenship - designing and making in response to community issues.

The important thing is that you should believe something and that this provides a rationale for the developments you undertake. Remember the words of St John in the book of Revelation:

'I know thy works, that thou art neither cold nor hot: I would thou wert cold or hot. So then because thou art lukewarm, and neither cold nor hot, I will spew thee out of my mouth.' (Revelation 3:15-27.)

You can use many of the chapters in this reader to help you discover exactly what it is that drives your passion for design & technology. It could be James Pitt and Margarita Pavlova's chapter on education for sustainability, Moshe Barak's piece on problem-solving, Frank Banks and Gwyneth Owen-Jackson's consideration of making. And of course what drives you is subject to change as you develop in the profession and discuss issues with other teachers. Using collegiality for professional development underpins much of Steve Keirl's chapter on the politics of the technology curriculum.

Discuss with others in your department what it is about design & technology that makes it so special.
Is there consensus?
If so how is this harnessed?
Or is there a wide variation of views?
And if so how do they play out in informing any development that is taking place?

08 Yrjo Engestrom, celebrated developer of activity theory.

09 Vera John-Steiner, celebrated author of "Creative Collaboration".

Engaging with the team

Developing a curriculum in response to national imperatives in the context of the requirement of local conditions (your school and its facilities, the needs of the pupils, nature of the catchment area and the employment possibilities in the region) is a challenging endeavour and you will need to be highly creative to be successful. Of course you cannot be successful working on your own. A design & technology department composed of disparate individuals, who do not work collaboratively, whatever their individual brilliance, are unlikely to make the impact of a department where the teachers work as a team. Cross-collaboration and working across lines of learning with other departments will often pay dividends. This can help understanding between departments and help reinforce pupils' learning. This can have great advantages where timetable time is tight.

'Knotworking' is an interesting means of creative collaboration in response to the problems involved in curriculum development. It was developed by the Finnish researcher Yrjo Engestrom, Professor of Adult Education and Director of the Center for Activity Theory and Developmental Work Research at University of Helsinki. 'Knotworking' involves solving urgent tasks where the combinations of people and the contents of the tasks are likely to change. Decision-making in such situations is distributed, as there is no central

authority in charge. The members of the group convened to tackle the problem are chosen on the basis of the experience in relation to the nature of the problem. In the case of a design & technology department such a group might consist of a mix of junior and senior members of teaching staff, plus ancillary staff. In such a group it will be important to put aside issues of status and position and concentrate on the task in hand, with each person making a contribution according to their relevant expertise. This may be an unusual activity, but the potential for professional growth of those involved is large and the impact on the ability of staff to collaborate in future will be high.

Vera John-Steiner is the Presidential Professor of Linguistics & Education at the University of New Mexico in Albuquerque. Vera has written at length about the issues facing those who wish to work across and within disciplines in her book "**Creative Collaboration**". She argues that it will require different sorts of partnership but they will all thrive on dialogue, risk-taking and a shared vision. Such successful collaboration always involves trust and this has to be earned by those working together. Without trust it is not possible to reveal and overcome the insecurities and uncertainties that underpin all creative endeavours. Working with colleagues in this way requires those involved take the bold step of becoming dependent on one another. This dependence is not a sign of weakness, but of strength; a dignified interdependence through which those working together have mutual respect and can forge achievements far beyond their individual, isolated capacities. As a new teacher becoming part of 'knotworking' groups and other associations within the design & technology department are an essential part of your early professional growth.

> To what extent does collaboration with others already take place in your design & technology department?
> If there is a tradition of successful collaboration try to identify the mechanisms that make it successful.
> If there is little collaboration try to identify the blockers that are preventing it.

Identifying areas of development

In deciding which area or aspect of the design & technology curriculum to develop you will have to take into account the current curriculum offering and any prevailing development plans that may be in place. Once you have established yourself as a competent and confident teacher you will almost certainly be asked to carry out particular development tasks. It is likely that you will need to show effectiveness here before being given the freedom to develop areas of your own choosing. It is worth considering which areas of design & technology education might be worth developing. There is no shortage of possibilities. Here are some examples:

• You might be interested in the place of making within design & technology having gained much satisfaction yourself from making. So what curriculum development might you do in this area? There is an interesting relationship between making with hand and hand controlled machine tool and using computer assisted manufacture. This could be explored through curriculum development that monitored the way pupils made progress in these two different but related ways of making.

• You might be interested in the place of designing within design & technology. In which case developing ways to enhance pupil's designing skills would be an appropriate area of development. You could take this further by trying to explore the effect of enhanced designing skills on performance elsewhere in the curriculum.

• You might really enjoy your own ability to understand how things work, your technical understanding, and want to enthuse pupils in this area. Hence developing the technical aspect of the designing and making assignments carried out in your school would be an intriguing and useful piece of development.

- You might find that the understanding of the influence of technology on society (and vice versa) to be under represented in your school curriculum and want to redress the balance. Developing a suite of resources that could be used by yourself and other colleagues related to this issue, and which do not consume too much curriculum time would be a challenging and worthwhile endeavour.

- You may be intrigued by the relationship of design & technology with other subjects, especially the extent to which why, how and when an idea from another subject (its utility) might be useful. An exploration of the utility of other subjects in different designing and making assignments would make a fascinating reading and might lead to enhanced cross-curricular activity.

- You might find new and emerging technologies fascinating and want to introduce them into the design & technology curriculum. Developing accessible accounts of such technologies with suggested ways of engaging pupils would be useful curriculum development which maintained the modernity of your school curriculum.

- You might find the different responses of boys and girls to design & technology

intriguing. In which case some curriculum development to ways of presenting designing and making assignments so that they are appealing to both sexes yet confront conventional gender stereotypical responses would be a particularly interesting piece of development.

It all depends on what you are interested in plus the current and intended state of the design & technology curriculum. Aligning your interests with ways to improve the curriculum will be an important strategy to enabling you to respond professionally to the challenge of curriculum development. Design & technology is in many ways unique and teachers can be opportunist and take advantage of emerging contexts and themes, both local and national. This will enable teachers to refresh their repertoire as an ongoing activity and as a distinct management process of the subject.

Discuss with colleagues what you and they might want to be the focus of curriculum development. Find out if there is any relationship between these interests and current concerns within the design & technology curriculum. Use these findings to develop proposals for curriculum development.

Becoming a reflective and effective practitioner

You can think of curriculum development as the creation of new professional knowledge. In 1998 David Hargreaves wrote a very useful short booklet about this "The role of teachers in the knowledge society". He breaks the process down into the following sequence of five activities:

1. Generating ideas

This involves a mix of learning by doing, sharing experience, dialogue and networking.

2. Supporting ideas

New ideas need to be welcomed and respected. Good ideas are often fragile and need protection. Hence being cynical is highly counterproductive.

3. Selecting ideas

Not all ideas can be fully developed. Some will need to be abandoned or postponed so that those selected can be implemented. This will inevitably lead to disappointment for those whose ideas are not pursued and it is important that they do not lose face.

4. Developing ideas into knowledge and practice

It is essential that the new knowledge is robust and trustworthy and leads to practice that is effective. It is not always easy to see immediately whether practice is effective. New practice may appear ineffective simply because it is new and unfamiliar with both teachers and students being unsure how to respond. So giving new practice time to prove itself will be important. Once new practice is validated it should lead to the abandonment of old practices that cannot be validated. And if new practice is ultimately found to be wanting then it must be adapted so that it becomes practice that is effective. If this is found impossible then it should be abandoned.

5. Disseminating knowledge and practice

It is likely that new knowledge and practices will occur initially in parts of the design & technology department, rather than across the whole. Once such knowledge and practices are validated it is important that they are made accessible to other teachers through internal networks. This will not happen by chance. It will be important to develop channels of communications by which the outcomes of knowledge creation are widely distributed for it is unlikely that such channels already exist.

If you can tackle curriculum development in your school using this model you will find that the result is extremely robust.

Underlying Hargreaves' approach to curriculum development is the powerful idea of the teacher as a reflective practitioner, someone who thinks about what they are doing and why, ponders the effectiveness of their actions and changes what they do in the light of their thoughts. The General Teaching Council has taken the idea of the reflective practitioner and embedded it in the Teacher Learning Academy. This is a national

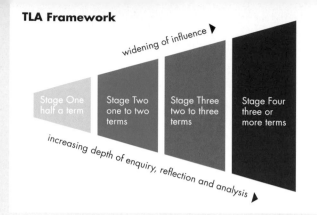

TLA Framework

widening of influence ▶

| Stage One half a term | Stage Two one to two terms | Stage Three two to three terms | Stage Four three or more terms |

increasing depth of enquiry, reflection and analysis ▶

10 TLA framework.

(From Stage one booklet, Teacher Learning Academy, General Teaching Council for England, 2006.)

10

system for teacher learning and offers teachers the opportunity to develop their professional abilities throughout their teaching career. There are four stages in this approach to professional development, shown above. Each stage of the framework differs progressively in terms of the:

• depth of enquiry, reflection and analysis;
• timescale;
• sphere of influence;
• presentation requirements.

Stage one provides an ideal opportunity for you to begin the professional development that should continue throughout your career. The requirements are as follows:

Depth: You will give a descriptive account of your learning;

Timescale: The project should take no more than half a term;

Sphere of influence: The impact on your work will be seen mainly in your own classroom, but other colleagues in your department or teaching the same year or key stage could benefit from your learning;

Presentation: Learning plan (written); Learning journal (any media; if written no more than 1500 words).

Activities typical of stage one include the following:

• observing another teacher, considering what you have learnt from this and adapting your own practice as a result;
• finding out more about a new initiative or teaching and learning strategy and

exploring ways in which it might benefit your class or school;
• attending a training day/seminar/workshop, identifying which skills you want to build on or acquire as a result and taking steps to do this;
• exploring an area of subject knowledge with which you are less familiar, introducing it into your teaching repertoire and evaluating its impact on your practice.

It is important that you disseminate the results of your successful curriculum development activities more widely than your own school. TEP's website, journal and other publications are an ideal launch pad for sharing ideas with a wide audience. The Design and Technology Association provides several different opportunities for this also. You can describe your activities in the following publications:

"**D&T Practice**" which includes articles highlighting the practical aspects of design & technology teaching, including case studies of good practice and resources used;

"**Designing**" which is a large format, highly visual publication that celebrates the design activities of schools, universities and professional designers;

"**Design and Technology Education: An International Journal**" which publishes high quality research, scholarly and review papers relating to design & technology education.

You can present your work as a poster session or a paper at the Annual Design & Technology Association Conference.

11 "D&T Practice".
12 "Designing".
13 "Design and
Technology
Education:
An International
Journal".

How realistic do you think Hargreave's approach to curriculum development is? Compare it with the way curriculum development is carried out in your department and discuss your findings with colleagues.

Further Reading

GENERAL

Engestrom, Y. & Tuomi-Grohn, T. (Eds.), (2003). "Between School and Work New perspectives on Transfer and Boundary Crossing". Oxford: Elsevier Science Ltd.

General Teaching Council for England (2006). "Stage One Booklet, Teacher Learning Academy". London: General Teaching Council.

Hargreaves, D. (1998). "The role of teachers in the knowledge society". London: Demos.

John-Steiner, V. (2006). "Creative collaboration" paperback edition. New York: Oxford University Press.

TO SUPPORT POSSIBLE AREAS OF CURRICULUM DEVELOPMENT

Clark, A. (2003). "Natural-born cyborgs: Minds, Technologies and the future of human intelligence". Oxford: Oxford University Press.

Gershenfeld, N. (2007). "Fab: The coming revolution on your desktop - from personal computers to personal fabrication" paperback edition. New York: Basic Books.

Gershenfeld, N. (2000). "When things start to think". New York: Henry Holt and Company.

Greenfield, S. (2004). "Tomorrow's people". London: Penguin.

Jackson, M. (2002). "What's happening to Home: Balancing work, life and refuge in the information age". Notre Dame IN: Sorin Books.

Kurzweil, R. (2005). "The Singularity is near". New York: Viking.

Mitchell, W. J. (2003). "Me++ The cyborg self and the networked city". Cambridge Massachusetts: Massachusetts Institute of Technology Press.

References

Design & Technology Association: www.data.org.uk

e-scape: http://www.qca.org.uk/downloads/qca-05-1513_creativity-in-dt_R_web.pdf Accessed March 3, 2007.

Engestrom, Y. and knot working: http://www.edu.helsinki.fi/activity/pages/research/newforms/

Hargreaves, D. (1998)." The role of teachers in the knowledge society". London: Demos.

Higgs, S., Baumfield, V. & Hall, E. (2007). "Learning skills and the development of learning capabilities". A report from the EPPI-Centre, Social Science Research Unit, Institute of Education, University of London. Available at http://eppi.ioe.ac.uk/cms/Default.aspx?tabid=1851.

John-Steiner, V. (2006). "Creative collaboration" paperback edition. New York: Oxford University Press.

Lyn, M. 2001 - Nuffield Primary D&T News item. Available at http://www.primarydandt.org/news/?type=archive&pageNo=5, accessed on 03.03.07.

Nuffield Design & Technology: www.secondarydandt.org

Qualifications and Curriculum Authority: www.qca.org.uk

Science Learning Centres: www.sciencelearningcentres.org.uk

SETNET: www.setnet.org.uk

TEP: www.tep.org.uk

Developing your own curriculum Nick Baldwin and David Barlex

The pupil as designer

Malcolm Welch

Malcolm Welch is an associate
professor in the Faculty of Education
at Queen's University, Ontario.
He teaches graduate courses in
research methods and curriculum
design and undergraduate courses in
teaching methods and design &
technology. He has directed several
research projects and has published
widely in academic journals.
Currently, he is principal investigator
on a three-year research study that is
investigating how pupils learn to
make design decisions. He has
worked on major curriculum projects
in England and Canada and has
co-authored eight textbooks.

The pupil as designer
Malcolm Welch

Introduction

Michael Shannon (1990) wrote that, *'design is a subject with profound cultural implications that needs to be addressed by public education…Designing the world we live in is everyone's opportunity and responsibility [and]…design must become a basic attitude about living that shapes every person's priorities'* (p. 29).

> What is your response to Shannon's contention that designing
> is a part of culture? Does everyone have an opportunity to contribute
> to the made world? If yes, what are those opportunities?
> In what ways would the made world be different if every citizen
> took responsibility, to some degree, for its design?
> How will you address these questions with your pupils?

This chapter, which has four parts, is about teaching pupils to design.
Part 1, subtitled "**Is teaching pupils to design important?**", provides a rationale for design education as an essential element in the education of all pupils, both elementary and secondary. Part 2, "**Teaching pupils to design**", will (a) describe the types of tasks you can use to teach pupils to design, (b) describe a pedagogy that supports pupils as they learn to design, and (c) list five interrelated abilities pupils must acquire in order to develop capability as a designer. In Part 3 of the chapter, you will be introduced to a model, developed by David Barlex, that describes the types of interrelated design decisions that pupils must learn to make. Part 4 provides an overview of ideation techniques and modelling skills pupils will need if they are to generate, develop, communicate and evaluate design ideas. The chapter ends with suggestions for further reading and a list of references.

Is teaching pupils to design important?

More than twenty years ago, in 1982, Nigel Cross laid the foundations of a rationale to support the inclusion of design as a mandatory component of general education for all pupils. This rationale contained three important ideas.

First, design develops the innate abilities of the pupil to solve a particular type of real-world problem. C. West Churchman (1967) described these problems as ill-defined or *'wicked'*. Wicked problems are those that, unlike the well-structured problems tackled in mathematics,

01 Everything we
- use has been
05 designed.

(Photograph 01 ©
Claudia Christen
for Smart Design.)

06 Nigel Cross.

are individual (each is unique), have
no definite formation (understanding
and describing the problem is the designer's
first step), do not contain all the necessary
information for their resolution, are not
susceptible to exhaustive analysis, have
no stopping rules (designing can continue
without time limits), and have no one correct
solution. One aim of design education is,
therefore, to allow the pupil to develop the
ability to understand the nature of ill-defined
problems, how to tackle them and how they
differ from other types of problem.

Second, design supports constructive thinking.
This is quite distinct from the inductive and
deductive reasoning common to the sciences
and humanities. Jerome Bruner claimed that
constructive thinking sustains the pupils'
cognitive development in their ability
to manipulate images in the mind's eye.

Third, design offers opportunities
for the pupil to develop a wide range
of abilities in nonverbal thought and
communication. While the humanities and
sciences rely on verbal, numerical and literary
modes of thinking, design thinking relies
on a range of modelling techniques that can
be used to externalise ideas that develop
in what Eugene Ferguson (1992) referred to
as *'the mind's eye'*. These non-verbal modelling
techniques include various forms of graphic
images (sketches, drawings and diagrams)
as well as three-dimensional models. Models
serve as an aid to internal thinking as well

as aids to communicating ideas to self
and to others.

In 2001 Richard Kimbell and David Perry
published a very important paper entitled
**"Design and technology in a knowledge
economy"**. This paper describes the *'distinctive
contribution which design and technology makes
to the school curriculum'* (p. 1).

According to the authors, this distinctive
contribution:
• Engages pupils in a task-centred activity
  (taking a project from inception to
  completion within the constraints of time,
  cost and resources);
• Requires pupils to tackle increasingly
  wicked tasks;
• Requires pupils to unpack the wickedness
  of a task and also acknowledge that design
  is not just about change but about
  improvement, which is value laden;
• Engages pupils in creative exploration,
  to conceive and plan what does not yet
  exist, to operate in a world of uncertainty
  and risk;
• Engages pupils in modelling ideas,
  an iterative process in which the pupil
  moves back and forth between models
  in the mind's eye and models in reality;
• Manages the complexities and uncertainties
  arising from tackling wicked problems;
• Leads to increasingly autonomous learners
  capable of taking responsibility for their
  decisions and living with their consequences
  (pp. 5-7).

07 Richard Kimbell.
08 David Perry.

How would you describe the concept of capability in the context of design education? What would you say to a parent who asked you to justify design education as part of his or her child's education?

Teaching pupils to design

Now that you have a rationale to support design education for all pupils, you will need to think about answering three questions:
(a) What types of tasks will encourage and promote learning to design?
(b) What pedagogy will effectively enable this learning? and
(c) What design skills must pupils acquire in order to be successful? The remaining sections of this chapter respond to these questions.

Setting appropriate tasks

Patricia Murphy and Sarah Hennessy (2001) have described the nature of tasks that teach pupils to design to a high standard. These authors refer to such tasks as *'authentic tasks'*. The next section of this chapter explores two aspects of authenticity: *personal authenticity* and *cultural authenticity*. While they are interrelated, they can be thought of distinctly.

A design and make activity that has *personal authenticity* requires the pupil to identify a need and is orientated towards clients and markets that he or she can relate to. Pupils will be involved in the context of the problem (e.g., helping a bed-ridden person avoid becoming bored). This leads to both the design and make activity and the tasks within to have personal meaning and relevance for the pupil. The pupil must also be given the opportunity to make significant decisions: decisions that allow him or her to be creative (e.g., identify the user, specify the product, propose a solution; not simply make relatively trivial decisions about colour or aesthetic elements of the shape). Being in control and having autonomy, including making a range of design decisions, are all part of what creates personal authenticity in pupils' learning experiences.

In addition to exploring the context of the problem, Patricia Murphy and Sarah Hennessy suggest that pupils need to see the context for its solution. *Culturally authentic* design and make activities relate to activity in the world outside school - in this case in the community of practice of technologists. This implies saying who the pupil is in the process (e.g., part of a company that produces wooden products), and the relationship to any client (e.g., the sibling or friend of a bed-ridden person). *Culturally authentic* design and make activities are sophisticated and 'real' (e.g., a system to detect whether an old has fallen over and summon help).

Identify some authentic design tasks for a Year 10 pupil living in a flat in a high-rise building. Now identify some design tasks that would not be authentic for this same pupil.

Pedagogy to promote learning to design

David Barlex (1995) has described a robust pedagogy that supports pupils as they learn to design using authentic tasks. This pedagogy has, at its centre, a *'capability task'*.

A capability task is a significant activity in which pupils have to use the knowledge, understanding and skill they have been taught in an integrated and holistic way. It forms a focal point in a teaching sequence and enables

09 – 15 What sort of design tasks leading to products like these will be both personally and culturally authentic for pupils?

(Photographs 9, 10, 11, 12, 13 & 15 © The D&T Association.)

pupils to reveal what they have learned through what they can do. A capability task requires pupils to intervene in, and make improvements to, the made world by designing something that they themselves can make and then making the product they have designed. Both the product and the processes by which the product is conceived, developed and realized are significant in this activity.

For pupils to be successful in a capability task they will need particular and appropriate knowledge, skill and understanding. These are taught through a series of *'resource tasks'*: short, highly structured and focused activities through which the pupil acquires the knowledge, skill and understanding he or she will need to successfully complete a capability task. Resource tasks are active. They require pupils to engage with design skills, technical

16 What sort of
- design tasks
18 leading to products like these will be both personally and culturally authentic for pupils?
(Photograph 16 © The D&T Association.)

understanding and making skills.
While a single resource task will usually
address a quite narrow topic, a sequence
of such tasks will lead to a pupil acquiring
a wide repertoire of design, technical,
constructional and aesthetic knowledge and
skill. The effectiveness of this teaching and
learning is evidenced through the quality
of response to the capability task.

For example, in a capability task entitled
"**Desk Lamp**", pupils are given a design brief
in which they are to design and make a desk
lamp with a light source that is focused and
fully adjustable for height and angle and with
an on/off switch. To be successful with this
design and make activity pupils must be able
to generate, develop and communicate ideas;
mark, cut and shape sheet materials to a high
degree of accuracy; use electric components
to build a circuit; use mechanical components
to achieve adjustability; and assemble parts.
Once a desk lamp has been designed and
made the pupil must evaluate the product
and his or her own learning.

Hence *before* responding to this design brief
(design and make a desk lamp) pupils will
complete the following resource tasks:
• Exploring existing products;
• Using a collage to generate ideas;
• Exploring simple, series and parallel circuits;
• Exploring reflective materials;
• Exploring mechanisms;
• Writing a design specification.

List the three major points
that you find intriguing
or interesting about using
'resource tasks' and
'capability tasks' as
a pedagogy for teaching
and learning in design
& technology.
In what ways is this
pedagogy different from
what you experienced
as a pupil?
What challenges do you
see for you, the teacher,
when implementing
this pedagogy?
What challenges do you
anticipate pupils will have
when engaging with
this pedagogy?

What must the pupil designer learn to do?

Teaching pupils to design in the formal
setting of the classroom is very demanding.
Although they will have been 'making stuff'
from an early age, this will have been largely
spontaneous, needs-driven, have used three-
dimensional materials and have been
completed in a non-structured environment.
However, be warned! Pupils frequently don't
respond enthusiastically to the often ritualized
designing required by teachers in the design

& technology classroom. According to Bob McCormick and Marion Davidson, (1996) the ritualisation of designing has become a significant problem in design & technology education. The Office for Standards in Education noted in its 2000 annual report that attainment in design & technology education is often limited because students spend too much time on superficial work associated with the presentation of their portfolios at the expense of the main core of designing and making activities.

If a pupil is to develop his or her capability as a designer, he or she must acquire a set of five interrelated abilities:
1. How to make design decisions;
2. How to generate design ideas;
3. How to develop design ideas;
4. How to communicate design ideas;
5. How to evaluate design ideas.

Reading through this list might suggest that designing a product is a linear, algorithmic process. But no designer proceeds in a straight-line path from the first step (describing a context) to the final step (evaluating the design proposal). Nigel Cross (2000) describes how designing is an iterative process that is heuristic rather than algorithmic, one that uses *'previous experience, general guidelines and rules of thumb that lead in what the designer hopes to be the right direction, but with no absolute guarantee of success'* (p. 29).

The next section of this chapter describes the types of design decisions pupils will engage with in your classes, and will exemplify and discuss ways to enable your pupils to generate ideas. This is followed by an overview of the modelling techniques that pupils may use to develop, communicate and evaluate design ideas. But before doing any of this, a small detour is in order.

A small detour!
Before we examine the skills you will have to teach pupils if they are to become increasingly competent as young designers, it is worth thinking about the prior knowledge of designing that pupils bring with them to your classroom. Prior knowledge is comprised of a pupil's images, reminiscences, experiences and intuitions that are lodged in the subconscious - what Michael Polanyi (1966) refers to as *'implicit knowledge'*. In the past, an assumption has been that the pupil arrives at the design class with little or no relevant prior knowledge, what Lev Vygotsy refers to as *'spontaneous concepts'* (Vygotsky, 1934/ 1986, p. 146). But recent research that I have conducted with David Barlex and Erin O'Donnell (2006) indicates that this may not be the case.

In Year 1 of a three-year study, Year 6 pupils were asked questions about the skills needed by a designer and what designers need to know in order to design particular products. Analysis of the data has revealed that students,

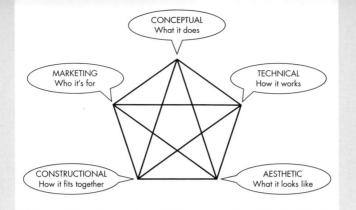

19 The design
decision
pentagon.
(© D. Barlex, 2007.)

who had no previous experience of design &
technology education, demonstrated a
considerable knowledge of not only what
designers do, what skills they need to have
and their personal characteristics, but also
substantial knowledge of what designers need
to know in order to design a range of
products. It appears as though elementary
students' beliefs about designers and what
designers do provide a significant fund of
knowledge relevant to learning to design.

These findings should not be surprising,
for a constructivist view of learning argues
that pupils do not arrive at any classroom
empty-headed, with a *tabula rasa*. Rather,
they arrive with lots of strongly-formed ideas
about how the world works (Brown, Collins
and Duguid, 1989). Effective teachers have
always recognized the need to begin
instruction *'where the pupil is'* (Ausubel, Novak
and Hanesian, 1978). For meaningful learning
to occur, new knowledge must be related
by the learner to relevant existing concepts
in that learner's cognitive structure.

?

Speculate on the experiences
relevant to learning to design
that your pupils may
have had.
What might you be able
to do to help your pupils
use what they already know
about designing?

Discuss your suggestions
with colleagues and work
out how you might build
this into your practice.

Design skills for the pupil designer

As you read earlier in the chapter, if a pupil
is to become an increasingly capable designer
then he or she must develop the ability to:
(a) make design decisions;
(b) generate ideas;
(c) develop ideas;
(d) communicate ideas, and
(e) evaluate ideas.
The next section of this chapter describes the
types of design decisions pupils will engage
with in your classes, and will exemplify and
discuss ways to enable your pupils to generate
ideas. This is followed by an overview of the
modelling techniques that pupils may use
to develop, communicate and evaluate
design ideas.

Learning to make design decisions
You read earlier in this chapter that a designer
is required to make design decisions that span
elaborating the overall concept to resolving
the small particulars. David Barlex (2005)
has suggested that in the context of school-
based designing, pupils should be given
the opportunity to learn to make five types
of interrelated design decisions:
(a) Conceptual;
(b) Marketing;

(c) Technical;
(d) Aesthetic;
(e) Constructional.

Conceptual decisions are concerned with the overall purpose of the design, that is, what sort of product it will be. Marketing decisions are concerned with, for example, who the design is for, where it will be used and where it will be sold. Technical decisions are concerned with how the design will work. Aesthetic decisions are concerned with what the design will look like. Constructional decisions are concerned with how the design will be put together.

This can be represented visually, as shown above, with each type of decision at a corner of a pentagon and each corner connected to every other corner.

This inter-connectedness is an important feature of making design decisions. A change of decision within one area will affect some if not all of the design decisions made within the others. For example, a change in the way a design is to work will almost certainly affect what the design looks like and how it is constructed. It may also have far-reaching effects in changing some of the purposes that the design can meet and who might be able to use it.

Donald Schön (1987) describes designing as a series of 'What if I did this' moves. Hence, we can envisage a pupil making a series of such moves as he or she considers possible decisions about a feature and its effects on decisions made or yet to be made about other features. Kees Dorst and Judith Dijkhuis (1995) describe designing as a reflective conversation with the situation in which the inter-connectedness of the decision-making can be seen as the pupil constructs his or her understanding of the emerging design proposal through a constructivist reflection-in-action paradigm. Donald Schön and Grant Wiggins (1992) suggest that the use of 'What if I did this' moves is more than a mere *ad hoc* tool to cope with the complexity of designing. Its repeated use also increases the pupil designer's understanding of the issues, thereby informing, guiding and stimulating further designing both within and outside the given design situation. Siang Kok Sim and Alex Duffy (2004) consider these iterations as a powerful tool that the designer uses to learn about the design proposal as he or she is creating it.

Generating ideas

Where do 'good' ideas come from? When you have a 'wicked' design problem to solve, what knowledge and resources do you draw from? Chances are that you do several things, including:

- Visit a store and look at existing products similar to the one you plan to design;
- Leaf through books and magazines to gather ideas;
- Think about other similar products you have designed;
- Talk to family and friends about your problem;

"Existing objects are a form of knowledge about how to satisfy certain requirements, about how to perform certain tasks"
(Cross, 1982, p. 225).

20 Pupils examining products.

• Sit quietly and think, doodle and sketch ideas;
• Draw upon your tacit knowledge about a wide range of areas, including the made world, design skills and technical knowledge.

What strategies do you use to help pupils learn from existing objects?
How will you bring the knowledge embedded in objects to pupils' attention so that they can learn from it?

There is an ancient Chinese proverb that states *'On a blank sheet of paper the most beautiful of marks can be made'*. While this may be a helpful idea for you or for a professional designer, it will not be helpful to most of the pupils you teach, who are novice designers. A blank sheet of paper will be very intimidating to many pupils. So you must teach strategies that will enable your pupils to produce (generate) a lot of ideas quickly.

There are a number of well-developed idea generation methods available to help pupils think more creatively. Methods range from logical, structured problem-solving procedures to those that are intended to encourage lateral thinking. Some of the techniques you can use with your pupils are listed below:

• **Brainstorming** is a technique for a group of people to generate a lot of ideas quickly;
• **Attribute analysis** is a technique to produce new designs from familiar objects;
• **Bubble charts** are a technique for recording answers to the questions: What? Where? When? Who? and Why?;
• **Observational drawing** is a technique that uses detailed drawings of an object (natural or made) to generate new design ideas;
• **Making connections** is a technique for connecting different ideas in a new way.

Discuss with colleagues the ways they encourage pupils to generate ideas. In what ways are these different from the strategies you use with pupils?

Using sketchbooks with pupils
Another powerful aide for pupils learning to generate design ideas is a designer's sketchbook. According to Gillian Robinson (1995) *'a sketchbook is an Aladdin's cave of visual ideas...a personal visual memory bank that can be used as a resource for...developing ideas'* (p. 14). Robinson advocates that pupils should be encouraged to keep a sketchbook so as to function as researchers. Andy Ash and colleagues (2000) describe how the use of a sketchbook can help pupils *'to develop self-awareness and skills as independent learners and critical observers'* (p. 193).

Pupils could be encouraged to acquire the 'sketchbook habit' early in their design & technology career and be taught to develop their sketchbooks in increasingly diverse and personalized ways as they mature and their confidence and skills grow. The sketchbook could be used for information gathering as a pupil searches for a creative solution to a design problem. According to Ash et al. (2000) this will encourage the development of a personal response, develop investigation skills, encourage critical and analytical skills, develop self-awareness as an independent learner, promote an active and creative approach to learning and help pupils develop documentation skills. A pupil's natural curiosity, enthusiasm and need for personal realization and expression will be reflected in his or her sketchbook as a personal vision.

21 Simple
- techniques for
25 generating ideas.

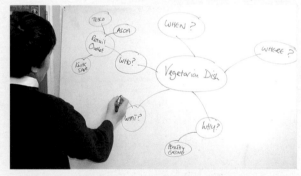

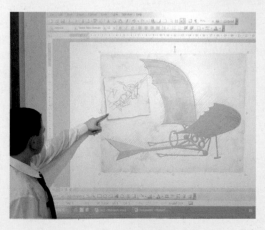

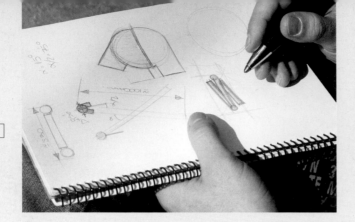

26 27 28

26 Sketching is
- an important
28 skill.
(Photographs
26 & 28 ©
The D&T
Association.)

Malcolm Welch and David Barlex (2003) have written a set of introductory guidelines and activities that provide support for teachers wanting to use a sketchbook approach to enhance their own creativity as well as introduce sketchbooks to pupils.

> Would using sketchbooks with pupils lead to increasingly creative responses to 'wicked' design problems? What strategies would you use to encourage pupils to maintain a sketchbook? Could a sketchbook carry over between key stages?

Developing, communicating and evaluating design ideas

Ideas in the 'mind's eye' (cognitive models) are tenuous - they can be forgotten easily and it is difficult to clarify them. The pupil designer needs to externalise these cognitive models so that they can be developed, communicated and evaluated. To do this the pupil can use various forms of modelling, which Bruce Archer (1979) has referred to as the *'essential language of design'* (p. 133). These include:

1. Sketching and drawing (two-dimensional [2D] modelling);
2. Making models from paper, card, other easy-to-use materials, and simple components

(three-dimensional [3D] modelling);
3. Using symbols (circuit diagrams and mathematical models);
4. Using computer aided drafting (CAD) and other software (spreadsheets and illustration packages).

Using two-dimensional modelling to support designing

Christopher Tipping (1983) considers it essential for pupils to be taught to sketch: *'Fluent sketching ability may be the single most important factor in developing any general design ability'* (p. 45). There can be little doubt about how useful sketching, defined as making lines freehand, is as a form of thinking. Various authors have identified how sketching serves the designer in four important ways.

First, sketching allows and encourages the designer to 'play' with ideas, an essential stage to creative idea development. Sketching is a powerful tool for formalizing, exploring and testing playful musings, to explore and manipulate the unknown.

Second, sketching helps the designer explicate needs, define and clarify the task. Sketching is a crucial part of the process of understanding and gaining insight into a design problem. Edward Robbins (1997) argues that *'until you delineate [a] design conception in a drawing you really cannot claim to understand it'* (p. 32). Renzo Piano, the international architect, claims that *'it is a mistake to believe that now I understand the problem and now I draw it.*

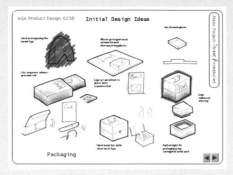

Rather, right at the time you draw you realize what the problem is' (quoted in Robbins, 1997, p. 27).

Third, as Edward Robbins (1997) has written, sketching is essential for communicating ideas, both with 'self' and others. In your classroom, a pupil designer's sketches will evidence to you, the teacher, what he or she is thinking. Sketching enables you, the teacher, and other pupils to reply rapidly and fluently to a pupil's sketches and contribute to his or her thinking.

Fourth, sketching facilitates the evaluation of a design proposal and the identification and restating of problems. Sketching provides a means of testing concepts, which in turn will encourage the further generation of ideas. As Stephen Temple (1994) wrote, evaluation permits progression *'from an innovative mental image to a vehicle for analysis and criticism'* (p. 24).

But the assertions made by the authors quoted above were written in the context of professional design practice. Hence, as teachers, we must ask to what extent a reliance on sketching helps or hinders the pupil designer.

What skills will you need to teach pupils if they are to become more fluent at sketching?
What opportunities will you create for pupils to use 2D modelling to explore design ideas?
What do you see as opportunities and challenges for you, the teacher, in requiring pupils to develop and communicate ideas using sketches?

Using three-dimensional modelling to support designing

According to Donald Schön (1987), *'designing is a creative activity. A designer's reflective conversation with the materials of a situation can yield new discoveries, meanings and inventions'* (p. 161). But when Donald Schön wrote these words, he was referring to the professional designer. So as teachers we must ask the question: Can pupils engage in a *'reflective conversation with materials'*?

The bulk of a pupil's untutored designing skill will have been acquired in the material world: building sand castles, using commercial construction kits, or constructing using found materials.

Research by this author (Welch, 1999) identified the critical role of modelling in three-dimensional materials as an aid to pupils' thinking. Modelling was used to support a range of activities:
- Increasing understanding of the problem;
- Stimulating the generation of solutions;
- Seeing what a design would look like;

• Testing, and continuously incorporating modifications and improvements into a solution.

What skills will you need to teach pupils if they are to become adept at using 3D modelling to develop, communicate and evaluate design ideas? What modelling materials will you introduce to pupils? What opportunities will you create for pupils to use 3D modelling to explore design ideas?

29
-
30

29 3D modelling.

The pupil as designer Malcolm Welch

What do you see as opportunities and challenges for you, the teacher, in requiring pupils to develop, communicate and evaluate design ideas using 3D models?

What does the phrase *'a reflective conversation with the materials'* signify to you?

Using symbolic modelling to support designing

Symbolic modelling uses symbols to represent objects, the physical properties of objects,

31 Symbollic
- modelling.
32

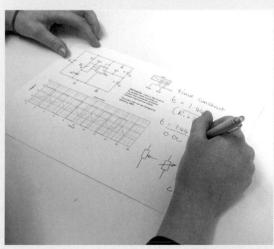

33 34

33 Modelling
- on screen.
34 (Photographs ©
The D&T Association.)

and the relationships between them.
For example, pupils may use mathematical
formulae to calculate the size of a resistor
needed in a circuit. They may collect data
and create a bar chart to illustrate
the nutritional value of various foods.
They may create graphs to show the
relationship between the cross section of
a beam and its rigidity. They may draw circuit
diagrams to show the connections between
electrical components. For particular forms
of symbolic modelling, for example circuit
diagrams, there are usually conventional
symbols. But sometimes pupils can make
up their own symbols as they struggle
to get to grips with their emerging ideas.

What skills will you need
to teach pupils if they are
to become skilled at using
symbolic modelling to
develop, communicate
and evaluate design ideas?
What opportunities will
you create for pupils to use
symbolic models?
What do you see as the
opportunities and challenges
for you, the teacher, in requiring
pupils to develop, communicate
and evaluate design ideas
using symbolic models?

Using computers to support designing

The computer-assisted design (CAD) software
available in schools may be used to explore
the form of an object, animate a mechanism,
explore a variety of finishes, perform
calculations concerning performance
and generate working drawings.
Spreadsheet software can be used to explore
the mathematical relationships between
features of a product and used to model both
technical and economic aspects.

What skills will you need
to teach pupils if they are
to become skilled at using
virtual modelling to develop,
communicate and evaluate
design ideas?
In what ways is virtual
modelling more useful and
less useful than 2D and 3D
modelling?
What do you see as
the educational advantages
and disadvantages
of virtual modelling?

Endnote

I will end this chapter by posing two
questions that I believe are central to thinking
about teaching pupils to design. For each
question, I will suggest some enabling

questions; starting points to stimulate your thinking. I also encourage you to discuss your responses to these questions with colleagues.

Question 1:
Is the modelling strategy used by pupils a function of the 'capability task'?
Which form of modelling would be most appropriate for pupils designing and making body adornment, an essentially aesthetic task?
Which form of modelling would be most appropriate for pupils designing and making a self-controlled moving toy, an essentially technical/constructional task? How will you ensure that pupils extend their repertoire of modelling skills and then use those skills appropriate to a particular task?

Question 2:
What is the most appropriate sequence in which to teach modelling strategies?
How does this sequence map onto the age, ability and experience of pupils? Given that most of the modelling techniques can be taught in some form at any age, how should capability tasks be sequenced to support progression in learning to model ideas?
How do we encourage pupils to use different modelling techniques in increasingly sophisticated ways?

Further reading

Archer, B. (1979). 'The Three Rs'. "Design Studies". 1. (1), 18-20.

Harrison, M. (1992). 'Modelling in Key Stages 1 and 2'.
In J. S. Smith (Ed.), "IDATER92: International Conference
on Design and Technology Educational Research and Curriculum
Development", (pp. 32-36), Loughborough, UK:
Loughborough University of Technology.

Lawson, B. (1990). "How designers think: The design process
demystified" (2nd edition). London: The Architectural Press.

Lawson, B. (2004). "What designers know".
Oxford: Elsevier Architecture Press.

March, L. J. (1976). 'The logic of design'.
In L. J. March (Ed.), "The architecture of form" (pp. 21-37),
Cambridge: Cambridge University.

Peto, J. (Ed.) (1999). "Design process, progress, practice".
London: The Design Museum.

Ropohl, G. (1997). 'Knowledge types in technology'.
"International Journal of Technology and Design Education".
7, 65-72.

Seymour, R. (1999). 'Design, a word you think you
know the meaning of until you try to define it'.
In Peto, J. (Ed.), "Design process, progress, practice"
(pp. 11-21). London: The Design Museum.

Vygotsky, L. (1986/1934). "Thought and Language",
(A. Kozulin, Trans), Cambridge, MA: Massachusetts Institute
of Technology.

Welch, M., Barlex, D., & Lim, H. S. (2000). 'Sketching:
Friend or foe to the novice designer?'. "International Journal
of Technology and Design Education". 10, 125-148.

References

Archer, B. (1979). 'The Three Rs'. "Design Studies". 1. (1), 18-20.

Ash, A., Hall, J., Meecham, P., & Montgomery-Whicher, R.
(2000). 'Attitudes to making'. In N. Addison & L. Burgess (Eds.).
"Learning to teach art & design in the secondary school:
A companion to school experience" (pp. 193-204).
London: RoutledgeFalmer.

Ausubel, D. P., Novak, J. D., & Hanesian, H. (1978).
"Educational Psychology: A Cognitive View" (2nd ed.).
New York: Holt, Rinehart & Winston.

Barlex, D. (1995). "Nuffield design and technology:
Teacher's guide". Harlow, UK: Longman.

Barlex, D. (2005, December). 'Approaches to Coursework
Moderation'. Paper presented at the "Qualifications and
Curriculum Authority Senior Examiners' Conference".
Coventry, UK.

Barlex, D. (2007). 'Capitalising on the Utility Embedded
in Design & Technology Activity: An Exploration of Cross
Curricular Links'. In E. W. Norman & D. Spendlove, (Eds.).
"The Design and Technology Associaition Education and
International Research Conference 2007 linking learning".
(pp. 5-10). Wellesbourne: The Design and Technology
Association.

Brown, J. S., Collins, A., & Duguid, P. (1989).
'Situated cognition and the culture of learning'.
"Educational Researcher". 18. (1), 32-41.

Churchman, C. W. (1967). 'Wicked problems'.
"Management Science". 14. (40), 141-142.

Cross, N. (1982). 'Designerly ways of knowing'.
"Design studies". 3. (4), 221-227.

Cross, N. (2000). "Engineering design methods: Strategies for
product design" (3rd ed.). Chichester, UK: John Wiley & Sons.

Dorst, K., & Dijkhuis. J. (1995). 'Comparing paradigms for
describing design activity'. "Design Studies". 16, 261-274.

Ferguson, E. S. (1992). "Engineering and the mind's eye".
Cambridge, MA: Massachusetts Institute of Technology Press.

Kimbell, R., & Perry, D. (2001). "Design and technology
in the knowledge economy". London: Engineering Council.
Available at www.engc.org.uk via Publications.

McCormick, R., & Davidson, M. (1996). 'Problem solving
and the tyranny of product outcomes'. "Journal of Design
and Technology Education". 1. (3), 230-241.

Murphy, P., & Hennessey, S. (2001). 'Realising the potential -
and lost opportunities - for peer collaboration in a D&T setting'.
"International Journal of Technology and Design Education".
11, 203-237.

Office for Standards in Education (2000). "OfStEd subject
reports secondary design and technology 1999-2000".
London: The Stationary Office.

Piano, R. (1997). 'The Building Workshop'. In E. Robbins, (Ed.),
"Why Architects Draw". (pp. 125-150), Cambridge, MA:
Massachusetts Institute of Technology Press.

Polanyi, M. (1966). "The tacit dimension".
New York: Garden City Press.

Robbins, E. (Ed), (1997). "Why Architects Draw".
Cambridge, MA: Massachusetts Institute of Technology Press.

Robinson, G. (1995). "Sketch-books: Explore and store".
Portsmouth, NH: Heinemann.

Schön, D. A. (1987). "Educating the reflective practitioner:
Toward a new design for teaching and learning in the
professions". San Francisco, CA: Jossey-Bass.

Schön, D. A., & Wiggins, G. (1992). 'Kinds of seeing and their
functions in designing'. "Design Studies". 13, 135-156.

Shannon, M. J. (1990). 'Toward a rationale for public design
education'. "Design Issues". 7. (1), 29-41.

Sim, S. K., & Duffy, A. H. B. (2004). 'Evolving a model of
design learning'. "Research in Engineering Design". 15, 40-61.

Temple, S. (1994). 'Thought Made Visible - the Value of
Sketching'. "co-design journal". 1, 16-25.

Tipping, C. (1983). 'Acquiring design skills for teaching -
a self-help suggestion'. "Studies in Design Education, Craft
and Technology". 16. (1), 12-14.

Vygotsky, L. (1986/1934). "Thought and Language",
(A. Kozulin, Trans). Cambridge, MA: Massachusetts Institute
of Technology.

Welch, M. (1999). 'Analyzing the tacit strategies of novice
designers'. "Research in Science and Technological Education".
17. (1), 19-34.

Welch, M., & Barlex, D. (2003). "Developing your creativity
using a sketchbook: Innovative materials for teachers and
students". Available at: www.nuffieldfoundation.org/curriculum/
issues/index.asp

Welch, M., Barlex, D., & O'Donnell, E. (2006).
'Elementary students' beliefs about design and designing'.
In E. W. L. Norman, D. Spendlove, & G. Owen-Jackson (Eds.),
"The D&T International Research Conference 2006"
(pp. 165-175), Wolverhampton, UK: Wolverhampton University.

Marion Rutland

Dr Marion Rutland is a principal lecturer for design & technology education at Roehampton University, England and teaches on primary, secondary initial teacher education (ITE), and masters programmes. She was a teacher and advisory teacher for thirty years in England and Sydney, Australia. She is a past chair for the Design and Technology Association ITE Advisory Group and currently an Ofsted Team Inspector. Research interests are developing curriculum materials, food technology, ITE, partnership and creativity in design & technology.

David Spendlove

David Spendlove was previously a senior teacher in secondary education before moving into Higher Education and is now the subject leader for design & technology at the University of Manchester. He co-edits both "Design and Technology Education: An international Journal" and the DATA international research conference proceedings. He is a director of the Design and Technology Association and his research interests are broadly based around learning, pedagogy, creativity, emotion and gender.

Creativity in design & technology

Marion Rutland and David Spendlove

Introduction

Creativity in our pupils' work is never an easy issue to address. Teachers will have different ideas on what they think is creative as it is a very subjective concept and they may even question the importance of creativity in their pupils' work. Many teachers you have met may think that it is much more important for the pupils to get the best marks they can by following examination boards' guidance rather than trying to be creative.

The focus of this chapter is to encourage you to think about your pupils' creativity. Do you think that creativity is important? And if so why, and how can you support and guide the pupils? Questions we want you to think about are:
• Are you a creative teacher?
• Are your pupils' creative?
• Does your teaching encourage creativity?
• Do your pupils' products show a creative response?
• How do you know?

 Some design & technology teachers question the importance of creativity. They argue that their task is to teach pupils to learn 'skills' and make well. What do you think?

The need to foster pupils' creativity has become an important issue in recent years in the UK. It was Ken Robinson's Report "**All Our Futures: Creativity, Culture and Education**" (1999) that first raised the issue of the lack of creativity in education. The report proposed a national strategy and made recommendations of how to foster pupils' creativity across the curriculum. Similarly, educational writers such as David Hargreaves (2000) have highlighted the importance of creativity in education, as have Richard Kimbell (2000) and David Barlex (2003a) in design & technology. This has been followed by government initiatives such as the "**Key Stage 3 National Strategy (Designing); Foundation subjects: design & technology**" (Department for Education and Skills, 2004).

The Design and Technology Strategy Group, supported by the Department for Education and Skills (Barlex, 2003b), recognised that there was a need to examine the approach to pupil

01
02 03 04

01 Is this work
- creative?
04 How do you
decide?

assessment in design & technology responding to Richard Kimbell's comment that assessment was *'widely regarded as having become formulaic, routinised and predictable'* (Kimbell, 2004, p. 100).

The Innovating Assessment research project was a response to the view that *'it has become increasingly evident over the last few years that a number of pressures have combined to reduce learners' innovative performance at GCSE in design & technology. "Playing safe" with highly teacher managed projects has been seen to be the formula for schools guaranteed A-C pass rate'* (Kimbell 2006). The project explored and developed approaches to assessment that enabled pupils to discuss, record and critique their 'designerliness' as they moved through a design task structured in a way to provoke and reveal their creativity.
See http://www.nuffieldcurriculumcentre. org/go/CurriculumIssues/Issue_292.html

What do you think?
In your experience do examining bodies credit pupils' creativity and if so how?

The early **"National Curriculum Design and Technology Orders"** (Department for Education, 1995) did not mention creativity. This was rectified through the 'importance of design and technology' statement in the 1999 Orders. Design & technology was the only subject where creativity was mentioned twice.

Pupils are expected to *'learn to think and intervene creatively...become autonomous and creative problem solvers'* (Department for Education and Employment and Qualifications and Curriculum Authority, 1999, p. 15). Recent pressures in education, such as rigid national examination systems, the introduction of national 'league tables' and regular school inspections from the Office for Standards in Education have, as noted by Richard Kimbell (2000, p. 211), *'contributed to the damping down of creative fire in design & technology'*. Ken Robinson's Report (1999) argues that that there is a shortage of teachers who aim to foster pupils' creativity, as there is excessive risk in being such a teacher for it involves discovery, risking, pushing limits and taking steps into the unknown. Ellis Paul Torrance supports this with the claim *'this is serious business - dangerous business and when you challenge students (or pupils) to be creative, you lose control'* (1995, p. 107).

The rest of this chapter will discuss definitions of creativity; explore strategies to foster creativity and teach pupils to be creative. It will describe examples of pupils' work that are creative and present a model for developing creativity in the design & technology classroom. It will also provide suggestions for further study.

Defining creativity

Defining creativity in general terms has not proved an easy task, giving rise to a wide range of suggestions. At a simple level John Dacey and Kathleen Lennon (1998) see creativity as the ability to produce new knowledge. Margaret Boden (1994, p. 75) adopts a more complex view, seeing creativity as *'a puzzle, a paradox, some say a mystery'* but essentially a novel combination of ideas that should include value. Edward de Bono (1992, p. 4) sees creativity as *'a messy and confusing subject, bringing something to life that was not there before'*. David Feldman, Mihaly Csikszentmihályi and Howard Gardner (1994) consider *'big creativity'* to be something that is of enduring value, contributing to an existing field of knowledge and transforming it. Whereas, *'small creativity'* is more humble, though equally valuable, as it is an activity that gives a fresh and lively interpretation to any endeavour. Richard Mayer (1999, pp. 450-451) suggests, *'there appears to be a consensus that the two defining characteristics of creativity are originality and usefulness'*. Teresa Amabile (1983, 1996) highlights the importance of a supportive social environment for creativity to occur. This has particular implications for the classroom in which the teacher is trying to teach pupils to be creative.

 Many teachers believe that 'small' creativity is something we see in the design & technology classroom. Try to give some examples from your experience.

However, a literature review indicates that there is still generally a lack of consensus over the meaning of the word 'creative'. In some cases the word is used to describe a product, in others a process, sometimes a personal quality and at other times a social quality. For some creativity is seen as rare, possessed by only a few, while for others it is a quality possessed in some measure by all. In the context of education the Robinson Report (1999) sees creativity as a universal quality that can be enhanced by teaching. The report defines creative activities in education as *'imaginative activities fashioned so as to produce outcomes that are original and of value'* (1999, p. 29).

Designing and creativity

Jacob Bronowski in 1973 described designing as the creative process that visualises the future, plans and represents it as images that are projected and move about inside the head. In education designing is referred to by Bruce Archer, Ken Baynes and Richard Langdon (1976) as cognitive modelling and described by Ken Baynes (1989, p. 2) as *'the task of creating the form of something unknown, the ability to image, to see in the mind's eye'*. Educational writers such as Richard Kimbell and David Perry (2001) and Bryan Mawson (2003) agree that this process underpins and lies at the heart of design & technology so highlighting its potential for pupils to be creative. David Barlex (2003a) notes that design & technology does not have a high priority in the Robinson Report (Department for Education and Employment, 1999), although there is recognition of the potential for creativity in *'designing'*.

Designing in the context of design & technology is a verb or a 'process' as it involves pupils carrying out a range of activities in order to find a solution to a brief or problem and meeting the needs of people. Designing is seen as a creative activity as it involves pupils carrying out a range of activities to bring ideas from the mind's eye into reality in response to peoples' needs and wants. The level of pupils' creativity will depend on the extent to which they have control of the ideas they eventually turn into products.

Teaching for creativity

The Robinson Report (1999, p. 89) considers creative teaching in two ways: first *'teaching creatively'* and second *'teaching for creativity'*. Teaching creatively is interpreted as teachers using imaginative approaches to make learning more interesting, exciting and effective. This could be described as 'good practice' where teachers themselves are highly creative and develop materials and approaches that interest and motivate pupils. In teaching for

creativity, the focus is on forms of teaching that are specifically aimed to foster or enhance pupils' own creative thinking or behaviour. Teaching creatively and teaching for creativity are both considered to include all the characteristics of good teaching including *'strong motivation, high expectations, the ability to communicate and listen and the ability to interest and inspire'* (Robinson, p. 95). Additional criteria needed to teach for creativity are techniques to stimulate curiosity and raise self-esteem and confidence in pupils. The report notes that teachers need to recognise when these techniques are required and balance structured individual learning with opportunities for self-motivation and group work. The report suggests that when teaching for creativity teachers should:

• Include broad and narrow experimental activities;
• Encourage a positive attitude to imaginative activity and self-expression;
• Provide space for generative thought that is free from immediate criticism and discouragement;
• Encourage self-expression;
• Understand the phases of creative activity;
• Be aware of the differing contexts for the development of ideas, the role of intuition, unconscious mental processes and non-directive creative thinking;
• Encourage and stimulate free play with ideas, the use of imagination, originality, curiosity and questioning and free choice.

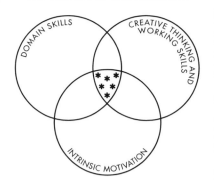

THE CREATIVITY INTERSECTION

05 The Creativity
Intersection.

(Adapted from
Amabile, Teresa M.
(1989). "Growing Up
Creative". New York:
The Creative Education
Foundation.)

Can you give examples
of these sorts of activities
for the design & technology
classroom?

Fostering creativity in design & technology

Facets of creativity

Traditionally, achieving functionality has been the main criteria for products designed and made in the design & technology classroom. However when teaching for creativity a wider perspective is required and other criteria become equally important. Creativity in design & technology requires a combination of clearly identifiable criteria where pupils make creative design decisions, including the overall concept plus its aesthetic, technical and constructional features. Marion Rutland (2005) has described these as:

• **Concept:** which requires the pupil to consider originality; novelty; feasibility, usefulness and function;
• **Aesthetic creativity:** which requires the pupil to consider *'ways in which the product will appeal to the senses'* - sight, hearing, touch, taste and smell;
• **Technical creativity:** which requires the pupil to consider *'how the product will work'* and the nature of the components and materials required to achieve this;
• **Constructional creativity:** which requires the pupil to consider *'how the product will*

be made' and the tools and processes needed to achieve this.

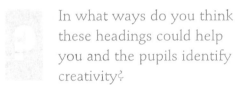

In what ways do you think these headings could help you and the pupils identify creativity?

The environment for creativity

Teresa Amabile (1983, 1989, 1996), an American social psychologist, introduced two important factors to be considered when teaching pupils to be creative when she highlighted the impact of specific social factors and intrinsic motivation on creativity. She describes creativity as the confluence of intrinsic, or self, motivation, domain-relevant knowledge and abilities and creativity-relevant skills. The creativity-relevant skills relate to strategies and approaches that the teacher teaches pupils so that they have some tools for being creative. Teresa Amabile argues that our culture places great emphasis on talent, skill and hard work yet they make up only two-thirds of the creativity formula with intrinsic motivation as the remaining third. Thus, when helping pupils to become their most creative selves, it is not enough to train them in skills, give them opportunities to develop their talents or develop good work habits. There is a need to help them identify the place where their interests and skills overlap, which she calls the *'Creativity Intersection'* and illustrates as shown above.

06 A Key Stage 3 example of playfulness in creativity: 'Walk on the wild side'.

07 Friendly melon bench.

(Produced by Richard Loxam.)

	1	2	3	4	5	6	7	8	9
Feelings	Lazy	Scary	Happy	Loving	Friendly	Chirpy	Grumpy	Energetic	Sad
Things you like to sit on	Tall box	Kerb	Bench	Horse	Chair	Sofa	Cushion	Rocking chair	Piano

Teresa Amabile argues that it is at the intersection that pupils' domain skills and creative-thinking skills overlap with his or her intrinsic interests and it is here that the pupil is most likely to be creative. Her focus on social factors as well as motivation is of great relevance for design & technology in that it emphasises the importance of the classroom or learning environment and the role of the teacher in ensuring an environment conducive to pupil creativity.

Artefacts to support pupil-pupil and teacher-pupil dialogue

Malcolm Welch and David Barlex (2004) interviewed several professional designers to find out what they used to support and enhance their own creativity. They revealed that they used sketchbooks (a personal record of generic research, with sketches, notes, doodles, not focused towards any particular end product, looking at surroundings and soaking up information) and ideas boxes (collections of items the designer finds intriguing, novel, appealing). To maintain a record of their designing as it occurred, the designers used job bags which contained everything to do with a specific project (every scrap of paper, sketches, and drawings, simple rigs, models, photographs, digital images of models etc.). Such artefacts are likely to be useful for pupils because (a) they support the 'internalised dialogue' that takes place in designing, (talking to yourself, inside your head, about your ideas as they are developing) and (b) they provide an arena for conversations between pupils and teachers. This often undervalued opportunity to talk and to explore ideas is an essential pre-requisite to the development and evaluation of new and novel solutions to problems. It helps pupils take risks in handling new ideas, deal with uncertainty, and develop and articulate reasoned arguments to support their thinking.

For further guidance on the use of sketchbooks visit the address below where you can download a guide to using sketchbooks in design & technology:
http://www.nuffieldcurriculumcentre.org/go/CurriculumIssues/Issue_93.html

What are your views on the present GCSE and 'A' level portfolios?
To what extent do they encourage pupils to be creative?

Playfulness in creativity

When encouraging children to be creative it is essential to provide the time and appropriate classroom environment to allow them to 'play around' with their ideas. It is inevitable that some ideas will have less potential than others. It is only by 'playing' with their ideas and speculating about their usefulness and feasibility that pupils will be able to identify those ideas that are worth pursuing and those which should be discarded.

	10	11	12	13	14	15	16	17	18
Feelings	Melancholic	Cheerful	Depressed	Lively	Blue	Peaceful	Angry	Spiteful	Resentful
Things you like to sit on	Suitcase	Railings	Rope	Fit ball	Bicycle seat	Table	Floor	Car seat	Carpet

Unfortunately some methods used within design & technology advocate efficiency to creative idea generation using the minimal number of iterations to come up with an embellished rather than divergent and novel response. Although this 'playfulness' is time-consuming and can appear as idle chatter, in reality this iterative process is an essential ingredient for creativity. This does not mean that the 'playing with ideas' should be unstructured - quite the reverse. Structure is essential for novice designers as they are unlikely to have strategies for playfulness. The materials from the Key Stage 3 National Strategy give a range of useful activities that provide a framework for structured playfulness and encourage children along 'unconventional' thinking paths. "Walk on the wild" side is an interesting example. This technique is a way of using unusual word associations to generate novel and divergent ideas from random words and is a way of de-structuring thinking whilst facilitating idea generation. Themes have words randomly associated to them and then a random linkage is made between the two discrete themes to come up with unusual associations, which form the basis of the next design iteration. The table above shows two lists of words. The first list is associated with the theme 'feelings'. The second list is associated with the theme 'objects to sit on'.

Some random associations for designing seating are an angry chair, a friendly bench, a resentful rocking chair. Some of these associations will be unfruitful but some will lead to interesting and unusual ideas. To increase the fun element spinners or dice can be used to generate genuinely random associations between the different categories. When using the dice the word lists can be numbered 1-6 (or any multiple of 6 e.g., 12, 18, 24 etc.) with pupils taking turns to throw the dice to see which random association they have to work upon. Note there is no shortage of combinations in the above example. There are 18 possible types of seat for each of 18 feelings giving 18 x 18 = 324 possible combinations.

If a pupil threw the dice and got a five (friendly) and a 3 (bench) then the question is what would a friendly bench be like? Who would the bench be friendly towards? Would it be in a friendly location? Or would it be environmentally friendly? Above is an example of a friendly bench based upon square melons. Why? Well why not? It is essential not to reject anything at the early stage and to see the associations as opportunities for creativity.

Using up to three dice and the lists above, have a go at generating your own random associations between feelings and something you sit on.

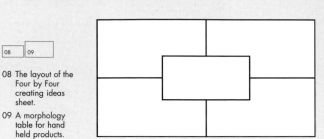

Colours	Style	Construction	Cost
Blue	Funky	Vacuum-formed	£1 - 3
Red	Futuristic	Injection-moulded	£3 - 5
Spotted pink	Retro	Blow-moulded	£5 - 7
Combination	Pop	Cast	£7 - 10

08 The layout of the Four by Four creating ideas sheet.

09 A morphology table for hand held products.

Here are three other examples from the National Strategy for design & technology.

Four by Four

Divide a large piece of paper into four with an additional large square in the centre as shown above. As individuals (or in a small group) you have four minutes to come up with a creative solution to a problem in one of the squares on the paper, e.g. Alternative uses for used CD's. After four minutes, you pass on your idea and receive another person's sheet containing their initial idea. You then have four minutes to work on the idea that you have received (whilst the other person works on your idea) in the next square. After four minutes, you pass on again and finally repeat for a fourth time. When you eventually receive your ideas sheet back, you can then review and synthesise the range of ideas in the final centre square.

Morphology

This is a way of generating large numbers of combinations by breaking down a product design in to different features. If a group of pupils is designing a handheld product they can break down the design into headings related to colour, style, materials, cost, construction and so on. The table above shows an example. By combining features from each column the pupils can generate descriptions of new products. One possible set of combinations is a spotted pink, futuristic, vacuum-formed design costing £7-10. As there are 4 features in each of four columns the total number of combinations is 4 x 4 x 4 x 4 = 256 combination. This is the perfect antidote to pupils who say they only have one idea!

An alternative to this is attribute analysis. You can find an example at this address: http://www.secondarydandt.org/resources/ks3/frk3_0000000013.asp

SCAMPER

This is a technique that encourages divergent thinking when pupils use the SCAMPER analysis tool to think about an object from different perspectives. Doing this allows pupils to think about redesigning an object from multiple perspectives. Therefore if redesigning a fork using SCAMPER headings pupils might think about it as follows:

- **S - Substitute** - We could use chopsticks, fingers;
- **C - Combine** - We could use fork and knife and spoon;
- **A - Adapt** - We could create a tuning fork;
- **M - Modify** - We could produce a baby fork, garden fork;
- **P - Put to other uses** - We could use it for planting seeds;
- **E - Eliminate** - We could pre-shred all food, use adapted spoon;
- **R - Reverse/Rearrange** - We could think of alternatives to a fork (as if it had never been invented).

Scamper does not provide answers but provides a re-conceptualisation opportunity

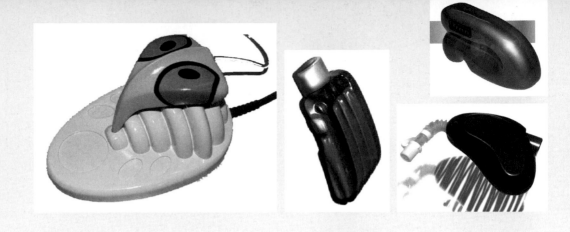

10 Product ideas
- from pupils.
13

that may spark idea generation. Note that Moshe Barak discusses SCAMPER and other problem-solving approaches to designing in his chapter.

> Think about how you might use these strategies in your own teaching.

Product parade 1

Look at the products shown above. They were all produced by pupils as minor projects.

> Before you read ahead, write down what you think each product might be and why you think this. A clue is that the products are all related so you can begin by asking yourself how products might be related.

The project that the pupils attempted embodies the principles outlined above in that the pupils had to work in an uncertain and risky way as they were operating outside of their existing knowledge base. The teacher did not pre-determine the outcomes. Clearly they are diverse in appearance and that alone suggests creativity.

In fact all the outcomes were produced in a medical product design project. This can be attempted with any age group in secondary school although the examples here are from pupils aged 14 and 16 years. These pupils were tasked with designing a product to be used in response to a specific medical condition. Such a task is immediately non-trivial and provokes genuine engagement unlike so many design tasks that pupils tackle. Not only did they need to consider the significance of the product, they also needed to consider the hidden (emotional) messages that the designs would create such as being reassuring, healthy and uplifting.

At the design stage, the pupils were very much encouraged to play with ideas. This was particularly evident with design 3 (image 12) where the student was playing with a 'Tipex' mouse by drawing out the white tape across the back of his hand. As he was playing he realised that this could be a way of applying medication across the skin without the need for injections (which was his original brief). Product responses 1 (image 11) and 4 (image 13) are redesigns of asthma inhalers with design 4 being aimed at the sports market and taking a stimulus from sports drinks plus making the product bigger than the usual inhaler for easier finding in a sports bag. Product response 2 (image 10) takes its stimulus from a wasp's tail as it stings and was a means of providing insulin for someone in early pregnancy.

14 15
16 17

14 Wrapped-filled
- food products
17 designed by
   pupils aged 15.

The development of each product was fraught with uncertainty. Pupils were given license to be risky and make mistakes from which they were able to recover. Achieving technical functionality was not an initial priority and did not drive the process. Playfulness was encouraged at the early stages, which translated into technical detail in the later stages. The results in terms of creativity speak for themselves.

How might this approach be used in one of the projects you teach? In what ways would you have to change the project?

Product parade 2

Look at the food products shown above. They were made when Year 10 pupils working in small groups were encouraged to design and make products with a 'wow' factor. The approach allowed the pupils to design more freely rather than addressing a very specific brief, for example design and make a '…' from the beginning. It could be described as the 'Ready Steady Cook' approach, with an open range of ingredients available where the pupils could draw on their previously learnt 'knowledge and skills' base to develop their own range of ideas for a named target market.

Their first task was a product analysis of existing products to rank order existing wrapped-filled products against a set of criteria for design decisions.
The criteria were:
• Desirable nutritional content;
• Flavour and odour;
• Colour;
• Cost;
• Effective use.

The results from the product analysis task were analysed and ranked using a series of star diagrams for their potential as a handheld product by a 'taste testing panel' consisting of the whole class. This activity enabled the pupils to identify key criteria for a 'handheld' product.

The pupils then experimented in groups with a range of fillings and wrapping to explore the development of flavour, odour and taste. They chose two fillings to develop with different wrapping into a food product for a specific market. It was at this stage that each pair of pupils wrote their own design brief for a range of 'handheld' products. Their ideas they came up with were wide-ranging and varied, including:
• a range of handheld pastry snacks for a new fast food franchise;
• a range of handheld snacks for a school trip;
• a sweet and savoury product for a children's packed lunch box;
• healthy, deli-based food products for a champagne picnic for two;

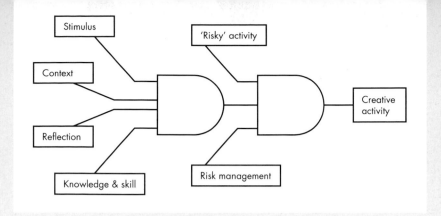

18 The inputs that need managing for creative activity.

- savoury handheld wrapped foods for an adult summer picnic;
- handheld wrapped picnic foods aimed at improving fruit consumption.

This work involved pupils writing their own brief around a theme. Could this work in your classroom? What difficulties might your pupils experience? How would you overcome these?

A model for developing creativity in the design & technology classroom

The Nuffield Design & Technology Project and the Qualifications and Curriculum Authority responded to the Robinson Report by inviting 20 teachers to attend a full-day meeting. The teachers presented pupils' work in art & design and design & technology that they considered creative. This was followed by visits to a selection of schools to watch lessons in progress and a further full-day meeting in which teachers presented and discussed pupils' work. From this overview it was possible to identify four features that had to be in place for pupils to act creatively in either subject:

- The activity had to be presented in a context to which the pupils could relate;

- The activity had to be supported by a significant stimulus which was often, but not exclusively, intensely visual;
- Focused teaching was necessary to provide knowledge, understanding and skills;
- An attitude of continuous reflection needed to be encouraged.

But these four features alone do not ensure creative activity. The deciding factor is the way they are managed. This must be done so that pupils can *handle uncertainty in exploring and developing outcomes*. There must be some risk associated with the endeavour in terms of the 'originality' of the activity as far as the individual pupil is concerned. If the outcome is certain to be successful, all possibility of 'failure' is eliminated, if there are no 'butterflies in the tummy' at some stage in the endeavour then the outcome will be mundane. This is illustrated above. These findings indicate clearly that the nature of the activity and the way in which the teacher manages the classroom are two factors that need to occur simultaneously when teaching for creativity.

Try to suggest means by which these inputs can take place in the way design & technology is taught.

Teaching *for* creativity is a complex and demanding activity in which the role of the teacher is crucial in creating a calm, supportive environment where pupils feel motivated, secure and confident to take risks.

Teaching *for* creativity and fostering creativity is dependent largely on the teacher's professional ability to manage his or her classroom environment to meet these requirements. We believe that providing an appropriate environment and expecting pupils to be creative within that environment is as least as important, if not more so, than developing exercises to assess their creativity.

Further reading

This chapter has merely scratched the surface of what is an enormous topic which is increasing in significance. The issue of the relationship between creativity and intelligence has not been explored, but if this is of interest to you read the work of Robert Sternberg listed below. If you wish to develop your nderstanding further then the publications below will give you a good starting point as well as providing you with further references.

Barlex, D. (Ed,). (2003). "Creativity in Crisis, Design and Technology at KS3 and KS4, DATA Research Paper 18". Wellesbourne, UK: DATA.

Craft, A., Jeffrey, B. and Leibling, M. (2001). "Creativity in Education". London: Continuum.

Craft, A. (2005). "Creativity in Schools; Tensions and Dilemmas". Oxon, Abingdon, UK: Routledge.

Cropley, A. (2001). "Creativity in Education & Learning; a guide for teachers and educators". London: Rogan Page.

Gardner, H. (1982). "Art, Mind and Brain". New York: Basic Books.

Gardner, H. (1983). "Frames of mind". New York: Basic Books.

Gardner, H. (1993). "Multiple Intelligences". New York: Basic Books.

Gardner, H. (1999). "Intelligence Reframed". New York: Basic Books.

Fisher, R., Williams, M. (2004). "Unlocking Creativity: Teaching across the Curriculum". London: David Fulton Publishers.

Norman, E., Spendlove, D., Grover, P., Mitchell, A. (Eds.). (2004). "Creativity and Innovation - DATA International Research Conference 2004". Wellesbourne, England: DATA.

Rutland, M. (2003). 'How do we show in design & technology that we value creativity?'. In J. R. Dakers & M. J. de Vries (Eds.). "PATT-13 (Pupils' Attitude Towards Technology) International Conference Proceedings, The place of design and technology in the curriculum". (pp. 71-83). Glasgow: University of Glasgow. Also available at www.iteaconnect.org/PATT13/rutland.pdf

Rutland, M. (2002). 'What can we learn about creativity from the practice of professional designers to inform design and technology classroom practice?'. In E. W. L. Norman (Ed.). "DATA Research International Conference", (pp. 153-159), Wellesbourne, UK: DATA.

Rutland, M. & Barlex, D. (2007). 'Perspectives on pupils creativity in design and technology in the lower secondary curriculum in England'. "International Journal of Technology and Design Education". (in press).

Sawyer, R. K. (2006). "Explaining Creativity".
Oxford: Oxford University Press.

Spendlove, D. (2005). 'Creativity in education: a review'.
"Design and Technology Education: An International Journal".
10. (2), 9-18.

Sternberg, R. & O'Hara, L. (2000). 'Intelligence and Creativity'.
In R. Sternberg, (Ed.). "Handbook of Intelligence".
(pp. 611-630). Cambridge: Cambridge University Press.

References

Amabile, T. (1983). "The Social Psychology of Creativity".
New York: Springer-Verlag.

Amabile, T. (1989). "Growing up Creative: Nurturing a Lifetime
of Creativity". New York: The Creative Education Foundation.

Amabile, T. (1996). "Creativity in Context: Update to the Social
Psychology of Creativity". Colorado, USA; West View Press.

Archer, B., Baynes K. & Langdon, R. (1976). "Design in General
Education". London: Department of Education and Science.

Barlex, D. (Ed.). (2003a). "Creativity in Crisis, Design and
Technology at KS3 and KS4, DATA Research Paper 18".
Wellesbourne, UK: DATA.

Barlex, D. (2003b). "Building on success: The unique contribution of
design and technology". London: Department for Education and Skills.

Baynes, K. (1989). 'Beyond Design Education'.
"Journal of Art and Design Education". 1. (1), 2.

Boden, M., (Ed.). (1994). "Dimensions of Creativity".
Cambridge, MA: Bradford Books, Massachusetts Institute
of Technology Press.

Bronowski, J. (1973). "The Ascent of Man".
London: British Broadcasting Corporation.

Dacey, J. & Lennon, K. (1998). "Understanding Creativity".
San Francisco: Jossey-Bass.

de Bono, E. (1992). "Serious Creativity".
London: Harper Collins Business.

Department for Education (DfE). (1995). "Design and
Technology in the National Curriculum". London: HMSO.

Department for Education and Employment (DfEE) & Qualifications
and Curriculum Authority (QCA). (1999), "Design and Technology:
The National Curriculum for England". London: HMSO.

Department for Education and Skills (DfES). (2004). "Key Stage
3 National Strategy. Foundation subjects: design and
technology. Framework and training materials". London: HMSO.

Feldman, D., Csikszentmihalyi, M. & Gardner, H. (1994).
"Changing the World: A Framework for the Study of Creativity".
West Point Connecticut: Praeger.

Hargreaves, D. (2000). 'Towards Education for Innovation'.
Lecture on 22nd November 2000 at the Qualifications and
Curriculum Authority (QCA), London.

Kimbell, R. (2000). 'Creativity in Crisis'. "The Journal of Design
and Technology Education". 5. (3), 206-211.

Kimbell, R., (2004). 'Assessment in Design and Technology
Education for the Department of Education and Skills'.
In H. Middleton, M. Pavlova & R. Roebuck, (Eds.).
"Learning for Innovation in Technology Education Conference",
Vol. 2, (pp. 99-112), Brisbane, Australia: Griffith University.

Kimbell, R. & Perry, D. (2001). "Design and Technology
in the knowledge economy". London: Engineering Council.
Available at www.engc.org.uk via Publications.

Mawson, B. (2003). 'Beyond "The Design Process":
An Alternative Pedagogy for Technology Education'.
"International Journal of Technology and Design Education".
13, 117-128.

Mayer, R. E. (1999). 'Fifty Years of Creativity Research'.
In R. Sternberg (Ed.). "Handbook of Creativity". (pp. 449-460).
Cambridge: Cambridge University Press.

Robinson, K. (1999). "All our Futures: Creativity, Culture
& Education". London: Department for Education and
Employment.

Rutland, M. (2005). "Fostering creativity in design and
technology at Key Stage 3". Unpublished PhD Dissertation,
Roehampton University, University of Surrey, UK.

Torrance, E. P. (1995). "Why fly? A philosophy of creativity"
(Creativity Research). Norwood, NJ: Ablex.

Welch, M. & Barlex, D. (2004). 'Portfolios in design
& technology education: Investigating differing views'.
In E. W. L. Norman, D. Spendlove, P. Grover & A. Mitchell
(Eds.). "DATA International Research Conference 2004".
(pp. 193-197), Sheffield, UK: Sheffield Hallam University.

Problem-solving in technology education: the role of strategies, schemes & heuristics

Moshe Barak

Moshe Barak is a senior lecturer in the department of Science and Technology Education at Ben-Gurion University of the Negev, in Israel. Previously he served as a lecturer and researcher at the Technion - Israel Institute of Technology, where he received his Ph.D. and M.Sc. degrees. He is a member of the editorial boards of the "International Journal of Technology and Design Education" and "Educational Research and Reviews". He has written many articles in academic journals and textbooks on subjects such as creativity, problem-solving and project-based learning in technology education.

Problem-solving in technology education:
the role of strategies, schemes & heuristics
Moshe Barak

Introduction

Problem-solving is considered one of the most complex intellectual functions. In spite of the fact that the nature of human problem-solving has been studied by psychologists over the past 100 years, the term has remained rather ambiguous. Some of the questions often discussed regarding problem-solving are: Is there a general method for solving problems in different areas and contexts? What characterizes a good problem-solver? To what extent can people learn problem-solving methods and improve their competencies in this regard? This chapter addresses these questions, with particular emphasis on teaching and learning technology in K-12 education. An effort will be made to propose a rationale for teaching pupils inventive problem-solving methods beyond the 'classical' problem-solving model often discussed in technology education literature. The chapter will end with a reflection on teaching this type of course to Israeli teachers and pupils, and conclusions about the effectiveness of teaching problem-solving methods.

Is there an all-purpose problem-solving method?

The question characterizing problem-solving in technology cannot be separated from the broader question - is there a general problem-solving method? This question is very difficult and ancient as well; Aristotle's works contain much regarding both. Let us examine concisely what two renowned educational philosophers wrote on this issue. John Dewey (1859-1952) had made problem-solving the very model of thinking (although he did not put it that way). In his 1910 book, "**How We Think**", Dewey distinguished five steps in thinking (or, as he put it, reflection), and what he described are in the steps involved in problem-solving: '*Upon examination, each instance reveals, more or less clearly, five logically distinct steps: (i) a felt difficulty; (ii) its location and definition; (iii) suggestion of possible solution; (iv) development by reasoning of the bearings of the suggestion; (v) further observation and experiment leading to its acceptance or rejection; that is, the conclusion of belief or disbelief* ' (Dewey, 1910).

In mathematics, ideas about problem-solving hark back to the mathematician George Polya, who pointed out in his book, "**How to solve it**", the following four stages in solving a problem: (a) understanding the problem; (b) devising a plan; (c) carrying out the plan; and (d) looking back. One can see that Polya's stages in solving problems very much resemble Dewey's suggestion. However, Dewey saw problem-solving as a kind of thinking (as opposed to, say, 'idle thinking'). Although Dewey called his book "**How We Think**" and not "**Physical Thinking**" or "**Mathematical Thinking**", he emphasized that thinking is always directed towards some

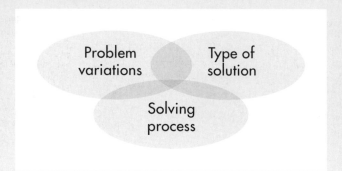

01 The three
dimensions of
problem-solving.

difficulty requiring unraveling, and therefore always takes place in a specific context. Indeed, during the last couple of decades, many voices have supported the 'domain specific' perspectives on learning, thinking and teaching. These include authors like Robert McCormick at the Open University in England (2004), David Perkins at Harvard University and Gavriel Salomon at Haifa University (Perkins and Salomon, 1989). In these circles, problem-solving must occur within a context and depends strongly on an individual's previous experience in similar situations. Perkins and Salomon, in their contribution entitled *'transfer of learning'* in the "**International Encyclopedia of Education**" (1992 edition), stress that transfer of learning from one context to another hardly occurs, and transfer to closely related contexts and performances (*'near transfer'*) seems to have a much better prospect than transfer to rather different contexts (*'far transfer'*). However, according to these authors, education can be designed to promote conditions fostering transfer, as will be discussed later in this chapter.

We can conclude this discussion by saying that no all-purpose problem-solving method exists, but there are some problem-solving approaches or representations that can be useful over several disciplines, and other methods that are unique to each subject separately. Technology educators, as well as educators in other fields, need to acknowledge diverse problem-solving approaches and be able to utilize them in different class contexts.

Accordingly, this chapter aims at highlighting several approaches for solving technological problems that have gained increased attention in areas such as engineering and management, and that could also be useful in technology education in K-12 schooling.

Is there room in the school curriculum for teaching special lessons in school for fostering general thinking skills, such as problem-solving or creativity?

What do technology, science or mathematics teachers know about problem-solving in subjects beyond their fields of expertise?

The nature of technological problems and their solutions

The term 'problem' expresses a state of difficulty, a situation, condition or issue that needs to be resolved, or a question raised for consideration for solution. What types of problems do we present to students in technology education? What kinds of solutions do we expect them to arrive at? Since this question relates closely to the more general question of what is technology, I will follow the approach suggested by Marc de Vries in his book "**Teaching about technology:**

02

02 How would you
   compare these
   three batteries?

An introduction to the philosophy of technology for non-philosophers" (2005), in which he describes technology as *'the human activity that transforms the natural environment to make it fit better with human needs, thereby using various kinds of information and knowledge, various kinds of natural (material, energy) and cultural resources (money, social relationships, etc.).'* We can combine this perception with the broader problem-solving model seen in image 01 (David H. Jonassen, 1997) to depict problem-solving in a technological context.

The three ovals are shown as partially overlapping each other to indicate that no sharp borders exist between the problem definition, the solving process and the solution itself, and that problem-solving is not a linear process. This model can help, however, in exploring problem-solving in technology, as discussed below.

'Problem Variations' is concerned, in general, with the context a problem is derived from, the setting, environment or background the problem relates to, its degree of complexity (specific versus multifaceted), degree of structuredness (well-structured versus ill-structured) and domain specificity (situated versus abstract). What makes a problem difficult to solve? The term 'ill-defined problem', which is often used in the psychological and educational literature, indicates that the difficulty level of a problem is first determined by problem definition or presentation, or in other words,

problem variations. Consequently, this is the first dimension of the problem-solving model seen in image 01. According to John Hayes (1978), ill-defined problems require solvers to contribute to the problem definition, such as reducing a general query to a specific question or a set of questions, making assumptions and determining criteria for a satisfactory answer. For example, if one is asked to compare the quality of three car batteries and no additional details are given, the solver has to determine what parameters to take into account. These might include the maximum current (in amperes) a battery can supply; its capacity (in ampere hours); the Cold Cranking Amps (CCA) parameter, which is the number of amperes a battery can support for 30 seconds at a temperature of 0°C; product maintenance requirements; price; and manufacturer's warranty.

Unlike problems in mathematics and science, solving technological problems often involves social norms and values. In the current example, these can be the implication of each battery's production or recycling in saving the environment, or the work conditions each manufacturing company provides to its employees.

How can we engage pupils in formulating problems as part of conventional teaching?

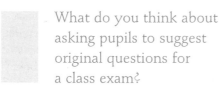

03 The Mango phone and an Israeli newspaper cutting announcing its release.

"New: a cellular 'phone for receiving calls only"

What do you think about asking pupils to suggest original questions for a class exam?

It is important to note that technological problems do not always arise from considering the explicit needs of individuals or society (food, clothing, housing, transportation, etc.), as is often presented in the educational literature. Many technological systems, for instance the microwave oven or the cellular telephone, were originated by inventors and engineers pursuing a technical possibility rather than in response to a request by people, simply because individuals cannot ask for products they have never heard about. The cellular telephone has responded to more than known needs. The advent of this artefact and its related services such as texting, also known as SMS (Short Message Service), have created a new technological market in response to previously unidentified needs.

To conclude, technological problems are often derived from several contexts and can involve social, economical, mathematical, scientific or technical aspects. Writers such as Marc de Vries (2005) and Charles Harris and his colleagues, in their book **"Engineering Ethics, Concepts and Cases"** (2000), argue convincingly that technological problem-solving and engineering in particular have to deal with issues such as moral dilemmas, ethical questions, responsibility, integrity,

reliability, risks, safety and environmental issues.

The *'Type of Solution'* regards the way a solution to a problem is put into practice, for example by changing the physical ttributes or function of components in a system or the entire system. Sometimes, but not always (as people often think), a technological problem is solved by the development of a new artefact or system. It is important to emphasize, however, that the essence of a solution to a technological problem is the idea behind the solution, while its practical application can appear in many forms. For example, an increasing number of today's technological systems are computerized, and technological problems are frequently handled through programming. Consider the following story: when the first generation of cellular telephones appeared on the market in the mid-1990s, the calls were so expensive that most organizations or families could not afford using this service. This was undoubtedly a technological problem having strong technical, economical and social aspects: how to limit people in using the telephone under only urgent or pressing circumstances. An Israeli company came out with a unique cellular telephone model called **Mango**, which was a regular cellular telephone in which the entire keyboard except for one key was blocked electronically; the user could receive calls but dial to only one pre-programmed number. The Mango was accepted as an innovative product, as seen in image 03.

The Mango was very successful on the market at the time: companies bought it for their out-of-house employees to keep in contact with the office, and parents gave it to their children to call home. In this case, a small functional change in an existing artifact, which solved the problem of limiting the cost of its use, enabled exposing people from diverse backgrounds to a new technology, which in turn advanced the entire field of cellular communication. The Mango case demonstrates that the term problem-solving in technology expresses a broader concept than the term design. Although many people consider these terms equivalent, it is worth mentioning that, unlike the concept of design, technological problem-solving does not always end up with the development of a new product.

Do you agree that a design always ends up with a new product? Can you think of an example that disproves this 'rule'?

'The Solving Process', the third dimension in the problem-solving model (see image 01), involves the method, course or procedure of proceeding from a given state to a desired goal state; this is the focus of the rest of this article.

Many people see problem-solving as a two stage process: first comes the collection of a wealth of ideas or optional solutions to a problem, and only later comes the examination of these ideas more systematically and the selection of the optimal one. Accordingly, terms such as 'thinking outside the box', 'free flow of thoughts', 'associative thinking' or 'brainstorming' are often mentioned in the context of problem-solving in technology. These terms, however, are used less in mathematics and science. This two stage view of problem-solving has become somewhat of a barrier for teaching problem-solving methods in school for two reasons: first, the concept of 'disordered thinking' is often perceived as strange, odd, inconsequential and not serious in comparison to convergent thinking, which characterizes problem-solving in science and mathematics; second, there is an inherent contradiction in trying to teach people to think in an unexpected way or to arrive at surprising ideas.

To learn more about the role of divergent thinking in solving technological problems, it may be instructive to ask the question: To what extent do expert problem-solvers use 'disordered thinking' as a working method? Phillip C. Wankat and Frank S. Oreovicz, who broadly discuss the issue of problem-solving in their book "Teaching Engineering" (1993), compare the ways novices and experts solve problems as follows:
'While novices memorize knowledge as small disconnected facts, experts have thousands of "chunks" of specialized knowledge and patterns stored in their brains in a readily accessible fashion; while novices have difficulties in describing

*a problem, experts use many techniques
to re-describe or re-define a problem; while novices
use trial-and-error, experts use strategies; while
novices do not break a problem into parts or harder
problems, experts analyze parts, proceed in steps
and look for patterns.'*

There is a wide consensus in the literature
that experts tend to concentrate on a problem
and use specific strategies to seek a solution
to a problem rather than rely on a random
search, as novice problem-solvers frequently
do (Joanne G. Kurfiss, 1988). David Jonassen
(1997) specifically stresses that individuals
who use domain-specific strong strategies are
better problem-solvers. Experts use strong
strategies effectively and less experienced
solvers can also learn to use them (Mayer,
1992). Margaret Boden (2004), a researcher
having a background in computational
psychology and artificial intelligence,
also stresses that constraints, as opposed
to random search or free flow of thought,
make creativity possible. According to this
author: *'To throw away all constraints would
be to destroy the capacity for creative thinking.
Random processes alone, if they happen to
produce anything interesting at all, can result only
in first-time curiosities, not radical surprises…
randomness can sometimes contribute to creativity,
but only in a context of background constraints.'*

John Hayes (1978) distinguishes between
random search to a solution, which he calls
'the most primitive search process', and heuristic
search, in which the problem-solver uses

knowledge to identify promising paths
in seeking a solution.

We can see, then, that in contrast to what
many people believe, organized thinking and
the consideration of prior knowledge and
constraints can contribute to successful
problem-solving more than methods like
'irregular thinking' or 'associative thinking'.
Lately, there is a growing recognition that
inventive problem-solving often requires
the integration of divergent and convergent
thinking, and good problem-solvers frequently
use these two types of thinking
simultaneously or alternate easily between
them (Frank Barron, 1969; Dennis R. Brophy,
1998; Paul A. Howard-Jones, 2002).
Arthur Cropley (2001) claims that the mere
production of variability via divergent
thinking runs the risk of generating only
'quasi-creativity' or 'pseudo-creativity' if it is
not explored and evaluated via convergent
thinking. Jacob Goldenberg and David
Mazursky (2002), in their book "**Creativity in
Product Innovation**", point out that most
brainstorming groups do not generate more or
better ideas than individuals working
independently. To get an inventive (simple,
surprising but efficient) idea, one does not
necessarily need to collect many ideas; it can
be more useful to utilize strategies or thinking
patterns that help in seeking a solution
through altering systematically with the
physical and functional attributes of a system's
ingredients. Some of these methods
are discussed on the following pages.

Strategies, schemes and heuristics for solving technological problems

Alex Osborn (1963) and Bob Eberle (1977) suggested the SCAMPER method for inventive problem-solving, which is mainly a framework of 'playing' with the traits and functions of components in a system, or their interrelations.

- **Substitute:**
  What could be used instead?
  What other components could be used?
- **Combine:**
  What parts or functions could be combined?
  What unrelated ideas or parts could we combine with this?
- **Adapt:**
  What else is like this?
  What could be copied?
  What idea could be incorporated?
- **Magnify:**
  What could be magnified, enlarged or extended?
  What could be exaggerated?
  What could be added?
  How about greater frequency?
  What could add extra value?
  What could be duplicated?
  How could it be carried to a dramatic extreme?
- **Modify:**
  Could we change an idea, practice or product slightly and be successful?
  What new twist could we introduce?
  What changes could be made in the plans?
- **Put to other uses:**
  What else could a specific component be used for?
  Are there new ways of using it?
  What else could be made from this?
- **Eliminate or divide:**
  What could be omitted or eliminated?
  What is not necessary?
  What could be condensed?
  Divided up?
  Split up?
  Separated into different parts?
- **Rearrange:**
  What other arrangement might be better?
  Other patterns?
  Other layouts?
  Other sequences?
  Change the order?
  Transpose cause and effect?
  Interchange components?
- **Reverse:**
  What are the opposites?
  What are the negatives?
  Reverse roles?
  Consider it backwards?
  Should I turn it around?
  Do the unexpected?

The case of the Mango cellular telephone mentioned earlier demonstrates the principle of solving a problem by eliminating a central component from the configuration of a system along with its function. In this case, the keyboard keys were not physically removed, rather their function was blocked.

04 Pharos of
Alexandria.

Jacob Goldenberg and David Mazursky (2002) show how 'the displacement template' in their terms is helpful in solving technological problems and developing surprising products; by removing legs from a chair, for example, we receive a chair useful on the ground, such as on beach sand.

Perhaps one of the most comprehensive works on inventive problem-solving in engineering was carried out by the Russian researcher Genrich Altshuller (1988) and his colleagues, who investigated the principles and knowledge that characterized more than a million patents and inventive solutions to technical problems. Altshuller's method, entitled TRIZ (the Russian acronym for the Theory of Inventive Problem Solving), comprises the following three stages:
(a) the resolution of technical and physical contradictions in a system;
(b) the evolution of systems;
(c) the reference to the ideal system and ideal solution.

Since TRIZ is not easy to learn or describe, it is often presented in the literature through **"40 Techniques for Overcoming System Conflicts"** such as (the first 10):
- Segmentation
- Extraction
- Local Quality
- Asymmetry
- Combining
- Universality
- Nesting
- Counterweight
- Prior counter-action
- Prior action

TRIZ is gaining increased attention in the world of engineering, design and creative problem-solving, and has been implemented in large corporations such as Motorola, Xerox, Kodak, McDonnell Douglas, General Motors, Ford and General Electric. At Rolls Royce, hundreds of engineers have been trained in TRIZ, which has become an integral part of the company's problem-solving culture.

Based on the roots of SCAMPER and TRIZ, Israeli researchers (Horowitz, 2001; Horowitz and Maimon, 1997; Goldenberg et al., 1999) developed a simplified version entitled 'Systematic Inventive Thinking' (SIT) or 'Advanced Systematic Thinking' (ASIT) that has been implemented successfully in a large number of companies in Israel and worldwide (Barak and Goffer, 2002). This method offers seeking a solution to a problem by the following manipulations with the system's ingredients:
- **Unification:** assign a new function to an existing component.
- **Multiplication:** introduce a copy (or slightly modified copy) of an existing object into the system.
- **Division:** decompose an object into its parts; slice, cut, snip or divide an object.
- **Eliminate:** remove an object from the system along with its function.

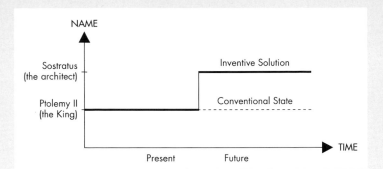

05

05 Solving a problem by making a connection between two variables.

• **Change relationships** between variables in a system; add, remove or alter the dependency between physical or functional attributes of components in a system.

Roni Horowitz (2001) suggested the 'closed world' principle, according to which an inventive solution to a problem is based on using existing resources in the 'world of the problem' or its closed environment. A conventional solution to a problem, on the other hand, often requires using extra resources such as components, materials or energy. The following example demonstrates how the 'change relationships between variables' template mentioned above can help in finding an inventive solution to a problem.

The Lighthouse of Alexandria, seen in image 04, was built in 3rd century BC and is considered to be one of the Seven Wonders of the World. Sostratus, the Lighthouse's architect, wanted his name to be perpetuated in the Lighthouse design. This was not allowed by Ptolemy II, the King of Egypt, who ordered his name to be carved on the huge structure. How could the architect solve this problem?

The lighthouse question was presented to 9th grade pupils who were studying a course in inventive problem-solving and to other pupils who served as a control group. The pupils who did not study the course suggested only a few solutions, such as writing the architect's name on the rear of the building, inside the building, or on a sign outside the building. The pupils who studied the course, in contrast, suggested many ideas, including:

• To carve architect's name in such a way that it could be seen from a distance;
• To hide architect's name graphically in a decoration on the building;
• To integrate architect's name graphically in the King's name;
• To write architect's name in a language unknown to the King (e.g., Chinese);
• To cast architect's name in a light beam to be seen at a distance by the lighthouse projectors.

Several pupils suggested ideas that were very close to the way Sostratus solved the problem: as history tells us, he first carved his name on the lighthouse, put plaster over it and then carved the King's name. After a number of years, the plaster bearing the King's name disintegrated and Sostratus' name appeared to one and all.

We can see that some pupils used the principle of solving a problem by assigning a new function of components that already exists in the system, for example the King's name or the light beam. Sostratus' solution, as some of the pupils also suggested, is based on the principle of adding a connection between a variable in the system, as illustrated in image 05.

The diagram in image 05 illustrates that while in a conventional state the King's name is permanently displayed on the building, the inventive solution is based on a change in the value of the variable Name (King's, architect's) over Time (present, future). Certainly, time is often an important factor (variable) in technological systems. Goldenberg and Mazursky (2002) demonstrate how the principle of adding connections between variables is useful in inventing interesting marketing ideas.

For example, imagine yourself calling a takeaway pizza service in which the price of the pizza depends on the delivery time: the longer you wait, the less you pay! What about connecting the pizza's price to its temperature? The idea of 'All You Can Eat' in many restaurants is based on the opposite action: eliminating the relationship between what or how much people eat and the price they pay.

Try drawing a graph that illustrates the concept of improving a system by 'changing relationships between two variables' for the two pizza takeaway services or the 'All you can eat' method promotion mentioned above; Use another independent 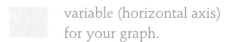 variable (horizontal axis) for your graph.

Outcomes from running inventive problem-solving courses to teachers and junior high school pupils

In this section I will describe the experience gained during several courses for inventive problem-solving with Israeli science and technology teachers and 9th grade pupils. The courses, which lasted about 15 meetings of two hours each, combined learning methods such as brainstorming, parts of de Bono's (1986; 1990) CoRT program, and inventive problem-solving principles derived from SCAMPER, TRIZ and ASIT described above. I have documented and evaluated some of the courses by videotaping class activities, interviewing the participants, analyzing the assignments the pupils or teachers prepared, and administrating pre-course and post-course quizzes and attitude questionnaires in the class (see Barak, 2006; Barak and Mesika, 2007). The following points of interest emerged from the courses.

• Many participants, teachers and students alike, commented that during the course they started to observe that many instruments or technological systems at home or on the street are

06 A universal dual-level counter for an amusement park: the aim is to enable wheelchair-bound individuals to buy tickets or play games next to other people.

based on the 'inventive principles' they learned. For example, a TV remote-control is just a modified version of an on-apparatus keyboard (the duplication principle), decaffeinated coffee utilizes the concept of eliminating a central ingredient from an existing product, and designating a road lane only for buses and taxis is based on connecting two or three variables in the system (type of vehicle, road lane location and time of day).

- Some pupils reported that they started using the 'inventive principles' they learned at home or in other subjects they studied at school. For example, a girl reported that when her mother asked her to clean the carpet in her room, she asked her: *'Why do I even need this carpet? Let's "delete" it.'* Later, when the mother asked her to clean the carpet in the living room, she said *'But it's such a difficult job.'* The mother responded, *'Then go and "duplicate" yourself.'* This example shows that the girl brought home the 'terminology' she had learned in the course and even taught her mother to implement this thinking pattern.

- A pupil reported that when she saw her mother arranging her clothes in her closet - winter clothing on the lower shelves and summer clothing on the higher ones, she suggested another method: to place the more useful clothes lower down, and the other clothes higher up. In the girl's world, she applied here the principle of 'making a connection between variables' that she had learned in the course.

- Many participants of inventive problem-solving courses mentioned that although at first they used the principles they had learned discreetly, gradually the diverse methods blended in their minds and they were often unable to state exactly what method had helped them in finding a specific solution. For example, in an 'amusement park' project, a group of pupils sought a method to allow pupils with disabilities to enjoy the park just like everybody else. They designed a universal model of a dual-level counter, seen in image 06. This counter could be used for ticket-selling, food-selling or shooting galleries often found in amusement parks. The pupils were convinced that they had applied the method they had learned in the course, but had difficulty in specifying whether they had used the 'duplication' principle, the 'division' principle or the 'change symmetry' approach. Actually, as the pupils said, the different methods they had learned frequently overlapped. For the pupils it is important that they can use appropriate methods fluently to find good ideas.

Although the follow-up of the above-mentioned experimental courses offered to teachers and pupils showed encouraging results, much further work is required to explore how people grasp the concept of

'systematic' problem-solving, and how 'ordered' and 'disordered' thinking merge in the problem-solving process.

Concluding remarks

This article puts forward the argument that inventive solutions to problems are often found through focused thinking, consideration of constraints and continued efforts, rather than by spontaneous discovery. We have seen that surprising but utilitarian solutions to problems are frequently based on using resources that are already available in 'the world of the problem' and its closed environment. People can learn how to systematically seek original solutions to problems by methods like assigning new functions to existing components in a system or changing relationships between variables in the system. However, one should consider these methods as flexible strategies and heuristics rather than as strict algorithms, and regard 'ordered' and 'disordered' thinking as complementary methods in problem-solving.

The discovery of penicillin by Sir Alexander Fleming in 1928 is often presented as an example of serendipity - the phenomenon of valuable discoveries by accident. On the other hand, there are those who claim that 'unexpected discoveries' always occur in the background of hard work and a wide knowledge base. What does your experience show in this regard? Will the teaching of problem-solving methods to pupils foster or impede their aptitude for finding original solutions to problems?

To conclude this chapter, let us return to the question of whether there is any benefit in teaching problem-solving methods, and to what extent people can transfer learning and thinking skills from one context to another. David Perkins and Gavriel Salomon (1992) point out that although the preponderance of studies suggests that transfer comes hard, a closer examination of the conditions under which transfer does and does not occur, and the mechanisms of transfer, present a more positive picture. These authors highlight several conditions and instructional approaches under which transfer might appear, such as:

- Thorough and diverse practice of performance in questions in a variety of contexts that can yield a flexible, relatively 'automatized' bundle of skills easily evoked in new situations;

- Including in the learning the explicit abstraction of principles and critical attributes of a given situation;
- Fostering active self-monitoring and reflection on one's thinking processes by teaching children not just to apply a specific strategy but also to monitor their own thinking processes in simple ways; and
- Arousing mindfulness and alertness to the activities one is engaged in and to one's surroundings, in contrast with a passive reactive mode in which cognition and problems unfold automatically and mindlessly (see, for example, Ellen Langer's 1997 book entitled "**The Power of Mindful Learning**").

Utilizing instructional approaches of the type identified above in class can encourage pupils to apply the problem-solving strategies they have learned in new contexts in school and outside it.

What kind of investigation could you carry out in your classroom to explore the role of 'ordered' and 'disordered' thinking in solving technological problems?

References

BOOKS

Altshuller, G. S. (1988). "Creativity as an Exact Science". New York: Gordon and Breach.

Barron, F. (1969). "The Creative Person and the Creative Process". New York: Holt, Rinehart and Winston.

Boden, M. A. (2004). "The Creative Mind: Myths and Mechanisms". New York: Basic Books.

Cropley, A. J. (2001). "Creativity in Education and Learning: A Guide for Teachers and Educators". London: Kogan Page.

De Bono, E. (1990). "Lateral Thinking". London: Ward Lock Educational.

De Vries, M. J. (2005). "Teaching about technology: An introduction to the philosophy of technology for non-philosophers". Dordrecht: Springer.

Dewey, J. (1910). "How We Think". Lexington, Mass: D.C. Health.

Eberle, B. F. (1977). "SCAMPER". Buffalo, NY: D.O.K. Publishers.

Goldenberg, J. & Mazurski, D. (2002). "Creativity in Product Innovation". Cambridge, UK: Cambridge University Press.

Harris, C. E., Pritchard, M. S. & Rabins, M. J. (2000). "Engineering Ethics, Concepts and Cases". Belmont, CA: Wadsworth.

Hayes, J. R. (1978). "Cognitive Psychology Thinking and Creating". Homewood, Illinois: Dorsey Press.

Langer, E. J. (1997). "The Power of Mindful Learning". Reading, MA: Addison-Wesley.

Mayer, R. E. (1992). "Thinking, Problem Solving, Cognition" (2nd ed.). New York: Freeman.

Osborn, A. F. (1963). "Applied Imagination: Principles and Procedures of Creative Thinking" (3rd ed.). New York: Scribner.

Perkins, D. N. & Salomon, G. (1992). 'Transfer of learning'. In T. Husen & T. N. Postlethwaite, (Eds.). "International Encyclopedia of Education". Oxford: Pergamon Press.

Polya, G. (1957). "How to Solve It". New York: Garden City.

Wankat, P. & Oreovicz, F. S. (1993). "Teaching Engineering". New York: McGraw-Hill.

ARTICLES

Barak, M. & Goffer N. (2002). 'Fostering systematic innovative thinking and problem solving: Lessons education can learn from industry'. "International Journal of Technology and Design Education". 12. (3), 227-247.

Barak, M. (2006). 'Teaching methods for systematic inventive problem solving: Evaluation of a course for teachers'. "Research in Science and Technological Education". 24. (1), 237-254.

Barak, M. and Mesika, P. (2007). 'Teaching methods for inventive problem-solving in junior high school. "Thinking Skills and Creativity". 2. (1), 19-29.

Brophy, D. R. (1998). 'Understanding, measuring, and enhancing collective creative problem-solving efforts'. "Creativity Research Journal". 11. (2), 123-150.

Goldenberg, J., Mazurski, D. & Solomon, S. (1999). 'Creative sparks'. "Science". 285. (5433), 1495-1496.

Horowitz, R. (2001). 'ASIT's five thinking tools with examples'. "TRIZ Journal". September. Available at http://www.trizjournal.com/archives/2001/08/c/

Horowitz R. and Maimon, O. (1997). 'Creative design methodology and the SIT method'. "Proceedings of DETC'97, ASME Design Engineering Technical Conference", Sacramento.

Howard-Jones, P. A. (2002). 'A dual-state model of creative cognition for supporting strategies that foster creativity in the classroom'. "International Journal of Technology and Design Education". 12. (3), 215-226.

Jonassen, D. H. (1997). 'Towards a meta-theory of problem solving'. "Education Technology: Research and Development". 45. (1), 65-95.

Kurfiss, J. G. (1988). 'Critical Thinking: Theory, Research, Practice, and Possibilities'. In "ASHE-ERIC Higher Education Report No. 2", George Washington University, Graduate School of Education and Human Development, Washington, D.C.

McCormick, R. (2004). 'Issues of learning and knowledge in technology education'. "International Journal of Technology and Design Education". 14. (1), 21-44.

Perkins, D. N. & Salomon, G. (1989). 'Are cognitive skills context bound?'. "Educational Researcher". 18. (1), 16-25.

The role of technical knowledge in design & technology

Gwyneth Owen-Jackson

Gwyneth Owen-Jackson is the subject leader for the design & technology PGCE course at The Open University in England. She has experience of working in secondary schools, initial teacher education and has worked with a number of organisations on developments within design & technology. She has edited several books for design & technology student teachers. Her main areas of research interest are the developing professional knowledge of student teachers and education in areas of conflict.

Torben Steeg

Torben Steeg is a freelance consultant and an honorary research fellow at the University of Manchester. Research interests include the interactions between design & technology, ICT, science and mathematics and, within design & technology, systems thinking, electronics and communications technologies. He works with the Nuffield D&T Project and is a curriculum advisor for the Electronics in Schools Strategy. He is a member of the editorial boards for DATA's "Journal of D&T Education" and the IEE's "Electronics Education" and of DATA's ITE Advisory Group.

The role of technical knowledge in design & technology

Gwyneth Owen-Jackson and Torben Steeg

What is technical knowledge?

Before we could begin to write this chapter we spent some time discussing what we understand by the term 'technical knowledge'. The Cambridge Dictionary (2006) defines it as *'knowledge of machines and methods used in science and industry'* or *'knowledge and methods of a particular subject or job'*. Well, this helps a bit, but what technical knowledge is relevant in school design & technology and how does such knowledge contribute to pupils' ability to design and make well?

> Think for a moment about something you have designed and made; this might be from your school education, your degree or something you have produced during your professional life.
> Take about 5 minutes to list the technical knowledge you needed to design and make this product.

The images overleaf show products produced by pupils; one was made in year 8 and one in year 11 and each represents good quality work for its level.

> Reflect on the technical knowledge that the pupils would have needed in order to design and make as successfully as this and for each artefact make a list of the technical knowledge you think each pupil would need to have mastered.
> Because the two products arise from different areas in the design & technology curriculum, you may approach this task as an expert for only one of them, or perhaps neither; this is fine, just use common sense and intuition.

What do your lists tell you about what 'technical knowledge' might mean?
What, in fact, does it mean for knowledge to be technical?

01 A year 8 food project.

02 A year 11 resistant materials project.

Thinking about technical and technological knowledge

The study of knowledge is a branch of philosophy called epistemology, and within epistemology the study of technical and technological knowledge has increasing stature thanks to the writings of authors such as Don Ihde (1997), Alistair Jones (1997), Robert McCormick (1997), Marc de Vries (2005) and John Dakers (2006). The ideas that have arisen from this study include:

- That technological knowledge includes both 'knowing-that' (propositional knowledge) and 'knowing-how' (procedural knowledge). This allows us to include skills (knowing-how) as relevant technical knowledge alongside facts (knowing-that).
- That much technological knowledge can't be expressed in words but arises in the 'mind's eye' and is best articulated visually, in two and three dimensions. On the other hand, some technical concepts are best expressed mathematically and others require the use of precisely defined language.
- That much effective work in design & technology relies on tacit knowledge; these are things that we have an instinct about but do not formalise as explicit knowledge (or we may have long forgotten such a formalisation). This may mean that pupils need opportunities to 'play around' with materials and ideas, to model and test out proposals, so that knowledge becomes embedded through the 'doing'.

- That those engaged in designing and making are generally more focused on practical than theoretical reasoning. For this reason technical knowledge is more often related to 'what works well' than to 'what is true'. Technical knowledge, therefore, is inextricably linked to value judgements; as soon as you ask 'what works well?' you are asking a value-laden question.
- Technology draws on knowledge from a wide range of other disciplines and, in the technical domain, especially science and mathematics. To become technically useful this knowledge usually needs to be re-worked into a form that allows it to answer 'what works well' type questions. This is not a trivial task and pupils are unlikely to transfer their knowledge between subjects without a great deal of support.
- It is sometimes useful to consider knowledge required for effective designing as two sorts of knowledge; knowledge of the problem or design situation (so it is fully understood) and knowledge required in order to create an effective design solution.

From this, we therefore suggest that technological knowledge includes all the aspects of knowledge that pupils may need in order to design and make, including technical knowledge, as shown in the illustration above right.

The interconnecting lines suggest that decisions in the technical (or any other) area

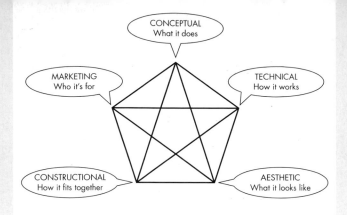

03 Knowledge
domains in
technology.
(© D. Barlex, 2007.)

04 1998 Apple iMac.
(Based on photograph
from Flickr (http://ww
w.flickr.com/photos/m
otoe/86835191)
by Masashige Motoe.
http://creativecommon
s.org/licenses/by-
sa/2.0/)

will affect and be affected by decisions made in the other areas.

This chapter focuses on technical knowledge; pupils' knowledge of how things work and how to make things work. We have taken this to include knowledge about the materials they use, the scientific and mathematical concepts related to materials and methods and, in some areas of design & technology, knowledge of structures and control systems. We don't deny the importance of the other vertices of the pentagon in the illustration above, but they are dealt with elsewhere in this book.

> Think about that first question again (the technical knowledge you needed to design and make a product); do you still think the things you jotted down were technical knowledge?

What technical knowledge might pupils need?

So, having considered what we mean by technical knowledge, how do we decide what technical knowledge to teach?

When Jonathan Ive and the design team at Apple computers started to work on what would become the first Apple iMac, what technical knowledge would they have needed?

The brief was multifaceted, including a desire to hark back to Apple's classic 'all-in-one' computer, a move away from 'beige boxes', a smaller computer that was easy to pick up and move, and improved ease of use through such things as minimising the number of leads and making setup intuitive.

The design decisions the team made took them into areas of technical knowledge they couldn't have predicted. For example they needed help with specifying the translucent colours to ensure consistency during high volume manufacture. Who has expertise in high volume production of translucent coloured items? Sweet manufacturers do, so that is where they went for advice. Similarly, keeping the computer quiet by dispensing with the fan led to rearrangement of the internal construction and the need to design in natural air circulation and venting.

Food product development often requires the development of existing products, and this brings its own demands. In developing the Crispy Savoury Pudding for Marks and Spencer, the manufacturers had to develop technical knowledge relating to the crispy outer layer of the product. Tests were undertaken to find out how this could be achieved then a way had to be found of doing this in quantity. The problem proved challenging and required many tests and experiments before a solution was found. Further challenges were presented by

05 Marks & Spencer had to develop technical knowledge in order to create their crispy savoury bakes.

06 Kevlar bulletproof vest.

07 Kevlar helmet.

08 Kevlar firefighter's jacket.

MARKS & SPENCER

The role of technical knowledge in design & technology

Gwyneth Owen-Jackson and Torben Steeg

the packaging of the product, again requiring research and testing. Food products are also driven by the need for food safety and consumer appeal, so the original concept and design brief had to be tightly adhered to whilst developing a product that had a 'home-produced' quality in which crispiness was combined with the chewiness more usually associated with puddings. (See www.foodforum.org.uk for further details).

With some products, it is the discovery of new technical knowledge that leads to the development of the product, as was the case with Kevlar (a synthetic fibre). In the 1960's Stephanie Kwolek, a chemist at DuPont, found whilst experimenting with fibre molecules that one experiment produced unexpected results. However, instead of throwing away the solution and starting again, Stephanie tried spinning the solution into fibres - and discovered that it created a fibre that was extremely stiff, yet lightweight and five times stronger than steel, and it could absorb energy by stretching rather than breaking. Kevlar is now used in products ranging from bulletproof vests to bridge cables.

Each of these case studies illustrates an important feature of the relationship between technical knowledge and designing and making. The process of creating a design brief will give you a broad idea of the kinds of technical knowledge that you are likely to need to draw on, but specific design decisions can lead you into completely unexpected areas of technical knowledge. Alternatively, looking for the solution to one problem could provide the answer to a completely different one. The conclusion is that it is not possible to know in advance what it is that you need to know to complete a brief. For many designers this is one of the attractive aspects of the job; designing becomes an expedition into unexplored territory where the route is not, and can not be, fully known.

In school, of course, we don't have the luxury of time and money to spend researching technical solutions to problems. Part of our role as design & technology teachers has to be helping pupils discover what they need to know and where to go to find it. They probably won't make new discoveries, as Stephanie Kwolek did, or create design icons, as Jonathan Ive did, but they will learn something new for themselves. We think that technical knowledge in design & technology should enable pupils to:

- Understand how things work so that they have knowledge on which to draw when making their own design decisions;
- Develop novel (for the pupil) and interesting ways for things to work;
- Understand what might be going wrong when something isn't working, and be able to consider ways in which to put it right.

09 Aberfeldy
suspension
bridge is
constructed using
Kevlar cables.
(© Robert Cortright,
Bridge Ink.)

10 Tyres use Kevlar
as it offers superb
puncture,
abrasion and
tear resistance.

Defining essential technical knowledge

If possible, carry out the following exercise with colleagues.

Select a focus area (eg. food, electronics, textiles, resistant materials) and use a table to list the areas of technical knowledge that you think a year 11 pupil really has to know to understand how things work.

Now, for each of those areas that you have identified in your table, spend some time thinking about what you would include in the area. Add a further column so that you can expand the area to say what each is about.

Before you write a piece of knowledge in, ask yourself:

- Is it really necessary for every pupil to know this? Perhaps it could be knowledge that some pupils might need but can find out for themselves when necessary.

- Is the level of detail right? It is easy to specify knowledge at a high level of detail when most pupils will never use the detail in their designing and making. Can you substitute the detail for some more general principles, coupled with advice on how to access the detail should they need it? Try not to be too influenced, during this part of the task, by what you know of the content of examination specifications; these are clearly important in defining what should be learned to pass an examination but not all their content is necessarily fundamental.

Once you have a reasonably comprehensive list of what you think is the essential knowledge content for the field you have chosen, you should put it to the test.

First, discuss your list with a colleague who has done the same exercise. You will probably find much on your lists that is essentially the same but this may raise issues to discuss:

- Do you agree on the level of detail specified?
- Have you placed it in the same row of the table; i.e., do you agree about the aspect of design & technology that this knowledge supports? And does this matter?

It is also likely that you will each have items of knowledge on your list that are not on your colleague's list. Some of these you will instantly agree should be there; one person may simply have not thought of it. It is the remaining items, those for which there is disagreement, that are the most interesting. You may be able to resolve some items through discussion, but it is likely that there will be some irreconcilable differences of opinion on what counts as essential technical knowledge. Don't fall out over this, instead recognise that you have got to the heart of what is a very difficult issue; what you count as essential depends ultimately on your underlying beliefs about aspects of education and aspects of design & technology.

You could also compare your list with a relevant GCSE specification. Are there any knowledge areas that you would consider to be essential at this level that are not in the specification? This would be quite surprising and might lead you to revise your own views of what is essential - or to question the comprehensiveness of the specification.

Remember that examination specifications are not written on tablets of stone; they are as subject to the errors of human thinking as any other document (including this one). Where there is technical knowledge in the specification that is not on your essential list, consider whether its presence is justified as a part of what pupils should learn at Key Stage 4.

The examination specifications direct much of what is taught in design & technology, but this may not always be what pupils need or want to learn. Over twenty years ago, the Department for Education and Science recognised that:

'The designer does not need to know all about everything so much as to know what to find out, what form the knowledge should take, and what

depth of knowledge is required for a particular purpose' (DES, 1981).

An examination specification that reflected this would be more in the spirit of design & technology!

How is technical knowledge best taught?

Given that we can identify appropriate technical knowledge for design & technology in schools - this leads to the questions 'how should we teach technical knowledge?' and 'when should we teach it?'

Constructivism and constructionism

Constructivism is a collection of theories about how learning happens (see Wood, 1998, for a clear introduction). These theories, which are currently accepted by many educationalists - including us - include the following principles:

- Learners interact with the world around them and construct their own knowledge models based on their experiences; these include models of how the physical and the social worlds operate.
- Social interaction has a significant role in establishing and supporting mental models.
- The constructed models are usually 'correct' in the sense that they account rationally for the experiences of an individual, but they may be based on restricted data or false assumption, so may not agree with scientific models. An example of such

a misconception is that many children, and adults, believe that a heavier object will fall with greater speed and hit the ground before a less-heavy one.

- Because these models are based on experience they are remarkably robust once they have been established. Change to a well-established cognitive model will only happen if there is sufficient evidence that it is incorrect. This suggests that a model of teaching based on telling pupils things is likely to be much less successful than one in which they experience things and interact with materials.

Constructionism is a constructivist theory of learning developed by Seymour Papert and others (Papert, 1980, 1994, Kafai & Resnick, 1996). The core argument of 'constructionism' is that people learn best when they are making something, be it a sandcastle on the beach or a theory in physics, because of the powerful interaction between thinking and action during construction. Learning is most powerful when two conditions apply; the construction environment is rich and there is ample opportunity to view the success of one's construction efforts (feedback).

Originally constructionism was used as an argument for putting children in control of computers through the use of LOGO; a programming language with a *'low floor and a high ceiling'* (easy to get into but limitless in its applications). The argument was that the child should control the computer, not the computer control the child. This work soon grew to encompass robotics, especially with the Lego 'Mindstorms' programmable brick, where the programming of the computer controlled not simply what happened on screen but also events in the real world. The link to work in design & technology should be clear; the nature of design & technology is that it is the subject most likely to have the curriculum flexibility to allow pupils to engage in constructionist activity and this makes design & technology a very good place for pupils to develop technical understanding.

Situated learning and communities of practice

Another constructivist strand of work (see Lave & Wenger, 1991) has pointed out that learning takes place in a particular context (situation) and, therefore, becomes bound to that situation. A consequence of this is that it is difficult for learners to transfer their knowledge from one domain to another. A growing body of evidence, much based on studies of the use of (especially mathematical) knowledge in the workplace, seems to support this view.

Jean Lave and Etienne Wenger also used the notion of *'Communities of Practice'* (see Wenger, 1998) to describe their understanding that social learning occurs when people who have a common interest in some subject or problem collaborate to share ideas, find solutions, and build innovations.

? What are the implications of these ideas for knowledge learning in design & technology?
Think about:
- Design & technology subject documentation which seems to suggest that the transfer of knowledge from other subjects is something that pupils can be expected to do without much difficulty.
- The role of group work in design & technology.

How should we teach technical knowledge?

So what do constructivism, constructionism and communities of practice tell us about how to teach design & technology? The ideas described above seem to suggest that we should be looking for ways to provide appropriate learning environments and activities to allow pupils to develop the skills to actively co-construct their own knowledge. Approaches commonly used to support technical learning in design & technology include:
- Product analysis;
- Case studies;
- Focused tasks.

Product analysis allows pupils to learn by examining and modelling existing products. For product analysis to be useful its focus has to be clear and relevant to the work that pupils are engaged in. Typical foci include: aesthetic features; the construction materials used; how materials have been formed; how products are assembled; the effectiveness of the user interface; technical operation (how does it work?) and the suitability of the product for the market sector. In food, product analysis often focuses on sensory evaluation, the ingredients and processes used and nutritional qualities.

Case studies also allow pupils to engage with products, especially those from other times and other cultures as well as those too large, small, dangerous or expensive to bring to the classroom. The Design Council's **"Product Profiles"** of 11 'Millennium products' also explain the design thinking behind the products, which otherwise can only be guessed at. Critical for the success of a case study is the inclusion of tools to actively engage pupils, for example through questions that prompt reflection, discussion or further research.

Focused tasks were inspired by the Nuffield Design & Technology Project's **"Resource Tasks"** (Nuffield, 1995). The aim of a focused task is to teach a specific element of knowledge or a skill in an active and practical way. The knowledge or skill could relate to a particular material area or to 'strategic'

skills relevant across all material areas. When a designing and making activity is being planned, it should be possible to include a range of focused tasks that will teach the underpinning technical knowledge and skills.

Look at a project that you have taught and sketch out how you could use the 3 approaches described above to help you focus the teaching of technical knowledge.

Systems thinking

Systems thinking is one approach to re-conceptualising scientific knowledge that has particular power. The core idea in a systems approach is that detailed concepts are abstracted to a 'higher', more useful level (See Steeg, 2000, for a detailed development of this). For example, in electronics teaching a systems approach is well-established that allows pupils engaging in introductory work to approach the design of a circuit at the level of what it should do (e.g., detect a changing light level) without having to engage in relatively complex scientific and mathematical ideas. A consequence of this is that a relatively small amount of technical knowledge can allow pupils to do a lot (to tackle a wide range of problems in a range of ways). By contrast the more traditional approaches to electronics teaching required pupils to learn a great deal

11 'Progression' model.

[From Bowen, R. (2002). 'Design and Technology in the primary school'. In G. Owen-Jackson (Ed.). "Aspects of Teaching Secondary Design and Technology Perspectives on Practice". (pp. 9-26). London: Routledge Falmer/ The Open University.)

of knowledge that they could do relatively little with.

> What do you think the balance should be between teaching pupils a lot of information they may one day need and teaching them how to find out what they need to know when they need to know it?
> How might you assess pupils' abilities in the second of these approaches?

When should we teach technical knowledge?

Rob Bowen (2002) suggests that design & technology in the primary school develops from mostly focused tasks, controlled by the teacher and designed to teach specific knowledge and skills, in the early years to more open design and make tasks, in which pupils have greater control over their activities and learning, as they move to year six. This suggests that by Key Stage 3 pupils have been well-prepared for openness in the design tasks they tackle. Sadly the experience of most pupils as they move from KS3 to KS4 mirrors their primary experience; they start with focused tasks controlled by the teacher and gradually move towards more open tasks.

In secondary schools a number of approaches have evolved; these include teaching technical knowledge:
• Prior to the design and make activity, pupils learn a body of knowledge then apply it to an activity;
• During the design and make activity, where knowledge is inserted at appropriate points during pupils' activity;
• As and when pupils need to know; Neil Gershenfeld (2005) has called this 'Just in Time' learning and contrasts it to the approach in the first bullet above which he calls 'Just in Case' learning.

> What do you think the advantages and disadvantages of the three approaches noted above might be for teachers and for pupils?
> Make a note of your responses.

These approaches are strongly linked to how other aspects of the design & technology task are organised. In particular the openness of the design task is a critical feature; if a task is tightly defined, with most technical decisions made by the teacher, it is easier to predict the required knowledge and teach it prior to the activity. If pupils are to be given the opportunity to engage with a task in a designerly way, making their own decisions about technical aspects, then it is much more

Gwyneth Owen-Jackson and Torben Steeg

Mechanisms Chooser Chart

12 Part of one of the Nuffield Design & Technology Project 'chooser charts'.

(With kind permission of Nuffield Design & Technology Project.)

likely that relevant technical knowledge will need to be provided as a task develops.

Using scientific and mathematical knowledge

The decision about when to teach aspects of technical knowledge might also be linked to when pupils learn about particular topics in science or mathematics. Design & technology has a special relationship with scientific and mathematical knowledge as this often helps designers to understand how things work, or how well they work or to calculate performances or expected results. Recognition of this led David Barlex and James Pitt to suggest in the "Interaction Report" that we should exploit this relationship to improve pupils' use of science and mathematics related concepts in their design & technology work (see Barlex and Pitt, 2000). Unfortunately this has proved to be less than straightforward. Two routes through which connections could be developed are (i) systematic links between the science/mathematics and design & technology curricula and (ii) by asking pupils to develop their own conceptual links (and ideally both strategies would be pursued together).

Sadly it turns out that, in the context of the current structure of the English National Curriculum, there is a range of fairly intractable structural difficulties that teachers face in working together across subject boundaries. "The Interaction Report" explored these difficulties thoroughly and

offered recommendations for development in this area, but there seems to be little incentive for most schools to devote energy to such work. The report "Becoming an Engineering College" (Barlex, 2005) showed that schools which are required to make explicit connections between science, mathematics and design & technology, find making such links difficult. Expecting pupils to make their own cross-subject links is likely to be equally problematic if the claims about situated learning noted above are correct.

In any case, studies of the ways that engineers and technologists make use of scientific knowledge carried out by David Layton (1993) suggest that it has to be re-conceptualised into a form that is relevant to the technological task at hand before it can be used. Re-conceptualisation of scientific concepts in a form that pupils can easily access to support work in design & technology has been popularised through the Nuffield Design & Technology Project materials (1995) in the form of 'chooser charts' and these have proved to be remarkably accessible to both teachers and their pupils.

Carousels

We should not leave the questions of 'how' and 'when' to teach technical knowledge without acknowledging the difficulties brought about by Key Stage 3 curriculum arrangements such as the 'carousel' or 'circus'. The circus limits the time available in each area and this, in turn, limits the opportunities for autonomous 'finding out' new knowledge by pupils (Steeg & Davies, 2005). One way of addressing this, perhaps, would be finding out what other colleagues are teaching and thinking about how you could build on this. This certainly applies if your six week scheme of work includes the teaching of, for example, writing a design specification. If you teach this to year 7 in September it may well be valuable new knowledge; if you teach it in May then they are likely to have already covered it elsewhere, leaving you more time to focus on the development of relevant technical knowledge. Find out, also, what is being taught in science and geography; there may well be areas that you can develop and build on. This does, we know, take time but if it allows you to spend lesson time on more appropriate and relevant learning then it must be time well-spent.

Alternatively, discuss with colleagues what the focus of each scheme of work will be. It may be that you 'give up' one of your schemes of work to focus on the development of design skills but, in turn, gain a scheme of work that focuses on the development of technical knowledge.

Rotational courses are a pragmatic response to the National Curriculum requirements in England, but they should be designed to work for the benefit of pupils, not to ease curriculum planning!

Implications for design & technology education

So what are the implications of all this for design & technology in schools; how does technical knowledge and understanding inform designing and making?

Robert McCormick (2002, p. 96) claims that research has shown that *'problem-solving skill is dependent upon considerable domain knowledge'*, indicating that pupils will need to have, or acquire, technical knowledge in the specific area in order to be able to successfully design and make. One consequence of this is that we, as teachers, need to think about what level of technical knowledge will be appropriate. For example, do pupils need to know about gelatinisation of starch molecules in order to be able to create a good sauce-based product or how polymer molecules respond to heat in order to be able to use the line-bending machine? Could too little, or too much, technical knowledge constrain pupils' design thinking?

In addition, good design and make tasks will be sufficiently 'open' that pupils are required to make decisions of their own, for example in relation to the mechanism to use or the fabric construction method. In these cases it is likely that pupils will require technical knowledge that was not predicted. As a teacher, then, you should be helping pupils to be able to identify when they need

new technical knowledge and developing their ability to learn independently; introducing them to areas of knowledge that are likely to be useful but then creating spaces, through the use of 'open' tasks, for the pupils to find out and construct their own knowledge. And the amount of knowledge 'out there' is vast, and growing; in what ways might we restrict what pupils learn by making decisions about what we teach?

But, we argue, technical knowledge is not needed by pupils just in order for them to design and make. Technical knowledge and understanding gives pupils an insight into how things might work, it helps them to understand how the world around them operates. Pupils who learn about the fantastic strength and toughness of spiders' web silk may be amazed and look afresh at spiders' webs. In the same way we remember one session with pupils on 'smart and modern materials' that introduced them to motion control gel, a lubricant used to give 'cheap and dirty' mechanisms a smooth and expensive feel. The pupils were amazed to see the way in which the gel allowed a travelling alarm clock case to 'glide' open and we began to discuss other ways in which this gel might be used. As a result of this experience these pupils now have a little more insight into the workings of the technological world they live in. This opening up of minds is, surely, part of the remit of design & technology education.

Further reading

Barlex, D. (2007). 'Creativity in School Design & Technology in England: a discussion of influences'. "International Journal of Technology and Design Education". 17, 149-162.

Catterall, C. (Ed.). (1999). "Food: Design and Culture". London: Laurence King Publishing in association with Glasgow 1999 Festival Company.

Chan, C. K. K. & Pang, M. F. (2006). 'Teacher Collaboration in Learning Communities'. "Teaching Education". 17. (1) 1-5.

Gardner, P. L. (1997). 'The Roots of Technology and Science; A philosophical and historical review'. In M. J. De Vries & A. Tamir (Eds.). "Shaping Concepts of Technology; From philosophical perspective to mental images". (pp. 13-20). Dordecht: Kluwer.

Harrison, I. (2004). "The Book of Inventions". London: Cassell.

References

Barlex, D. (2007). 'Capitalising on the Utility Embedded in Design & Technology Activity: An Exploration of Cross Curricular Links'. In E. W. Norman & D. Spendlove, (Eds.). "The Design and Technology Associaition Education and International Research Conference 2007 linking learning". (pp. 5-10). Wellesbourne: The Design and Technology Association.

Barlex, D. (2005). "Becoming an Engineering College: A report describing emerging and developing good practice". London: Specialist Schools Trust.

Barlex, D. & Pitt, J. (2000). "Interaction: The relationship between science and design and technology in the secondary school curriculum". London: Engineering Council.

Bowen, R. (2002). 'Design and Technology in the primary school'. In G. Owen-Jackson (Ed.). "Aspects of Teaching Secondary Design and Technology Perspectives on Practice". (pp. 9-26). London: RoutledgeFalmer/The Open University.

Dakers, J. R. (Ed.). (2006). "Defining Technological Literacy; Towards an epistemological framework". New York: Palgrave Macmillan.

Department for Education and Science (DES) (1981). "Understanding Design and Technology". London: HMSO.

De Vries, M. J. (2005). "Teaching about Technology; An introduction to the philosophy of technology for non-philosophers". Dordecht: Springer.

Gershenfeld, N. (2007). "FAB: The coming revolution on your desktop - from personal computers to personal fabrication" (paperback edition). New York: Basic Books.

Ihde, D. (1997). 'The Structure of Technology Knowledge'. In M. J. De Vries & A. Tamir, (Eds.). "Shaping Concepts of Technology; From philosophical perspective to mental images". (pp. 73-79). Dordecht: Kluwer.

Jones, A. (1997). 'Recent Research in Learning Technological Concepts and Processes'. In M. J. De Vries & A. Tamir, (Eds.). "Shaping Concepts of Technology; From philosophical perspective to mental images". (pp. 83-96). Dordecht: Kluwer.

Kafai, Y. & Resnick, M. (Eds.). (1996). "Constructionism in Practice". Oxford: Lawrence Erlbaum (Routledge).

Lave, J. & Wenger, E. (1991). "Situated Learning: Legitimate Peripheral Participation". Cambridge: Cambridge University Press.

Layton, D. (1993). "Technology's challenge to science education - cathedral, quarry or company store?". Milton Keynes: Open University Press.

McCormick, R. (1997). 'Coneptual and Procedural Knowledge'. In M. J. De Vries & A. Tamir, (Eds.). "Shaping Concepts of Technology; From philosophical perspective to mental images". (pp. 141-159). Dordecht: Kluwer.

McCormick, R. (2002). 'Capability lost and found?' In G. Owen-Jackson (Ed.). "Teaching Design and Technology in Secondary Schools - A Reader". (pp. 92-108). London: RoutledgeFalmer/ The Open University.

Nuffield Design and Technology Project materials. (1995). Harlow: Longman. (also available at http://www.secondarydandt.org).

Papert, S. (1980). "Mindstorms: Children, Computers and Powerful Ideas". New York: Basic Books.

Papert, S. (1994). "The children's machine: rethinking school in the age of the computer". Hemel Hempstead: Harvester Wheatsheaf.

Steeg, T. (2000). 'Systems Thinking and Practice; A review and analysis of key ideas and their implications for practice'. In R. Kimbell, (Ed.). "Design and Technology International Millennium Conference". (pp. 203-214). Wellesbourne: DATA.

Steeg, T. & Davies, L. (2005). 'Slow Down; How to stop spinning at KS3'. In E. W. Norman, D. Spendlove & P. Grover (Eds.). "DATA International Research Conference 2005". (pp. 51-56). Wellesbourne: DATA.

The Cambridge Dictionary (2006). Available at
http://dictionary.cambrige.org (accessed 13.10.06).

Wenger, E. (1998). "Communities of Practice".
Cambridge: Cambridge University Press.

Wood, D. (1998). "How Children Think and Learn"
(2nd edition). Oxford: Blackwell.

Websites

Awarding Bodies (for examination specifications):
AQA: www.aqa.org.uk
EDEXCEL: www.edexcel.org.uk
OCR: www.ocr.org.uk
WJEC: www.wjec.co.uk

iMac design resources:
• Digital Design Museum; iMac 1998:
  http://www.designmuseum.org/digital/jonathan-ive-on-
  apple/imac-1998
• Jonathan Ive describes the rules behind the design of the iMac:
  http://www.fastcompany.com/magazine/29/buy.html
• The man behind iMac:
  http://edition.cnn.com/TECH/computing/9809/22/
  imacman.idg/

Handling collections and case studies:
• Design Museum:
  http://www.designmuseum.org/education/secondary
• The Design Council:
  http://www.designcouncil.info/educationresources/
  schools.html
• Dyson:
  http://www.international.dyson.com/education/
• Nuffield D&T:
  http://www.secondarydandt.org
• BAE Systems:
  http://baesystemseducationprogramme.com/
  systemsengineering/
• Practical Action:
  http://practicalaction.org/?id=resources_online

The role of making in design & technology

Frank Banks

Frank Banks is director of the Centre for Research and Development in Teacher Education and director of Professional Studies in Education at The Open University. He has been a school teacher of technology, engineering science, and science at both secondary and primary levels, and was a visiting professor at Staffordshire University. He has acted as a consultant to Egyptian, South African and Argentinian government agencies and for UNESCO. He researches science and technology education, teacher education and development and he has published extensively in these areas.

Gwyneth Owen-Jackson

Gwyneth Owen-Jackson is the subject leader for the design & technology PGCE course at The Open University in England. She has experience of working in secondary schools, initial teacher education and has worked with a number of organisations on developments within design & technology. She has edited several books for design & technology student teachers. Her main areas of research interest are the developing professional knowledge of student teachers and education in areas of conflict.

The role of making in design & technology

Frank Banks and Gwyneth Owen-Jackson

Introduction

We were talking recently about why we were attracted to design & technology and we decided one of the main reasons was because we could make things. It wasn't just writing, it was doing. Of course we made things in other areas too. Art and design was good - one of us still has the pouting thin plaster head, carefully sculpted when in Year 11, that looks a bit like an emaciated Easter Island figure and the Toby jug made from papier mache by the other stood for years on the shelf in her parents' home. But the usefulness - in the broadest sense - of the artefacts made in design & technology made the subject special. The embroidered needle holder made over thirty years ago and the wooden bedside table-lamp with small bookstand base (now a bit wobbly) that seemed to take most of Year 10 to make are both still in use, although the wailing electronic musical instrument called a 'Glissandovibe' made in the design & technology club has thankfully long given up the ghost!

We don't think we are alone in our love of making things. Mark, a local builder, was chatting as he installed a new bathroom. *'I hated school'*, he said. *'Except D&T of course, I could see the point of that'*. Mark was not at all academic, but his intelligence for making, problem-solving and being creative with his hands was recognised. Learning by doing, the cornerstone of many school subjects including science and mathematics, is at its most obvious in design & technology. This is not new. Although we think that suspending the timetable to give a whole day (or even a week!) to a design & technology cross-curricular project is a recent trend, John Dewey was teaching by 'doing' at the University of Chicago Laboratory School over a hundred years ago. His idea for learning biology and chemistry through cooking breakfast in school has some very modern links to what underpins food technology lessons today (See Dewey, 1897 pp. 77-80). Indeed, learning through what we make has a long and respected pedigree.

What drew *you* to teach design & technology?

Think of an incident that made you particularly proud of what you had done or what you had achieved in your own design & technology work. How useful was the artefact you made?

No doubt like us, the people at home treasured your efforts - but did *you*? Did you *really* use that 'key fob'?

Will the current Year 9 CD rack project *really* be used at home when so many thousand songs fit onto their MP3 player?

01 02

01 What do pupils
- learn through
02 making simple
products such as
these when they
have little control
over the design?

Do pupils always need to make what they design?

But how important is the making to pupils' learning? Have we just changed the label of the subject from woodwork and sewing to CDT and textiles and now to design & technology, or have we changed the subject as well?

The 'Glissandovibe' mentioned above was a real pain to make and was done rather half-heartedly, especially counting the four lots of 250 turns on the coil, but the teacher said that a video recorder was too hard to make. Life has moved on and domestic video recorders are in most homes - but they are often very badly designed, as are many other domestic and leisure products. Without the restriction of having to make the product, we could all suggest ways to improve badly-designed ones.

On a piece of paper, brainstorm what your video recorder /DVD player can do. Circle those functions that you most use and those you *never* use.
Compare your results with a friend.
What does this tell you about the design of that common artefact?
This can be done with almost any product - mobile phones, food processors, and even the local supermarket!

Surely, being creative and designing what we make is what design & technology is all about. Was the bedside lamp or needle holder creative? No, not really, we all made one and there were few design decisions to make. Does the need to make what they have designed restrict pupils' creativity? Is there a problem?

'As creativity is now explicitly acknowledged as an essential feature of design & technology it is important to explore the reality of the subject in secondary school classrooms to find out if indeed there is a crisis in creativity' (Barlex, 2000).

Creativity can be described in different ways, here we assume that it always involves thinking or behaving *imaginatively*. Second, overall this imaginative activity is *purposeful*: that is, it is directed to achieving an objective. Third, these processes must generate something *original*. Fourth, the outcome must be of *value* in relation to the objective (DfEE, 1999a). But how far do current teaching approaches allow pupils to achieve this kind of creativity in their work? Here are some comments about the quality of designing and creative thinking in design & technology.

03 What do pupils
 - learn through
05 making simple
   products such as
   these when they
   have little control
   over the design?

'…pupils are taught trivial aspects [of food product development/designing] such as arranging toppings decoratively on a pizza or using complex engineering CAD software to produce very simple drawings of icing on cakes…' (Ofsted, 2006, p. 5).

'The development of creativity in students, the opportunity for them to propose imaginative solutions, take risks, be intuitive, inventive and innovative in their work has been side-lined by an approach which has become far too mechanistic' (Parker, 2003 p. 7).

The *'approach'* that Jon Parker, former senior curriculum advisor for design & technology in Northamptonshire, refers to is the teaching and learning style where *'students are compliant rather than enthusiastic'*. He is clearly critical of the narrow requirements of the examination system. Jon is supported in his views by OfSTED (2000, p. 3) who suggest that *'teachers provide coaching which allows pupils to pass through the assessment "hoops" for D&T GCSE coursework at the expense of following the rationale of wider D&T learning objectives'*. Jon is also supported by research evidence:

'…public examinations in design & technology have, on the one hand, enabled many pupils to achieve success in terms of performance, whilst on the other hand, they have wasted valuable education opportunities for the development of high order thinking skills at a crucial stage in a pupil's education' (Atkinson, 2000, p. 277).

In food technology, creativity may also be restricted by the requirement for pupils to bring in their own food ingredients. If their choices are limited to what is available at home, or what can be afforded, this can limit their opportunities to learn. And because parents provide the ingredients they expect an edible dish to be taken home, which is the purpose of food product development but which cannot be guaranteed every time. The rationale for pupils providing ingredients is not convincing and harks back to the days of 'cooking'. Pupils don't provide learning materials in science or art, why are they required to do it in food technology?

Do you think that these are fair criticisms? Is it right to blame the 'hoops' of the examination system as a barrier to allowing pupils to work more widely in design & technology? If pupils do well in their design & technology exams, isn't that all that is important? And should pupils be expected to bring in food ingredients, or pay for what they use in textiles or materials technology?

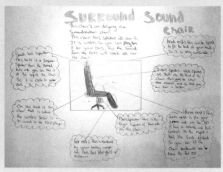

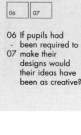

06 - 07

06 If pupils had
- been required to
07 make their
designs would
their ideas have
been as creative?

Is enabling pupils to be more creative worthwhile? This is not a trivial question; it has implications for how we treat pupils, how we value their ideas and suggestions, and how - given the reality of teaching a large group of pupils - we can really allow opportunities for them all to be creative.

We may think it is worthwhile, but what can we, as design & technology teachers, actually do to enhance pupil creativity specifically when they are designing? One programme that has tackled this head-on is "Young Foresight". "Young Foresight" is a 12-week programme for 14 year-olds that stimulates their creativity by challenging the orthodox in design & technology. It does this in seven ways.

1. Pupils design but do NOT make.
2. Work is done in groups.
3. Designs are for products and services for the future, not for now or for an immediate market.
4. Mentors from industry work with teachers to support the pupils.
5. Design ideas are based on the use of new and emerging technologies.
6. Ideas are presented to pupils' peers, their teacher and mentor and to others.
7. Pupils develop their own design briefs for the needs and wants of people in the future and the possible new markets that might exist or could be created.

Young Foresight (Barlex, 2000) also shakes up our usual expectation of what we, as teachers, should do to help pupils be more creative. We should ensure that the learning is:
• clarified to the pupils so they know what is expected at each session;
• active, and that all participate;
• personally relevant;
• in groups so that discussion is encouraged;
• involves problem-solving so that, in their groups, pupils can face up to conflicting demands and unanticipated difficulties;
• important and relevant to the pupils so that they engage with the problems and feel that opinions matter - they are valued.

The teaching is through:
• appropriate questioning;
• modelling ways of working;
• connecting the thinking of the pupils so that individual tasks are related to the whole design enterprise.

What are your first reactions to the ideas from "Young Foresight"? Is design & technology without making, not really design & technology at all? Is this programme feasible in the schools you know about? Would you be willing to experiment with this approach?

08 Using these tools
- well requires
10 tuition and
practice.

When considering food technology, the question *'do pupils always need to make what they design?'* brings a slightly different response. Although it is possible to develop ideas for new food products and model them for nutrition or cost, with food it is the look, smell and taste that determines whether a product will work or not - and this can only be done by making. However, pupils could be asked to design without making in food if the learning objectives are clearly defined. For example, the work could be planned to develop pupils' design strategies or skills, their ability to clarify and research a 'problem' or need or develop a specification, in which case designing without making would be appropriate.

Claire Catterall writes passionately about the importance of food:
'What we eat describes who and what we are, and how we should like to be. It tells of our society, the culture and age we live in; it speaks of politics, economics and geography. It encompasses love, friendship, family; marks ritual, celebration, solace; articulates hopes, dreams and aspirations. The history of food shows us the history of mankind itself' (Catterall, 1999, p. 23).

Although written about food, and suggesting a new way in which we might teach food technology, this statement could be applied to all areas of design & technology. Learning about and engaging in the design of products allows pupils to explore so many different aspects.

Do pupils always need to design what they make?

Peter Williams has strong views on the place of making in design & technology.
'In the development of design & technology from the earlier subjects of manual training, handicraft and technical studies, there was a swing away from the skill-based imitative tradition towards an investigative, design-based approach. However, skill in handling tools and materials is critical if the design/make/evaluate process is to be effective'. (Williams, 1994, p. 1).

How important are specific making skills? On early courses in control technology, pupils would often model a solution to a problem in Meccano or Lego as the final outcome of a project and never consider the aesthetics of the design or how it could ever be manufactured. Making skills were considered almost unimportant. Other courses, however, from a craft tradition continued to stress the importance of skill acquisition.

What is your view on this - how important are 'making' skills in design & technology? Why?

In 1992, Alan Smithers, Patricia Robinson and others criticised the original national curriculum for England and Wales for not clarifying sufficiently the making skills needed

11 12 13

11 Using these tools
- well requires
13 tuition and
practice.

for producing artefacts of quality - references to *'Blue Peter technology'* were made. That such criticism could be voiced, whatever its validity, was due to a swing away from the emphasis on making skills that was typical of woodwork, metalwork, cookery and sewing courses of years ago. The argument was that such skills were irrelevant for modern production methods and that it was really only the design process, transferable to different situations, that was important.

The argument that *'making is unimportant'* seriously undervalues the pride pupils have in producing a quality product. The quickly revised curriculum, in 1992 *'recommend that pupils should be required to make a manageable range of good quality products'* (DES/WO, 1992, para. 13), although it failed to define what it meant by 'quality', and that is the case today where the GCSE specification talks about 'quality products'. In a report on the design & technology resistant materials examination in 2002, the examiner said:
'The best work from centres was varied in its range of tasks and was of "marketable" quality. Many of these centres used the disassembly and recycling of an existing product as a starting point for, or an extension to, project work. The level of demand is still a key factor in the final grade. Some centres are continuing to use the same theme for all their candidates. Although there is no prohibition on this, it does tend to stifle individual candidates' creativity which is often the greatest spur to producing high quality work. Most projects were of wood or plastics with few "engineered" or

metal projects being seen and again a large number of "toy" or "box" type projects were in evidence. Physically smaller projects tended to have a better "surface finish" which helped their grade and allowed for rapid development. More use was seen of jigs for constructions and one or two centres are beginning to consider the commercial aspects of product design. Challenging tasks, which exhibit a variety of skills, are required for the highest grades." (AQA, 2002, p. 14)

So, making is important - but not high level craft skills? How valid is this position? And given time constraints on design & technology in school, what level of making is important - and how much attention to the use of tools and equipment should be given? Peter Williams suggests that we:
'imagine a pupil is being taught how to use a hacksaw for the first time. After the workpiece has been marked out, the pupil is helped to secure it in the vice with cut line vertical; the pupil is then shown how to hold the saw in two hands. In making the first cutting strokes, the pupil must be taught how to keep the saw cut on the "waste" side of the line, and should be encouraged to work out how the saw blade actually cuts into the material. Once this process has been assimilated and practised, the pupil could be introduced to the file as a cutting tool which is held in an identical fashion to that of the hacksaw. Because the stance and cutting actions of the two tools are almost identical, attention should be drawn to these similarities. Not only will skill in filing be acquired quickly and efficiently, but the practice in filing will actually help to consolidate skill in hacksawing.

14 Lots of
- construction,
15 but is it making?

As other tool skills are introduced, it is essential to draw attention to the similarities and differences in stance and hand positions between those tools already used and the new ones. This will continue the process of consolidation and speed up the learning process." (Williams, 1994, p. 5)

Sometimes we might ask pupils to make a product for a specific learning purpose, for example in food experimental and investigative work would require making skills. Pupils could be taught how to make a rubbed-in scone mixture then experiment with different ways of cooking it; they could be taught how to make a whisked sponge then asked to vary the sugar levels - they would be making but there would be no designing involved, does this make it less of a learning experience?

? Is such instruction in the use of tools still appropriate? How much time should be spent? Do all pupils need to learn this? What making techniques that you learnt at school would you say were a waste of time?

Claire Catterall writing in 1999 has suggested that we might be *'losing sight of the traditional culture of cooking'* and Ofsted (2006, p. 6) acknowledge the tension *'between teaching about food to develop skills for living and using food as a means to teach the objectives of design & technology'*. This tension could be applied to other focus areas; do pupils learn making skills in order to be able to carry out DIY at home or is there some other purpose?

Supporting pupils in making what they design

When we, as teachers, set pupils a design and make task they may know what they want to do but not be able to realise their solution because they do not have the required knowledge or skills. Wanting to build that video recorder might have been an extreme case - the technical understanding and the skills in soldering and mechanisms were missing - but more apparently 'well matched' tasks can founder through a lack of appropriate skills. More critically, when planning their work pupils may not even consider certain approaches to a problem because they are ignorant of the existence of equipment or a technique which might help them. And here we refer not only to making skills but also to a lack of exposure to other techniques that impact on making such as sequencing tasks and fault finding.

The approach suggested by the Nuffield Design & Technology Project, and emphasised in the national curriculum, was to advocate a carefully planned selection of shorter

Communication Chooser Chart
Use the chart to decide which technique or drawing system to use.

What you want to communicate	Technique or drawing systems to use
Realistic appearance of products	rendering on perspective or isometric views
Realistic appearance of clothing	fashion drawing
Realistic appearance of food	photography
Giving impact	put drawing or photograph against a background
Putting the product in a picture	single point perspective
Plans for food	

Food Wrapping Chooser Chart

Wrapping	Dip-coat	Wrap-around	Hold	Physical properties	Appearance	Texture
Deep-fried batter	✓	✓	✓	solid and brittle	brown with bubbles on surface; takes shape of food it covers	crisp and crunchy
Shallow-fried batter (pancake)		✓		solid, soft and pliable	cream with brown speckles	soft and chewy
Samosa			✓	solid, brittle when hot, softer when cold	golden brown, some bubbles on surface	crisp when hot
Shortcrust pastry						

Strategies Chooser Chart

Strategy	Comments			
Identifying needs and likes				
Observing people	B	◔	☆	
Interviewing	B	◔	☆	
Looking in books and magazines	B	◔	☆	
PIES	B		☆	
Looking at aesthetics				
Style, colour, feel, space and harmony	B	◔	☆	
Image boards	B	◔	☆	
Using briefs and specifications				
Writing design briefs	B	◔	☆	
Writing specifications	B	◔	☆	
Generating design ideas				
Brainstorming	B or M	◗	☆	👥
Observational drawing	B or M	◗	☆	
Making connections	B or M	◗	☆	
Attribute analysis	B or M	◔		
Modelling				

16 These charts help
- pupils choose
18 tools and techniques but they don't teach skills.

(With kind permission of Nuffield Design & Technology Project.)

projects, focused or *'resource tasks'* which allow pupils to learn and practice specific skills and techniques. Then when engaged in longer, more open design and make assignments or *'capability tasks'* they can draw on the skills and techniques that they need. Nuffield Design & Technology has produced a series of 'chooser charts' from which pupils can select a sequence of making operations and associated tools to produce a particular outcome from a starting piece of material. For example, to decorate fabrics they could choose from tie-dying, batik, fabric marker pen, transfer printing, block printing, appliqué, embroidery, or screen printing - all with advantages and disadvantages depending on the circumstances. Similarly, if a pupil wants to cut an irregular shape in material they can choose a coping saw, tin snips or abrafile depending on the nature of the resistant material.

But does it work in practice? Research on the Nuffield Design & Technology Project suggests the answer is yes - if the teaching is right and 'capability tasks' (longer project work) are supported by pertinent 'resources tasks' that teach techniques which are likely to be useful. Chooser charts then remind the pupil about techniques they have previously been taught or suggest possible new equipment, tools or processes for them to consider. This way of teaching also fits in with the government's concern that pupils lack *'cooking skills'*. The 'resource tasks' can be used to teach a range of practical skills, for example fruit and vegetable preparation or pastry making. In a design and make activity, or 'capability task', pupils then have a range of skills on which to draw to help them in their product development. An important question to raise here, though, is what skills are important, what should we be teaching in the 'resource tasks'? With the constraints mentioned above, access to ingredients and the limited time available in practical lessons, skills are often limited to those that are 'do-able', for example biscuit-making and cake-making. Are there other skills that we should be teaching? And shouldn't we be teaching the use of modern equipment: food processors, combination ovens, temperature probes?

How widely would you define 'skills' in design & technology? What advantages and disadvantages do you see in the idea of allowing pupils to 'choose'?

What is the place of CAD/CAM?

A question which has emerged over the last few years, as CAD/CAM programs and equipment have become more affordable for schools, is how we should balance the new skills of using computer support for design and manufacture with the development

19 PC & design software communicates with CAM peripherals.

20 Laser cutter cuts complex shapes from flat material.

21 Rapid prototyper builds up 3D designs layer by layer.

22 Computerised sewing machine embroiders rapidly.

23 New generation microwave oven cooks automatically acording to weight & type of food.

of psychomotor skills that are promoted through basic hand and machine tools?

Steve Rutherford, a senior lecturer at Nottingham Trent University is clear about the benefits and limitations of CAD/CAM: *'CAD/CAM is just another tool. It's not a killer application that allows anybody to be a designer. It is capable of being misused as a pencil. Yet we adore it, promote it and pretend that it will save the world. [...] We need to backtrack and consider what is really important for design education in the 21st century. CAD/CAM is certainly important, but what about areas so crucial to this period in history: areas like sustainability, team working, cross-disciplinary collaboration, and risk taking?'* (Rutherford, 2005, pp. 24-25).

Pupils are increasingly using CAD/CAM to design, for example with ProDesktop, Inventor, SpeedStep, SolidWorks and Techsoft, and to make, with CNC lathes, mills and routers, laser cutters and computerised sewing machines. It is now possible in almost all schools to define a design that is then produced by a computer-controlled machine, just as in industry, to an accuracy a pupil could rarely achieve. And as the software improves in its usability, the time invested in becoming competent shortens and outcomes can move from 'mass production' to one-off. For example, MIT's Fab Lab has a number of projects with community groups and developing communities that help them to participate in creating their own technological tools for finding solutions

to their own problems (MIT, 2006).
Pupils can now use CAD to develop designs that they could not make using traditional 'school making skills' but which they can realise using CAM. That with CAD/CAM pupils can now design and make artefacts that would otherwise be difficult to achieve is no doubt a considerable step forward in design & technology learning.

Of course the use of ICT is not restricted to applying CAD/CAM to designing and manufacturing. The internet can be used for research and communication; drawing software can help pupils to communicate information about the final product as well as to investigate initial ideas; digital photos can be taken using cameras or mobile 'phones and audio comments can be inserted using the web, a PDA or mobile 'phone to provide a record of the development of a project. ICT, like all other teaching and learning tools, has its place in design & technology but we should always be sure about why we are using it and how it is helping pupils' learning.

However, research has identified that there still needs to be a clearer understanding of the learning experience that CAD provides (Hodgson and Fraser 2005, p. 102). The same could be said of CAM, and we would encourage you to discuss the position and purpose of CAD/CAM in design & technology and the balance between 'high tech' and 'low tech' skills, knowledge and understanding.

? How would you justify teaching CAD/CAM in schools? Is it to service the needs of industry or are there other reasons? How much time needs to be spent on learning to use the software effectively? What might be lost by spending this time on CAD/CAM? Draw up a list of core basic design & technology hand skills that you think should never be replaced by CAD/CAM resources.

Conclusion

What might pupils think about the role of making in design & technology? Might they see it as a happy release from the rigours of the more cerebral elements of the curriculum both within design & technology and other subjects? Or do they view it as an integral part of design & technology intimately bound up with the cognitively demanding activity of designing? Does developing skill in making enhance a pupil's ability to model in 3D? Does the experience of handling materials through working them with tools enhance a pupil's appreciation of their usefulness in particular applications? Is making through handcrafts to produce a bedside lamp, CD rack, a t-shirt or a loaf of bread a sufficient experience for pupils or should this form of making be added to or even supplanted by a hi-tech approach?

Our view is that making *is* important to design & technology, that through the making process pupils learn technical knowledge - the properties and characteristics of materials and ingredients - and develop other skills - planning, independent learning, problem-solving. Making can also contribute to pupils' emotional development by fostering decision-making, motivation and self-esteem.

Your view of the role of making in design & technology will influence profoundly your view of the role of design & technology in the curriculum. If making is there to provide dexterity in manual skills for those who will need this in future employment this moves design & technology into a vocational position within the curriculum and one not inclusive of all pupils. If however making is seen as an integral part of design & technology contributing to both practical and intellectual development then design & technology moves into a position justified by its appropriateness for all pupils whatever career path they choose.

What do *you* think?

References

Assessment and Qualifications Alliance (AQA). (2002). "Report on the Examination: Design and Technology, Resistant Materials". Manchester: AQA.

Atkinson, S. (2000). 'Does the need for higher levels of performance curtail the development of creativity in Design and Technology project work?'. "International Journal of technology and Design Education". 10, (3), 255-281.

Barlex, D. (2000). "Young Foresight Book One Teacher Guide". London: Young Foresight Limited.

Catterall, C. (Ed.). (1999). "Food: Design and Culture". London: Laurence King Publishing in association with Glasgow 1999 Festival Company.

Department of Education and Science, Welsh Office (DES/WO). (1992). "Technology for Ages 5 to 16". London: HMSO.

Department for Education and Employment (DfEE). (1999a). "All our futures: Creativity, culture and education, the National Advisory Committee's report". London: HMSO.

Department for Education and Employment (DfEE). (1999b). "Design and Technology: The National Curriculum for England". London: HMSO.

Dewey, J. (1897). 'My Pedagogical Creed'. "School Journal". 54. Available at http://dewey.pragmatism.org/creed.htm accessed 12/8/06.

Hodgson, T. & Fraser, A. (2005). 'The impact of computer Aided Design and Manufacture (CAD/CAM) on school-based design work'. In E. W. L. Norman, D. Spendlove & P. Grover (Eds.). "DATA International Research Conference 2005". Wellesbourne: Design and Technology Association.

Nuffield Design and Technology Project materials. (1995). Harlow: Longman.
(also available at http://www.secondarydandt.org).

Office for Standards in Education (OfSTED) (2000). "OfSTED Subject Reports Secondary Design and Technology, 1999-2000". London: The Stationery Office.

Office for Standards in Education (OfSTED) (2006). "Food technology in secondary schools". ref. no. HMI 2633. Available at www.ofsted.gov.uk accessed 01/07/06.

Parker, J. (2003). 'Weaknesses Revealed'. In Barlex, D. (Ed.). "Creativity in Crisis, Design and Technology at KS3 and KS4, DATA Research Paper 18". Wellesbourne, UK: DATA.

MIT (2006) available at http://fab.cba.mit.edu/accessed 21/10/06.

Rutherford, S. (2005). 'CAD/CAM: Just another tool?'. "DATA Practice" 6, 22-25.

Smithers, A. & Robinson, P. (1992). "Technology in the National Curriculum: Getting it Right". London: The Engineering Council.

Williams, P. (1994). "Working with Resistant Materials". Milton Keynes: Open University PGCE.

Useful assessment for design & technology:
formative assessment, learning & teaching

Stephanie Atkinson

Dr Stephanie Atkinson is a reader of design & technology education at Sunderland University. She has taught at both secondary and tertiary levels and now concentrates on design & technology initial teacher education, industrial design, and the supervision and external examination of PhD students. Research interests include creativity, cognitive style and assessment. She regularly publishes articles in books and international journals and is a member of three editorial boards for prestigious journals in the UK and America.

Paul Black

Paul Black worked as a physicist for twenty years, before changing to education. He has contributed to curriculum development in science and in technology, and to assessment research. He chaired the government's 1998 Task Group on Assessment and Testing and also served on advisory groups of the USA National Research Council. He is Professor Emeritus at King's College London. His recent work on formative assessment with the King's Assessment for Learning Group has had widespread impact.

Useful assessment for design & technology:
formative assessment, learning & teaching
Stephanie Atkinson and Paul Black

Background history

In 1998 Paul Black and Dylan Wiliam produced a small booklet entitled "**Inside the Black Box**" (Black and Wiliam, 1998a). It is now widely known, having sold over 50,000 copies, and the ideas have had a wide influence. One reason for this impact was that the authors based their arguments on a thorough review of research which revealed that there was a great deal of rigorous evidence to indicate that formative assessment could raise pupils' attainments (Black and Wiliam, 1998b).

However, whilst their booklet made many practical recommendations, Black and Wiliam knew that they had to work with a group of local teachers to find out whether, and how, these ideas would work in practice in the normal life of today's schools. So with colleagues at King's College - Chris Harrison, Bethan Marshall, and Clare Lee - they set up a two-year project with a group of forty teachers from six secondary comprehensive schools to explore the practical applications of formative assessment. Many practical ideas were developed in this work; at the same time almost all of the teachers were positive about the project's effects for them, and there were significant gains in test performance for the classes involved. The King's team summarised their findings in a second short booklet "**Working inside the black box**" published in 2002 and more fully in a book written for teachers and schools "**Assessment for Learning: putting it into practice**" published in 2003.

Since then, formative assessment has become a central feature of several national and regional initiatives. One finding of the King's team, who have now worked with teachers in all subject areas, is that formative assessment has both generic features, which apply to learning across all stages and all school subjects, and also features which are specific - to primary teachers and to individual secondary subjects.

In this chapter we first discuss the meaning and implications of formative assessment. We then examine its application to teaching and learning in design & technology. After these introductory sections, we discuss in detail various classroom practices, namely dialogue in learning, feedback on the range of types of work that pupils might produce, the development of peer- and self-assessment, and the formative use of summative tests; these discussions will be illustrated by examples. The last main section presents a brief discussion to relate the ideas to the summative assessment practices and pressures within which teachers have to work. A closing summary reviews the principles, of learning, motivation, and collaboration which should underlie and guide formative practices.

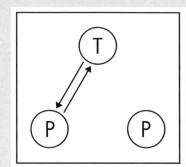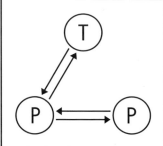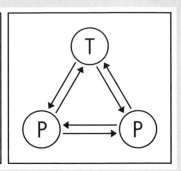

01 Effective learning
   interaction.
   T= teacher.
   P= pupil.

The meaning and implications of formative assessment

As the ideas have become more widely known, the terms *'formative assessment'* and *'assessment for learning'* have been more and more widely used, often with different and diverse meanings. It is not surprising that confusions and misunderstandings have arisen. A key point here is that effective learning demands interaction, started by the teacher to evoke the pupil's ideas, leading to feedback, from pupil to teacher and from pupil to pupil and then back again to the pupil, along lines and at levels determined, not by some pre-ordained plan, but by the needs revealed through the pupil's response. The teacher has to use this feedback to modify the teaching plan, so that new vocabulary and structures can be introduced through challenging activities that extend pupils' learning. This dynamic interaction can be illustrated as shown in the diagram above.

AfL - What exactly is it?
Here are three descriptions of Assessment for Learning:
- Are they all saying the same thing? or
- Do they usefully complement one another? or
- Do they contradict one another?

'Assessment for learning is any assessment for which the first priority in its design and practice is to serve the purpose of promoting pupils' learning. It thus differs from assessment of learning designed primarily to serve the purposes of accountability, or of ranking, or of certifying competence' (Black and Wiliam, 1998a).

'Assessment for Learning (AfL) is the process of seeking and interpreting evidence for use by learners and their teachers to decide where the learners are in their learning, where they need to go and how best to get there' (Assessment Reform Group, 2002).

'An assessment activity can help learning if it provides information to be used as feedback, by teachers, and by their pupils in assessing themselves and each other, to modify the teaching and learning activities in which they are engaged. Such assessment

Materials technology	Electronics & communication technology
Textile technology	Food technology

becomes "formative assessment" when the evidence is actually used to adapt the teaching work to meet learning needs' (Black et al., 2003).

These processes implement two principles of learning. The first is that one must start from where the learner is, rather than to present strange new ideas to overlay the old and so cause confusion. The second principle is that learning cannot be done *for* learners, it has to be done *by* them, albeit with the teacher supporting any new input.

The context of design & technology teaching

The distinctive contribution that design & technology makes to the curriculum is clearly stated in National Curriculum (NC) documentation (Department for Education and Employment/ Qualifications and Curriculum Authority, 1999) and the revisions to be introduced in September 2008 (Qualifications and Curriculum Authority, 2007).

In design & technology the level descriptors show progression in each of the three aspects of
- generating, developing, planning and communicating ideas,
- working with tools, equipment, materials and components to make quality products,

- evaluating processes and products, whilst specifying knowledge and understanding that will support attainment in each of these three aspects. Curriculum 2000 restated the need for a balance of teaching and learning activities in which capability was achieved through activities which developed designing and making skills, at the same time as knowledge and understanding. Most recently, the Qualifications and Curriculum Authority (2007) has restated this position: *'The NC specifies the activities through which design & technology should be taught: product analysis, focussed practical tasks and design and make activities. These differing activities all provide teachers with ideal opportunities to combine a range of assessment strategies to ensure that assessment is integral to their teaching and the pupils' learning'* (Ofsted, 2003).

There has been a great deal of focus on the holistic nature of capability in design & technology. The Design and Technology Association (2006) suggests that this may *'...lead to an over-emphasis on summative assessment and insufficient attention being given to formative assessment'*. They go on to explain that one of the reasons for this is that attainment in design & technology tends to be expressed primarily in terms of process. This use of process as a vehicle for assessment is understandable when one considers the nature of the activity being assessed and the unwieldy breadth of skills, knowledge and understanding that would have

03 Interaction
between teacher
and pupils.

to be specified to cover the four specialisms (see previous table) encompassed in the design & technology curriculum.

We believe that this concentration on a holistic and summative view of assessment is neither necessary nor appropriate. There are many ways that process can be effectively assessed formatively, thereby providing learners with an understanding of how to improve their ongoing process whilst giving teachers insight into specific knowledge, skills and understanding that learners require to support that process. It is also often the case that summative assessment provides (formative) feedback that would have been a more appropriate learning tool for the pupil if it had been provided earlier. For example rather than at the end of a design project, formative feedback during the project regarding, for instance, a lack of three-dimensional modelling at the development of the chosen idea stage could lead to a better understanding by the pupil of its value in decision-making. It may also highlight a lack of knowledge about appropriate, quick modelling materials.

Questioning and dialogue in classrooms

The essential two-way interaction between teachers and pupils can be achieved in several ways, but the crucial ingredients are:
• questions to encourage open discussion;
• challenging activities;
• strategies to support participation by all learners.

A good example of such interaction, in the context of design & technology, can be found in **"Good Assessment Practice"** (Ofsted, 2003):
'Year 9 pupils discussed and justified their design ideas in small groups. The teacher listened to the discussion and invited individual pupils to explain to the class how they were solving specific aspects of the design task. He quizzed them about their decisions on the materials and processes that they were using. Pupils were encouraged to try ideas and research possibilities, with no guarantee of success and links between pupils with related ideas were fostered. After the lesson the teacher jotted short notes on the record cards of some pupils, identifying those that had made significant progress or had encountered problems in the lesson' (Ofsted, 2003:1).

If questions are to serve a formative purpose in the design & technology classroom, it is necessary to focus attention on how well they serve this purpose - which factual questions usually fail to do. Why do you think this is?

Collaboration between teachers to exchange ideas and experiences about good questions can be very valuable. It could be part of professional development to reconsider questioning techniques and develop skilful 'laddering' and spiralling from simple to complex questions. Questions could be designed that would allow for factual responses, for imaginative and speculative ones and for developing pupils' competence in asking meaningful questions themselves.

Promoting discussion

Here are some examples of types of questions which you might ask to help encourage further discussion in class. Can you think of others?

- What can we add to Yagnesh's answer?
- Do you agree with Suzie's suggestion?
- Can someone improve on Jack's solution?
- Dean said…and Monica thought…How can we bring these ideas together?
- Do you think Sarah's idea will work or not? And why do you think so?

Any of these might work, but sometimes they might not

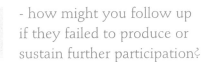

\- how might you follow up if they failed to produce or sustain further participation?

However, the central role of teachers in a formative approach is to promote thinking by encouraging pupils to express and then reflect on their ideas, leading them through such interactions to develop and change their thinking. Well thought-out questions can help both start and keep alive such 'thinking talk'. For example, in a scenario concerning designing a lantern for a religious festival, the teacher could challenge the pupils with such questions as *'Where will your lantern be used?'* and *'What safety aspects do you need to consider?'* and *'If we are to use a tea-light candle, how will you hold it safely in place inside the lantern?'*

Challenging activities

Questions play an important role in opening up and sustaining thoughtful discussion, but they can be most fruitful if they are 'built-in' to a challenging activity, i.e. an activity which challenges pupils to both think and perform. The test is whether or not an activity helps the teacher to find out what pupils understand and/or can do, rather than just what they know and can recite from memory. In design & technology this can be achieved in all design and make tasks, for example when pupils are asked to design and make a pop-up calendar with constraints that it must pack flat and fit into a certain envelope size.

04 Pupils looking for
a suitable place
to site a litter bin
in a playground.

Using the example of designing and making a pop-up calendar can you make a list of

- What pupils should understand,
- What pupils should be able to do,

in order to tackle the process successfully and produce a creative outcome for their pop-up calendars?

Challenging activities can take many forms and can include both individual and group work, with the aim of the latter being to encourage pupils to co-operate in planning, to share responsibility, to learn to allocate tasks and to foster teamwork. In design & technology using, for example, the context of sustainability when designing a litter bin for use in school, the teacher could start by asking the pupils to discuss with one another where in the school a litter bin would be useful. The next round of questions from the teacher could ask which recycled materials could be used, leading to the pupils devising their own questions concerning how they could cut, join or finish the materials they propose. At each stage, pairs or groups could be asked to present their ideas and compare one another's in a whole class discussion before going ahead to the next stage.

Strategies to support participation by all learners

Through formative questioning, the teacher hopes to collect rich evidence of the pupils' understanding. It's the opposite of assessment of learning, where we try only to find out what pupils already know, for the aim is not simply to find out what they know but also what they don't know and possibly, more importantly, what they partly know. Teaching is about helping youngsters realise this and then guiding them to upgrade their part-knowledge to a fuller understanding. To achieve these aims any activity and its associated questioning must have the potential to stretch and deepen the thinking of the pupils.

Frank Banks writing in 2002 talks about closed and open questioning and the cognitive level required of pupils to answer them. The above table is based on his idea of illustrating the differences using, as an example, a project on making a mechanical toy. Try to use this to generate a set of lower-order and higher-order questions, which would be relevant for a project appropriate

Low-order cognitive questions	
Recall	What is the name of this type of saw?
Comprehension	Why do we use that type of saw for this type of work?
Application	If we are going to cut this complicated shape in this piece of hardboard, which saw should we use?
High-order cognitive questions	
Analysis	To make this pull-along toy I need to cut out the different parts. What would be the best sequence to do that so that I can make sure they all fit together?
Synthesis	What will happen to the head of the pull-along duck if we use this cam and this rod together?
Evaluation	You've heard the different ideas from the different groups. Explain to me which of the suggested combinations of cams and rods you think will be most robust to work together to control the head and wings.

05 Example of low-order and high-order questioning.

to your own design
& technology specialism.

Demanding questions require time for the learner to work out an answer, so the teacher ought to wait for some time before expecting a response. Mary Budd Rowe writing in the "Journal of Research in Science Teaching" in 1974 reported that the wait time in primary science classes was very low, less than 1 second. In the secondary classrooms Paul Black and his colleagues reported in 2003 that teachers could, with practice, increase their wait time to around 3-5 seconds and that this had dramatic effects on the involvement of pupils in classroom discussion. Their research showed that:

- longer answers were given than previously;
- more pupils were electing to answer;
- fewer pupils refused to answer;
- pupils commented on or added to the answers of other pupils;
- more alternative explanations or examples were offered.

Even when wait time is increased, some learners are reluctant to offer answers. To overcome this some teachers adopt a 'no hands up' strategy, taking the view that if sufficient wait time is given, everyone should be expected to answer, so they select individuals to answer. Such techniques can remedy the unsatisfactory situation of the quick thinkers with hands shooting up either dominating or feeling

unacknowledged because they are ignored.

However, pupils often are reluctant to commit to an answer because they feel they may reveal their inadequacies. The teacher's role here is to act as a facilitator, a provider of scaffolding when necessary whilst encouraging pupils both to try to answer and to listen carefully to the answers from their peers; after all, wrong or imperfect answers can be essential guides to the ways in which peer interaction or teacher intervention might best be used.

Planning scaffolding that may be required before a question and answer session is important. This scaffolding will be different for pupils of different ages and/or ability. What scaffolding do you think is needed for a question and answer session regarding the mechanical advantage achieved by various levers
- with less able pupils meeting this concept for the first time?
- with a top set of key stage 4 pupils?

06 Classroom
dialogue.

Peer discussion plays an essential part in creating such an environment. If pupils can first discuss their tentative responses to a question within a small group, they can explore, articulate and check ideas before they reveal their group's combined effort to the whole class.

Taking a design task appropriate to your specialism, identify at least four separate instances where peer discussion could be advantageous to the pupils' learning.

Underlying these ideas about challenging activities and questions is the principle that we all learn as much from discussion as from reading and writing. Indeed, it is partly because they put this principle into practice that formative methods improve pupils' learning. So the underlying aim is to promote dialogue in the classroom as a key component of effective learning.

In his book "**Towards Dialogic Teaching**" (2006) Robin Alexander stresses the poverty of much classroom dialogue:
'Clearly, if classroom talk is to make a meaningful contribution to children's learning and understanding, it must move beyond the acting out of such cognitively restricting rituals'.
and explains why improvement is essential:
'Children, we now know, need to talk,

and to experience a rich diet of spoken language, in order to think and to learn'.
(Robin Alexander, 2006)

He classifies classroom dialogue under the following five headings:
1. Rote;
2. Recitation;
3. Instruction/exposition;
4. Discussion;
5. Dialogue.

Try to describe the difference between them.
Which of them are you, or your colleagues, using most frequently?
Does it matter?

Feedback on pupils' work, as writing or as a designed or constructed product

Research by Ruth Butler (1988) and Carol Dweck (2000) into the motivation and self-esteem of learners has explored different kinds of feedback specifically on written work although the connection between their conclusions and design & technology project work is easy to see. One kind of feedback gives only marks or grades. This is a judgement on the work and helps to develop 'ego-involvement' in pupils; its effects on both motivation and on subsequent test attainment are negative. It discourages low attainers, but also makes high attainers reluctant to tackle tasks if they cannot be sure of success, for failure would be seen as bad news rather than as an opportunity to learn. The second kind gives only comments on what needs to be done to improve. Ruth Butler found that comment-only develops what she called *'task-involvement'*. She found that its effects are positive for it can encourage all pupils, whatever their past achievements, that they can do better, and that they can learn from their mistakes. Furthermore it also produces better test results. If feedback provides both marks and comments, the negative effects follow because pupils tend to ignore the comments and attend only to the marks. Thus, marks give no formative feedback and emphasise competition rather than personal improvement, whereas comments can be formative and so ensure that they contribute to learning.

Effective Comments

Questions are useful ways of framing comments. Compare these two comments on a pupil's work when designing a poster about recycling:

'A nice sketch but you need to add more detail.'

'Your poster catches my eye but I am wondering why I should really want to recycle my rubbish! Can you persuade me? How about some imperatives? Some statistics that might

encourage me to take action! What can I do? What should I do?'

If you were the pupil which would you find more useful? Can you explain why? We think the second comment initiates thinking immediately, enabling the learner to discuss their thoughts either with the teacher or a peer, whilst the questioning nature also encourages the pupil to initiate improvement. The first comment simply describes the deficit in the piece. Do you agree?

Targets can form part of helpful comments, and the more focussed the target is, the better. General statements, as in the first example, should be avoided. Points that need to be considered next time may be useful but comments that prompt and guide immediate action are better. It may help if the feedback comment relates to success criteria or to a description of quality that might be shared with or devised by the pupils, so that they can learn to consider the criteria as their work progresses. For example, if pupils are asked to create an attention-catching poster about conservation

and recycling, then what is required is:
• facts and figures to 'persuade', using strong qualifiers;
• suggestions about what individuals can/should do using, e.g. modal auxiliaries;
• visual interest.

The second example relates to these criteria in an effective way.

Creating the improving classroom
The opportunity to respond to comments is essential, for learners need to see that the teacher really wants the work improved and that improvement is being monitored.

This might mean providing opportunity in lesson time for learners to read comments on their work and to discuss with their teacher or with peers the necessary improvements.

One simple way to achieve these aims is to record comments on a sheet of paper each time a piece of work is comment-marked: the learner slips this between the appropriate pages of his/her folio/workbook. The sheet then contains an accumulation of comments and allows both learner and teacher to recognise where improvements have been made or where specific problems keep arising. An example of such comments are the following:
'On your drawing of your chair design you need to specify the angle of the back cushion so that it supports a person comfortably when they are sitting using a laptop computer.'

The teacher (T) had written the above comment on the sheet in a design folio; the pupil (P) responded with the following comment which pinpointed the learning difficulty that she was having:
'I do not know what angle that should be. Where can I find out?'

Or it could have been:
T: *'You could make your box using the vacuum-former rather than gluing lots of pieces of plastic together.'*
P: *'I have never used the vacuum-former so I do not know what forms I can achieve.'*

If learners could be this precise and open about their uncertainties, then teaching would be much simpler. What do you think? We would suggest that this level of recognition by the learner initiates the desire to sort out uncertainty; in this way, feedback drives formative action.

The use of post-its on design sheets can cut down on writing time for teachers if thereby they no longer have to explain which design sheet they are referring to on their feedback sheet before they can start to add their comment. It can also overcome the problem

07 Using post-its on design sheets can cut down on writing time for teachers and also overcome the problem of teachers not wishing to write or draw on pupils work.

Useful assessment for design & technology: formative assessment, learning & teaching   Stephanie Atkinson and Paul Black

of teachers not wishing to write or draw on pupils' work. Or pupils not wishing to have the presentation of their work spoiled! Using a permanent pen on the plastic wallet-type portfolios that are popular for holding design sheets can also achieve the same objective, allowing corrections or suggestions for improvements to be applied at the relevant point.

Another useful formative assessment tool to assist pupils to develop drawing skills is to use tracing paper on top of design sheets to illustrate corrections to drawings. This enables pupils to improve both their understanding of perspective drawing and also see how to improve the communication of their ideas without the teacher having made marks on their actual work. The speed of giving feedback in this way is also a plus point for the teacher in that 'a picture is often worth a thousand words'.

It is not necessary for teachers to mark every page of a design folio, theory workbook or practical task - and there can be advantage in having some work checked by peer assessment. This latter method can also begin to move the responsibility for assessment onto the shoulders of the learners.

Self- and peer-assessment

Developing effective self-assessment is an essential part of managing one's own learning. It requires the pupil to have a clear picture of the learning targets, understanding of what would count as good quality work that meets them, an idea of where one stands in relation to those targets, and a means to achieve them. Pupils often lack this clear picture, are not aware of the rationale behind specific tasks, and cannot find their way to attain their individual targets.

Taking a suitable design and make task appropriate to your specialism:

1. Design a formative assessment sheet that you could give pupils at the start of the project. This must provide:
   - a list of the learning targets for the project;
   - a method of indicating where pupils stand in relation to achieving each learning target.
2. What teaching aids could you use to provide them with an understanding of what counts as good

quality work?

3. What skills, knowledge and understanding would you need to teach pupils in order that they could meet the learning targets you have specified?

The overall aim is to achieve meta-cognition, which is the power to oversee and steer one's own learning so that one can become a more committed, responsible and effective learner. Work with teachers has shown that peer-assessment helps pupils develop their self-assessment skills. Pupils can be taught to recognise both quality and inadequacies in other pupils' work even if their own level of competence is different from the level of the work being scrutinised. Discussion focussed on criteria for quality can develop pupils' awareness of successes and problems in pieces of work thereby enabling them to assess their own work with greater clarity and to see how small changes, or different ways of approaching parts of the work, can easily raise its quality.

Schemes of work might well be reassessed by teachers to ensure that there are sufficient numbers of peer-assessments reasonably spaced throughout each project. For example peer-assessment could be carried out at the end of the main research collection stage, when early 3D modelling has been produced,

during the detailing of the chosen idea and again at the end of the process. This makes the marking load more manageable whilst also giving pupils time for work on improvement before the next detailed feedback is due. Peer-assessment that requires several paragraphs, rather than one word or a single sentence, can provide a richer source of evidence to help the teacher appraise the learning of individual pupils and so provide individually useful advice.

A primary teacher gave her pupils a firm structure for assessing one another's work. She called it **"Two Stars and a Wish"**. The 'two stars' are two pieces of positive feedback, identifying successful outcomes. The 'wish' identifies an aspect that could be improved in some way. The following is an example of star and wish peer feedback:

∗ *'You have identified all the ingredients that will be used in your chosen ready meal.'*

∗ *'You have explained what else you would serve with it.'*

Wish - *'You should include the nutritional values that Mr Smith asked us to talk about.'*

This form of peer-assessment encourages pupils to give usefully targeted peer-assessment. Pupils can usually identify aspects that need improving;

08 Traffic light icons in use.
09 Pupils discussing folio work, with reference to assessment sheet.

however by also commenting upon successes they will develop confidence to use that understanding on future occasions. Can you think of specific instances where you might use this method of assessment?

With assessment applied in such a way, pupils gradually acquire the habits and skills of collaborative learning from a very early age, and, through peer-assessment, develop the objectivity required for self-assessment.

The use of traffic light icons can also help develop self-assessment skills. Pupils could be asked to label their theory work for example in electronics, or food technology, green, amber or red according to whether they think they have good, partial or little understanding of the topic or concept. If many pupils use red, then the teacher can see that this work has to be revisited. Conversely, a plethora of greens indicates that the class is ready to move on. A mixture of reds, greens and ambers calls for different action; teachers could pair up green and amber pupils to help one another, leaving them free to deal with the problems of the red pupils.

Where pupils do not understand the meaning of a target, or have little idea of what a piece of work that will meet the target criteria would look like, it might help if they discussed existing examples. For instance, at the start of a project to design a teenager's disco 'handbag', teachers could find it beneficial to use existing solutions or bought examples to clarify the often difficult-to-understand abstract criteria, that will be used to judge the pupils' chosen solution.

Taking the above example of a disco handbag or a project related to your own design & technology specialism can you make a list of the criteria you would use? Can you now highlight the more abstract criteria you believe will be difficult for pupils to understand and think of ways you could explain each of these to your pupils?

A combination of self- and peer-assessment during design activity can be very beneficial to the learner as well as providing the teacher with a better understanding of the learning requirements of individuals within a cohort. In this example the whole class assesses their own partially completed design activity against a set of appropriate criteria devised by the teacher in collaboration with the class.

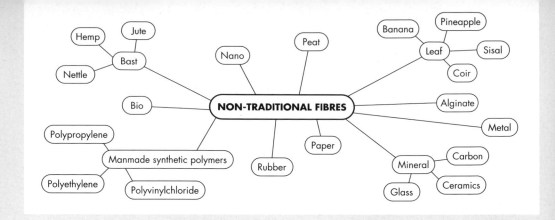

10 Mind map of non-traditional fibres in textiles.

The assessment is carried out by ticking whether: *'very good progress'*, *'some progress'*, *'a little progress'* or *'no progress'* has been made against each criterion. The teacher then gets the class to work in pairs and to exchange their self-assessment sheets. They then take turns to choose an instance where one of the pair has said he/she has made *'very good progress'* and discuss whether there is explicit evidence of that *'very good progress'* to be found in the folio. They then swap over and repeat the activity with the other folio. The next stage is for them to look at where they have each made little or no progress and discuss why this may be. Then in a class session these problem areas can be discussed with the teacher who may be able to provide a quick solution or may become aware of a future learning need of a number of pupils or even a whole class. If this assessment method is used on several occasions throughout the project using the same self-assessment sheet it can build up to provide both pupil and teacher with a clear picture of where progress is being made and where stumbling blocks are occurring.

Formative use of summative tests

Preparation for a test can be a formative opportunity. Classes can use traffic light icons as a guide to their revision, applying them to test items or to examination syllabuses and then working in groups on common problem areas. Through these activities, pupils are able to plan their revision for high stake tests more effectively. Mind mapping is also a useful technique, for instance, during textile technology lessons pupils can map what they know about smart materials, then add to this as they increase their knowledge of the topic, so giving them a list of revision topics in a diagrammatical form to use during revision.

Another useful approach is to analyse test responses to see which questions are causing the main problems and then return the scripts to pupils, asking them to mark one another's answers to these questions, inventing the mark schemes themselves. This makes pupils think through what counts as a good answer. Teachers then use the time after marking to revisit problematic questions and to give pupils further examples to try. For test questions where only a few have answered incorrectly, pupils can ask successful peers to help them.

In the Black and Wiliam research (2003), one teacher decided to give his class the end-of-topic test in the first lesson of the topic so that results could inform him of what the class did or did not know, by pupils using traffic light icons to indicate their familiarity with the skills or the understanding required. The teacher could then plan to concentrate on the areas of unfamiliarity or difficulty.

11 Teachers
moderating
pupils' projects.

Summative assessment

Given the emphasis of this chapter
on the formative, only a few comments
will be offered about summative assessments.
Such assessments serve a different purpose
from formative; nevertheless the same
information can often be used for both,
provided that it is interpreted appropriately,
so that, for example, a modest design might
both be recorded as such, whilst it may also
be an occasion for feedback advice to guide
future improvement. Often it may be fair
to record a summative assessment after
a pupil has had opportunity to improve
in the light of feedback.

Summative assessments made within school
and for internal purposes can have important
effects on a pupil's progress, so it is essential
to ensure the quality of the judgements made.

Ensuring quality in teachers' summative assessments
• Select tasks on which pupils can show
  their full potential.
• Have enough tasks to cover all criteria.
• Check and confirm agreement on the criteria
  being applied.
• Two or more teachers to mark samples
  independently.
• No marks on scripts to ensure independence.
• Compare and discuss results to secure consensus.
• Resolving differences can build shared
  understanding.

Short formal tests have very limited reliability;
for a typical written paper used for Key Stage
or GCSE testing the probability, even with
question papers that are carefully set and
marked, that any one pupil will be wrongly
graded is about 30% (Black and Wiliam, 2006)
- so exclusive reliance on such results is most
unwise. The error arises because the sample
of the pupil's attainments is too small
in relation to their variability. Thus a variety
of design & technology work collected over
time, which might include results from tests
and other assessments made en route,
can give a more reliable result. The exchange
and discussion between teachers of samples
of pupils' work is essential to ensure equality
of standards and as protection against bias
(which can often be unconscious).

Conclusions

Principles of learning
At several points in this chapter we have
emphasised that the practices described
are based on well-established principles
of learning. These are:
• Start from the learner's existing
  understanding;
• Encourage active involvement of the learner;
• Develop the learner's overview in terms
  of the aims and criteria of quality learning;
• Involve the learner in discussion to promote
  learning through social interaction.
In addition, it is essential to encourage
self-esteem and motivation through feedback

which is focussed on improvement
and not on judgement and competition.

Learning together: learning from others
Our experience shows that teachers taking
on the development of formative assessment
need to work in a team for mutual support
in sharing ideas and resources. That team
must have a plan that has support from
the department and school, since some
innovations may be, or may be seen
to be, contrary to some aspects
of departmental or school policy.

Strategy for change
It is not easy to put AfL
ideas into practice. Teachers
need mutual support
and a commitment from their
leaders to help sustain
the process of change.
Here are some ideas that
might form a framework for
making a departmental plan.
Try to think of further
headings or details that ought
to be included in any plan.
Audit
To what extent are the four
formative practices already
well established?

Strategy
Involve all staff from
the start, or should a small
group take the lead?
Action
Try all the ideas together,
or one at a time?
Support
How can the innovators
be helped, e.g. given extra
time to plan and reflect?
Reflection and evaluation
How could progress
be monitored?
And experience shared
with others?
See Black et al. 2003, chapter 7.

Our experience has shown us that most teachers
have found this work very rewarding, but also
challenging when adopting changes to the way
they work with pupils and to the way that
pupils take responsibility for their own learning.
These do fit well within the current culture
in design & technology where learners are
required to exhibit independence, reflection,
creativity and criticality in their work in order to
achieve capability. However, assessment for
learning often seems risky. Indeed, what is
involved is best seen as a voyage of discovery,
a journey into new territories of teaching and
learning for pupils and teachers alike.

Further reading

Alexander, R. (2006). "Towards dialogic teaching:
Rethinking classroom talk" (3rd edition). Cambridge, UK: Dialogos.
See also www.robinalexander.org.uk.

Black, P., Harrison, C., Lee, C., Marshall, B. & Dylan, W. (2002).
"Working inside the black box: assessment for learning in the
classroom". London, UK: nfer Nelson.

Black, P., Harrison, C., Lee, C., Marshall, B. & Dylan, W. (2003).
"Assessment for Learning: putting it into practice". London: OUP.

Design and Technology Association (2006). "Key Stage 3
Assessment". Available at http://web.data.org.uk/data/
secondary/ks3_assessment.php accessed 12.04.2006.

Office of Standards in Education (Ofsted) (2003).
"HMI 1472: Good Assessment Practice in Design and
Technology". London: Office of Standards in Education
(Ofsted) Publications.

References

Assessment Reform Group (ARG) (2002). "Assessment for
Learning: 10 Principles". London: Institute of Education.

Banks, F. (2002). 'Teaching strategies for design and technology'.
In G. Owen-Jackson (Ed.). "Aspects of Teaching Secondary Design
and Technology". (pp. 75-89), London: Routledge Falmer.

Black, P. & Wiliam, D. (1998a). 'Assessment and classroom
learning'. "Assessment in Education: Principles Policy and Practice".
5. (1), (pp. 7-73).

Black, P. & Wiliam, D. (1998b). "Inside the Black Box: Raising
standards through classroom assessment". London UK: nfer Nelson.

Black, P. & Wiliam, D. (2006). 'The reliability of assessments'.
In J. Gardner (Ed.). "Assessment and Learning". (pp. 214-239),
London: Sage.

Butler, R. (1988). 'Enhancing and undermining intrinsic
motivation; the effects of task-involving and ego-involving
evaluation on interest and performance'.
"British Journal of Educational Psychology". 58, 1-14.

Department for Education and Employment (DfEE) (1999).
"Design and technology: The National Curriculum for England".
London: Department for Education and Employment (DfEE)
and the Qualifications and Curriculum Authority (QCA).

Dweck, C. S. (2000). "Self-Theories: their role in motivation,
personality and development". London: Taylor & Francis.

Qualifications and Curriculum Authority (2007).
"Design and technology programme of study:
ks3 The importance of design and technology".
Full text available at http://www.qca.org.uk/libraryAssets/media/
D-and-T_KS3_PoS.pdf accessed on 15.08.07.

Rowe, M. B. (1974). 'Wait time and rewards as instructional
variables, their influence on language, logic and fate control'.
"Journal of Research in Science Teaching". 11, 81-94.

Mind (not) the gap... Take a risk

Interdisciplinary approaches to the science, technology, engineering & mathematics education agenda

Dov Kipperman

Dov Kipperman is a curriculum developer for technology and science education at the ORT Moshinsky Center for Research, Development and Training in Israel. He has developed a variety of instructional materials for k-12: textbooks, websites, lab activities as well as programs for technology teacher training. He has published and presented papers at technology education conferences (ITEA, PATT, DATA). Currently he serves on the editorial board of the "International Technology Education Series".

Mark Sanders

Mark Sanders is professor and program leader for technology education and affiliate faculty of engineering education at Virginia Tech, located in Blacksburg, Virginia, USA. From 1989 to 1997, he was founding editor of the "Journal of Technology Education" and currently serves as associate editor. He is author of the textbook "Communication Technology: Today and Tomorrow", co-author of "Technology, Science, Mathematics Connection Activities" and has published numerous book chapters and journal articles. Before earning his PhD at the university of Maryland, he was a high school industrial arts teacher in New York state.

Introduction

There are gaps in the curriculum. These are the gaps between subjects. Students' understanding is diminished by these gaps. Bridging the gaps is not an easy task and not without hazards. But we believe it is worth the effort and the risk! Hence this chapter explores various approaches to establishing interdisciplinary connections between design & technology and other school subjects, particularly science and mathematics. The application of technological, scientific and mathematical principles, tools, and processes is, in effect, what it means to 'engineer' a technological solution to a problem. 'STEM' is now used widely to refer to science, technology, engineering and mathematics. We use the term 'interdisciplinary STEM' throughout this chapter to refer to the inherent connections among these four disciplines. We believe that incorporating more science and mathematics principles, tools and processes into the designing, building and testing of technological solutions has the potential to enhance the already robust pedagogy of design & technology.

Part I: Justifying the interdisciplinary approach

All good teachers draw upon students' prior knowledge, whether this is knowledge previously acquired in the subject being taught, knowledge learned in other subjects in the school curriculum or knowledge gained by students' experience in the world outside school. Design & technology is no exception. Designing, making and evaluating solutions to technological problems draws upon knowledge from a wide range of school subjects: art (aesthetics and visual design), the humanities (socio/cultural/environmental impacts), and English (technical writing, idea presentation). In addition, there is enormous potential for students to apply knowledge, principles and processes learned in mathematics and science classes in designing, constructing and testing the technological solutions they create in design & technology classes.

You can think of interdisciplinary teaching as a continuum that runs from approaches in which the subject areas remain relatively separate from one another, to approaches that completely integrate subject matter and teaching practices. Arthur Applebee, Robert Burroughs, and Gladys Cruz, writing in 2000, described this continuum as ranging from *correlated* to *shared* to *reconstructed* knowledge (shown overleaf).

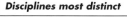

CORRELATED KNOWLEDGE	SHARED KNOWLEDGE	RECONSTRUCTED KNOWLEDGE
Represented as: Multidisciplinary Complementary Juxtaposed Parallel, sequenced Thematic (passive) Webbed **Characterized by:** Related concepts	**Represented as:** Thematic (active) Interdisciplinary Integrated Broad-field curriculum **Characterized by:** Preserving disciplinary boundaries Overlapping concepts Emergent patterns Disciplines mutually supported	**Represented as:** Synthesized Blended, fused Core curriculum Problem-centred Integrated/ive **Characterized by:** Eliminating disciplinary boundaries

Disciplines most distinct ➝ **Disciplines most blended**

01 The Interdisciplinary Continuum.

Mind (not) the gap...Take a risk

Dov Kipperman and Mark Sanders

Physics Teacher:
'What's the big deal about interdisciplinarity?
I already do technology in my physics class.
For example, teaching "energy transformations" I provide examples of machines like the electric engine motor.
That's technology!'

Technology Teacher:
'What's the big deal about interdisciplinarity?
I already do science in my technology education class.
For example, in my "resistant materials" workshop, students learn about different properties of materials. That's science!'

What do you think?

Contemporary learning theory supports interdisciplinary teaching

Over the past few decades, cognitive scientists have begun to study teaching and learning as it occurs in classrooms like yours. Many of their key findings were summarized and published in 2000, in the book **"How People Learn"**, produced by the National Research Council (US) Committee on Learning Research and Educational Practice. A good many of the conclusions cognitive scientists have drawn from this research may not come as a surprise to you, as they tend to underscore the robustness of established design & technology teaching practices. For example, some of their key findings include:

- Learning is an active process and learners construct new understandings in the context of what they already know.
- Abstract ideas are learned more effectively if 'situated' in a more familiar and concrete context (situated cognition).
  Thus, for example, Newton's laws of motion are more easily understood when students think about - or better yet, design, build and test - a scaled model roller coaster. Along the same lines, students are more likely to understand mathematical relationships among speed, weight and angle of descent in a moving object if addressed in the context of designing and making a model roller coaster, rather than as an abstract 'word or symbol based problem'.
- Learners benefit enormously from discussions they have with one another about their perceptions and ideas.
  For example, describing to one another what they believe is happening in various design/build components of the rollercoaster problem allows students to clarify and evaluate their ideas and 'understandings'. In other words, social

Need	How the need is met	Science contribution	Technology contribution	Engineering contribution	Mathematics contribution
Food	Corn				
Clothing	Outdoor coat				
Shelter	House				

interaction is a very important and powerful component of effective teaching and learning.

• Learners achieve their full learning potential by getting just enough outside assistance to enable them to move from what they currently know to a higher level of understanding.

As tackling design & technology problems often reflects so many of these key findings of learning research, Ann Marie Hill and Howard Smith, among others, referred to the type of learning that often occurs in design & technology classes as 'authentic learning'.

Research findings such as these directly support the idea that interdisciplinary teaching that engages groups of students in hands-on designing and making is more likely to promote effective learning of abstract and complex ideas such as those commonly taught in mathematics and science, than do the traditional methods of mathematics and science instruction.

The world outside school is interdisciplinary

Even a cursory analysis of our human-made (technological) world reveals how difficult it is to separate the scientific, mathematical, technological, ethical, aesthetic and socio-cultural components of technological endeavour. We need look no further than the production and consumption/use of outcomes to meet our most fundamental physical needs - food, clothing and shelter -

for endless examples of science, technology, engineering and mathematics principles, processes and applications at work.

Can you identify the contributions made by science, technology, engineering and mathematics to meeting the needs identified in the table above?

In our educational institutions, we generally separate the disciplines as a convenience. In many ways, it is easier to prepare teachers, organize curricula, and teach individually compartmentalized subject areas than to re-think our pedagogical approach with the goal of revealing the interconnected nature of the knowledge, principles and practices within the separate subject areas. Research on teaching and learning informs us that when we study one subject in isolation from another, it is very difficult to transfer the knowledge from one domain to the other. In 1983, Ernest Boyer chaired an expert group which conducted a comprehensive study of secondary education in America and then drew this conclusion:

'While we recognize the integrity of the disciplines, we also believe their current state of splendid isolation gives students a narrow and even skewed vision of both knowledge and the realities of the world.'

Educational reform initiatives from around the world support interdisciplinary teaching approaches

Educational reform efforts in the US have called for interdisciplinary STEM approaches. The 'Science, Technology and Society' (STS) movement that began in the 1970s promoted the study of the interconnected nature of science, technology and our society/culture. Many of their ideals were incorporated into the national science, technology education and social studies standards.

'Project 2061' is a massive science education reform project that has been guiding science education reform in the US since the mid-1980s. Project 2061's underlying philosophy, spelled out in their 1993 publication **"Benchmarks for Science Literacy"** speaks directly to the need for interdisciplinary approaches to math, science and technology education. The report states *'The basic point is that the ideas and practice of science, mathematics and technology are so closely intertwined that we do not see how education in any one of them can be undertaken well in isolation from the others...'* (pp. 321-322).

In 1989 the National Council of Teachers of Mathematics promoted the ideal that *'Problem situations can establish a "need to know" and foster the motivation for the development of concepts...In developing the problem situations, teachers should emphasize the application of mathematics to real-world problems'* (p. 75).

The US Standards for Technological Literacy are equally clear about the relationship between science, mathematics and technology. *'Science and technology are like conjoined twins. While they have separate identities they must remain inextricably connected in order to survive... Mathematics and technology have a similar relationship. Mathematics offers a language with which to express relationships in science and technology and provides useful analytical tools for scientists and engineers'* (International Technology Education Association, 2000, p. 44).

Interdisciplinary approaches to STEM education are emerging elsewhere in the world as well. Israel is a strong case in point. As a result of the 1994 report of the Tomorrow '98 Project written by Haim Harari, in 1994, the science and technology education curricula in Israeli junior high schools (grades 7-9) were combined into one mandatory subject - 'Science & Technology'. In addition, a new 'Science & Technology' national curriculum was developed, with collaboration between science and technology education as a central ideal:
'...Collaboration between science and technology is essential because of the growing linkage between scientific subjects and relevant technologies and also because of the unclear borders between them' (Israeli National Curriculum for Science and Technology 1996, p. 5).

It was believed this approach *'will expose the student to science and technology aspects and will introduce the social connections while emphasizing

03 James Dyson, the inventor of the dual-cyclone vacuum cleaner.

the combination between them'
(Israeli National Curriculum for Science and Technology 1996, p. 6).

In 2002, the Israeli Ministry of Education and Ort Israel began developing and implementing new high school level science and technology/pre-engineering disciplines and subjects that reflect relationships between science and technology in new multi-disciplinary ways. As Professor Kenny Price, Head of the 'Amos De-Shalit Science Teaching Center' at the Hebrew University described it: *'The concept behind this curriculum differs substantially from the traditional curricula teaching methods of science and technology, especially regarding contents interrelationships and particularly the teaching method. Technology is presented as an integral part of the science curriculum; learning about various types of technologies is combined with science education, so that students develop a viewpoint of science and technology as an unified whole'.*

The most recent rewrite of the programme of study for design & technology in England includes the statement: *'make links between design & technology and other subjects and areas of the curriculum'* (Qualifications and Curriculum Authority 2007, p. 57)

In addition, specialist Engineering Colleges, catering for students aged 11 to 19 years, have the following as part of their vision statement:

'Through a focus on enhancing understanding of the relationship between design & technology, mathematics and science, underpinning a broad curriculum, engineering colleges will raise standards of achievement for all students across the ability and subject range, leading to whole school improvement by providing increased diversity through opportunities for students to follow a wide range of vocational pathways'.
(Barlex 2005, p. 12)

James Dyson, the inventor of the dual-cyclone vacuum cleaner and advocate for design & technology education, has recently unveiled plans for a new college aimed at encouraging young people to become engineers. The Dyson School of Design Innovation - due to open in 2009 in Bath - will teach 2,500 14 to 18 year olds design, engineering and enterprise.

What are your views?
Despite educational reform efforts that encourage interdisciplinary efforts among STEM and other school subject areas, successful implementation depends largely on the ability of the teachers involved to make it happen. The reasons noted above provide a rationale for doing so… but examining this issue from your perspective is a very important first step. You need to decide where you stand.

Given the support for an interdisciplinary approach it seems obvious that teachers should pursue this path.

But is it really that simple? Consider what Franzie Loepp and John Williams have to say:

'Educational researchers have found that an integrated curriculum can result in a greater intellectual curiosity, improved attitude towards schooling, enhanced problem-solving skills and higher achievement in college'
(Austin, Hirstein and Walen 1997; Kain, 1993) (Quoted in Loepp, 1999).

'While the relationships between science and technology are undeniably significant, the differences between the two areas are just as important, particularly in terms of the goals of the developing area of technology education... the differences in methods, aims, use of knowledge and types of knowledge are fundamentally significant enough to teach them separately...'
(Williams, 2002).

Who do you think is right? State your reasons for taking sides. Develop some arguments to persuade those who think differently from you.

When James Pitt and David Barlex investigated the views of science and design & technology teachers in England in 2000 they found that the teachers had shared and consistent views of the subjects they taught but there was considerable ignorance of each other's subjects. A case study of science and design & technology teachers in a large secondary school in Sheffield carried out by David Barlex, Colin Chapman and Tim Lewis in 2003 revealed that this ignorance could lead to antagonism that was counterproductive in forming a useful relationship between the subjects. So it is important to develop an understanding of the curriculum areas you don't teach as well as those you do.

Do you know what your colleagues think about the subject they teach? Here's a chance to find out. Get together with other STEM teachers and complete the table below collectively, discussing ideas as you go.

Delete the 'sample' information in the 'Science' column before you begin... it is included here only to clarify the intent of this activity.

04

04 Interdisciplinary Connections among STEM Disciplines.

Criteria	Science	Technology	Mathematics	Engineering
Primary domain of concern?	Natural world			
Provides answers to the question...?	What is?			
Activity guided by...?	Inquiry, observation, theories, principles			
Primary endeavor?	Explain natural world			
Success determined by...?	Theories validated by other scientists			
Disciplines organized by...?	Laws and principles			
General approach	Research			
Resulting outcomes?	New explanations and theories			
Formal education occurs at what levels?	Grades K-16			
Signature pedagogy	Inquiry			
Connections with which (if any) of the STEM disciplines?	Technology, math & engineering			

05 Students in years 7 and 8 use a slope to investigate the effects of friction and velocity while working on a car safety problem.

Designing and making as a focus for STEM

Design problems commonly used in technology education generally require students, working individually or in teams, to:

1. identify and clarify problems;
2. conduct research which might involve investigations;
3. generate one or more design proposals;
4. develop these so that they can be scrutinised for predicted performance and social/environmental impact;
5. construct a prototype of the most promising design, experimenting with subcomponent designs as necessary;
6. test/evaluate the constructed solution.

During this process the students should document all design, construction and testing procedures; and be involved in communication with their peers and teacher. It is tempting to see 1 to 6 as a linear process but in reality we know that the stages not only inform one another but are to be revisited according to the demands of the emerging design. Hence students will use their mathematics and science as and when they need to, depending on the particular issue they are trying to resolve.

The various phases of the designing call on the use of mathematics, science and designerly speculation. Mathematical prediction and analysis will be useful in 1, 4 and 6. Scientific enquiry will be useful in 1, 2 and 5. Designerly speculation will be required in 3,

4 and 5. This is sometimes referred to as 'trial and error' but this term devalues the importance of this activity. Asking a series of 'what if' questions about changes to a subcomponent and using these to move to an improved design requires rigorous thinking that can be informed by mathematics and science. Thomas Edison, for example, said he found 5,000 ways to make a light bulb that wouldn't work! Engineers routinely employ all three strategies: mathematics, science and 'designerly speculation' methods, in the design of technological solutions.

One of the unique aspects of design activities is their ability to support developmentally (age) appropriate math, science and trial and error problem-solving. Even simple design problems generally have the potential to support the application of scientific inquiry and/or mathematical analysis at any level of sophistication, thereby offering appropriate challenges for students who come to the activity with robust science and math knowledge. Likewise, trial and error methods range in sophistication, depending upon the ages of the problem-solvers and the prior knowledge they bring to the problem. Teachers may gear the sophistication of the science, mathematics, and technological applications to align with students' current developmental capabilities. In practice, students may 'self-select' the level of sophistication at which they work. If students choose to go beyond the teacher's comfort zone with their

06 07 08

06 Developing
- inflatable
08 safetywear for
cyclists.
Bicycle airbag
'test drive'.

mathematics, science or technological inquiry, the teacher should take heart in the fact that design activities allow students to reach their maximum learning potential in each of the STEM areas. This may be the time and place for design & technology teachers to involve fellow science and/or mathematics teachers in the activity.

Here are some examples of some technically focused designing and making activities that might be called engineering.

The **"West Point Bridge Designer"** software, used in many schools in the US and England (http://bridgecontest.usma.edu/index.htm) allows students to analyze bridge truss designs instantly after changing one of the components in the design. The software quickly computes a cost associated with a change in the truss design. In a problem like this, algebra might be used to determine the strength to weight (supported) ratio of a particular truss design. Mathematical analyses like these inform the design process, enabling students to make better design choices than they might, had they not used any analytical procedures. Similarly, a scientific investigation of the strength of materials used for bridge design could assist students in designing and re-designing bridge components. The prototype construction phase of the design process generally allows opportunities for designerly speculation, a way of problem-solving, an important and most useful aspect of designing.

In Israel students in years 7 to 9 study a science & technology curriculum. Although it has been established as one subject (science & technology), it is recommended that there should be different teachers who specialise in different topics of the curriculum and collaborate in their teaching through project-based learning. In the example shown above left, students are working on a car crash safety design problem. Naturally they conduct experiments using physical science concepts such as force, friction, velocity, acceleration and momentum. In the example above students were developing the design of an inflatable safety device for cyclists. This was based on the idea that inflation would occur just before the bicycle tipped over but would remain deflated during normal use including cornering at speed. The need to sense and measure velocity and angle to some degree of accuracy was necessary. Clearly no shortage of mathematics or science here and this demanding project won first prize in a national competition.

A particular tricky question is just what makes the engineering component different from other forms of designing and making. Is it simply the use of science and mathematics? Or in tackling engineering style designing and making do students need particular knowledge, understanding and skills not required for other areas of designing and making?

Help these poor characters below figure out the relationships among science, technology, mathematics and engineering education!

Make your own illustration to describe these in general terms.

Describe an engineering activity and use your illustration to show the interactions that take place.

09 What are the relationships between science, technology, mathematics and engineering education?

Here are some designing and making activities. What potential does each have for using mathematics and science?

- A high-energy food bar for use on an expedition in a cold climate.
- A child's outdoor coat that is easy for the child to put on and take off.
- An alarm clock that comes on just as the sun rises.
- A pop-up greeting card with an audio message.
- Outdoor seating that can be folded up for easy storage.

The Royal Academy of Engineering (2000) defines engineering as *'the knowledge required, and the process applied, to conceive, design, make, build, operate, sustain, recycle or retire, something of significant technical content for a specified purpose; a concept, a model, a product, a device, a process, a system, a technology' (p. 5).*

Given this definition do you think any of the activities listed could be called engineering? Explain your reasons.

Pick a design activity with which you are familiar and identify and describe opportunities for students to engage in:

1. qualitative analysis (e.g., involving careful observation rather than mathematics);
2. quantitative analysis using age-appropriate math;
3. scientific investigation and the use of scientific concepts; and
4. designerly speculation.

Because technological design problems offer such a rich environment for revealing the connections among the STEM subjects, technology educators may play a key leadership role in interdisciplinary STEM teaching, primarily by taking advantage of the math and science opportunities inherent in technological problem-solving.
An interdisciplinary STEM approach

10 The "Interaction" report.
(David Barlex and James Pitt; © Engineering Council UK.)

Dov Kipperman and Mark Sanders

is fundamentally about seizing rather than avoiding the opportunities to incorporate math and science into the technological design problems used in technology education.

Part II: Interdisciplinary STEM approaches

If you wanted to connect the STEM disciplines, what do you think would be the best way to go about it? That is, what do you think the ideal working relationship among the science and technology and mathematics teachers would look like?

As noted earlier, interdisciplinary teaching approaches fall along a continuum, from those that involve relatively little collaboration between/among the teachers involved, to the full merger of content of two or more disciplines to create an entirely new course. Recently David Barlex and James Pitt used the experience of secondary schools in England to write the Interaction Report about the relationship between science and design & technology in the curriculum. They describe three possible interdisciplinary approaches that mirror those identified by Arthur Appleby and his colleagues:

coordination, collaboration, and integration.

The coordinated curriculum approach

The coordinated curriculum approach... *'involves teachers in each subject being au fait with the work carried out in the other and planning their curricula so that the timing of topics within each subject is sensitive to each other's needs'.* It is the least disruptive of these three approaches. In theory, each teacher continues to teach what and how they've taught in the past, simply re-scheduling when they teach these concepts/activities, so students encounter similar and complementary ideas concurrently in each of the participating subject areas. For example, a course in physical science might address magnetism and electromagnetism at the same time students in technology education design, construct and evaluate magnetic levitation vehicles powered by a small electrical motor. The math teacher might instruct students on algebraic relationships - in parallel with the idea of electromagnetic strength relative to the number of windings on a coil. Each teacher might reference this unit in the other two classes, highlighting the cross-curricular connections, without substantively altering their approach to the unit they're teaching. Curriculum frameworks such as the National Curriculum in the UK are a good first step in facilitating coordinated teaching, as they draw attention to what is being taught in each of the subject areas, including design & technology, science and math.

This 'framework' begins to make it possible to see the content connections among the subjects, which in turn allows teachers to coordinate their teaching.

The collaborative curriculum approach

Given typical scheduling constraints in education, it is problematic to completely coordinate teaching schedules in different subject areas. For that reason, it may be more plausible to work toward interdisciplinary collaboration rather than coordination. In the 'collaborative' model, STEM and other teachers might work together to identify an educational activity that has potential for cross-curricular connections. Technological design problems are ideal for this purpose, as they present ample opportunities to apply technological design principles, scientific inquiry and mathematical analysis.

Objectionable noise

Consider working on this reflective activity collaboratively with a science and/or math teacher in your school.

Part I
1. Review the article "The Noise Around Us" at this URL http://www. iteaconnect.org/Conference/PATT/PATT13/PATT13.pdf
2. Consider the noise and noise-related problems in your immediate environment (home, neighborhood, school).
3. What noises are there that are bothersome or potentially harmful to your hearing?
4. Is there anyone in your family with a hearing problem?
5. What are the social implications of noise and/or hearing problems?

Part II
Science concepts associated with sound include vibration, frequency, amplitude, wavelength and loudness. Math students learn to plot graphs of data to help us visualize patterns and relationships.
1. How might you develop this activity in a way that

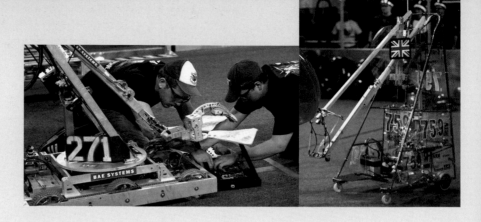

11 FIRST Robotics.
& (Photographs by
12 Adriana M. Groisman,
courtesy of FIRST.)

would engage students in the use of principles, concepts and processes from science and mathematics?

2. Develop a 'design brief' that challenges students to design solutions to objectionable 'noise problems' in their community (home/school/ neighbourhood).

3. Identify ways of structuring this activity in your particular school setting that would facilitate collaboration among technology education, science and math faculty.

The integrated curriculum approach

Barlex and Pitt describe the integrated curriculum approach as the merging together of multiple subjects - in this case, science, technology education, engineering and mathematics - into a single 'integrated' course. They consider this an inappropriate arrangement, because *'science and technology education are so significantly different from one another that to subsume them under*

a "science & technology" label is both illogical and highly dangerous to the education of pupils'.

How do you feel about the 'integrated curriculum' approach, in which science, design & technology and math would be taught as one subject? Can you envision such a course? If so, what would it look like? Would you be comfortable teaching such a course? If so, why, if not why not? What do you think it would take to enable you to feel comfortable teaching such a course? If such a course were developed and taught effectively - perhaps by a team comprised of all three (design & technology, science and math) teachers, do you think students would benefit more or less from this approach than from the coordinated or collaborative models described above?

13 14 15

13 FIRST Lego League.
- (Photographs by
15 Adriana M. Groisman,
   courtesy of FIRST.)

Extracurricular interdisciplinary STEM approaches

Educational infrastructures create significant challenges to those trying to make interdisciplinary connections during the regular school day. The remarkable global success of programs such as "Odyssey of the Mind" (founded by a technology teacher educator) and the "FIRST Robotics" and "FIRST Lego League" competitions (founded by an engineer) are testimony to the vast potential of interdisciplinary STEM activities. A great part of their success results from the fact that they are extracurricular activities. By moving these activities out of the conventional classroom/curriculum the following advantages, among others, may be realized:

- students and teachers may concentrate on the application of math, science and technological principles to 'authentic' problems, rather than focusing on a specific set of ideas to be formally assessed with 'high stakes tests';
- competitions often challenge/motivate students in a way conventional coursework rarely can;
- collaboration/social interaction - known to facilitate more effective learning - is more likely to occur, since students are not competing against one another, as is often the case in conventional classrooms;
- scheduling problems are a non-issue, since students are free to use math, science and technological principles and methods at any point in the process.

This is not to say extracurricular interdisciplinary STEM activities aren't without a downside. Drawbacks to the extracurricular approaches include the following:

- there are often significant expenses involved (e.g., "FIRST Robotics" is a very expensive program to operate);
- most extracurricular competitions are relatively short in duration (e.g., "FIRST Lego League" engages students actively for only about 6 weeks during each school year;
- they often engage only a small percentage of students (for example, the FIRST competitions typically involve fewer than 5% of students in participating schools; and
- most schools and students choose not to participate in extracurricular design activities.

How might some of the benefits associated with extracurricular interdisciplinary STEM activities be incorporated into the regular school day?

Part III: Pathways to interdisciplinary STEM connections

Interdisciplinary connections between technology education and other disciplines aren't likely to occur unless someone takes the initiative. If the idea of 'making connections' between design & technology and other school subjects interests you, don't wait for the others to come to you (you'll likely be waiting for a *long* time!). Rather, begin to promote this idea to fellow teachers and administrators in your school. Start small. See if you can begin a collaboration between science and design & technology, math and design & technology or math and science. If you can get that working, try to bring in the third subject area as well. Before you venture out with this idea, know that interdisciplinary teaching in state schools *is an attainable goal!* We know this, because many middle schools throughout the US - serving youngsters approximately 11-13 years of age - have managed to change their philosophy, infrastructure, curriculum and teaching practices to develop and implement highly successful interdisciplinary teaching. The National Middle School Association has publicly espoused interdisciplinary teaching since the 1980s. The 2002 version of their **"Position Statement on Curriculum Integration"** stipulates *'We must encourage middle level educators to push themselves beyond the conventional, separate subject format and to expand their use of integrated curriculum formats, ranging from intra-team planning of interdisciplinary units at a basic level to more advanced implementation of full-scale, integrative programs in democratic classrooms'.* Their position statement includes the following bold assertions:

1. *'The greater the degree of integration, the greater the benefits;'* and
2. *'Students in integrated curricula generally do as well or better on standardized tests than do those in conventional curricula'.*

Bringing administrators and collaborators on board

Successful transition to interdisciplinary teaching requires commitment from school administrators, participating teachers and the community. Administrators must be willing to provide a supportive environment, which includes planning time for teachers and flexibility with respect to class facilities scheduling. Design & technology educators should look for willing collaborators in the STEM disciplines, but may also reach out to the art, social studies and English teachers. Again, it's good to start small, and expand the partnership, expanding with cautious optimism as you gain confidence. 'Purposeful socializing' may help you get started. The cultures of the STEM disciplines are very different from one another. Differences between strangers are often perceived as barriers, but those same differences might be seen as learning opportunities among friends. So conversations are a very important first step.

Getting Started - Purposeful Socializing

Interdisciplinary teaching isn't going to occur as long as the participating educators (e.g., STEM faculty) are strangers to one another. Make a plan to have lunch with one or more prospective collaborators, with the idea that you'll chat informally about your teaching. If collaborative opportunities present themselves, consider experimenting with those opportunities. Start small and build from there.

Also, consider inviting a math and/or science teacher to observe your students as they present their designs to classmates…an ideal way for them to begin to see the possibilities for interdisciplinary connections.

As you talk with other STEM educators, it might be helpful to point out that one design problem can challenge all levels of students. For example, one student might approach a design problem requiring volume estimation by using water displacement to arrive at an estimate; another might resort to a 3D CAD program for this, and a third might turn to calculus. Alternative approaches like these are consistent with contemporary ideas about mathematics teaching.

In conclusion

Karen Zuga observed in 1996 in the book "Science-technology-society as reform in Science" 'Communities of technology and science educators have been passing as two ships pass silently in the night without speaking to each other about their relationships' (p. 227).

This is a sad but true reflection on the state of interdisciplinarity. Despite the patently obvious relationships among the STEM disciplines beyond the walls of the school, STEM educators have become estranged from one another. The differing interests and dispositions of these individuals led them to four distinctly different directions, yetthere are undoubtedly grounds for some forms of working together. Political and economic realities make it easier to work in isolation than in collaboration, yet we are forced to ask: Would STEM education be significantly better if approached collaboratively rather than competitively? Would the whole be greater than the sum of its parts? Would students and teachers benefit in the long run? Would the relatively unproven claims of STEM education reformers be substantiated if the experiment were carried out to its logical conclusion?

Vera John Steiner has written at length about the issues facing those who wish to work in an interdisciplinary way in her book "Creative Collaboration".

Vera argues that it will require a wide range of partnerships over a prolonged period of committed activity. These partnerships thrive on dialogue, risk-taking and a shared vision. These partnerships will need a high level of support. The work of these partnerships will be highly demanding but essential. Collaboration in creating an interdisciplinary STEM curriculum will be an emotional as well as an intellectual process. Successful collaboration always involves trust and this has to be earned by those working together. Without trust it is not possible to reveal and overcome the insecurities and uncertainties that underpin all creative endeavours. The decrease in personal autonomy that accompanies close collaboration can best be achieved in an environment of trust where people come to value each other's contribution that expands their own resources. To achieve this, those working in collaborative STEM endeavours will need to take the bold step of becoming dependent on one another. This dependence is not a sign of weakness, but of strength. It is a dependence that will allow individuals to make substantial professional growth through partnership. Above all it is a dignified interdependence through which those working together have mutual respect and can forge achievements far beyond their individual, isolated capacities.

So we urge you **MIND (NOT) THE GAP... TAKE THE RISK!**

References

American Association for the Advancement of Science (AAAS) (1993). "Benchmarks for science literacy". New York: Oxford University Press. See also http://www.project2061.org/

Applebee, A., Burroughs, R., and Cruz, G. (2000). 'Case studies of interdisciplinary instruction'. In S. Wineburg & P. Grossman (Eds.). "Interdisciplinary Curriculum: Challenges to Implementation". New York: Teachers College Press.

Barlex, D. (2005). "Becoming an Engineering College: A report describing emerging and developing good practice". London: Specialist Schools Trust.

Barlex, D. & Pitt, J. (2000). "Interaction: A report for the Engineering Council on the relationship between Science and Design and Technology in the secondary school curriculum". London: Engineering Council.

Barlex, D., Chapman, C. & Lewis, T. (2007). 'Investigating interaction between science and design & technology (D&T) in the secondary school - a case study approach'. "Research in Science & Technological Education". 25, 37-58.

Boyer, E. L. (1983). "High school: A report on secondary education in America". New York: Harper Colophon.

International Technology Education Association (2000), "Standards for technological literacy: Content for the study of technology", Reston, VA: International Technology Education Association.

Hill, A. M. & Smith, H. A. (2005). 'Research in purpose and value for the study of technology in secondary schools: A theory of authentic learning'. "International Journal of Technology and Design Education". 15, 19-32.

John-Steiner, V. (2000). "Creative collaboration". New York: Oxford University Press.

Loepp, F. (1999). 'Models of Curriculum Integration'. "The Journal of Technology Studies". Fall issue. Retrieved January 29, 2007 from this URL: http://scholar.lib.vt.edu/ejournals/JOTS/Summer-Fall-1999/PDF/Loepp.pdf

Ministry of Education, Culture, and Sport, Science and Technology (1994). "Tomorrow '98: Promoting science, technology and computer studies". Jerusalem: Science and Technology Division, State of Israel.

Ministry of Education, Culture, and Sport, Science and Technology (1996). "Israeli National Curriculum for Science and Technology". Jerusalem: Science and Technology Division, State of Israel.

National Council of Teachers of Mathematics (1989). "Curriculum and evaluation standards for school mathematics". Reston, VA: National Council of Teachers of Mathematics.

National Middle School Association (2002). "NMSA position statement on curriculum integration". Retrieved January 29, 2007 from this URL: http://www.nmsa.org/AboutNMSA/PositionStatements/CurriculumIntegration/tabid/282/Default.aspx

National Research Council (1994). "National science education standards". Washington, DC: National Academy Press.

National Research Council (U. S.) Committee on Learning Research and Educational Practice, National Research Council (2000). "How people learn". Washington DC: National Academy Press.

Qualifications and Curriculum Authority (2007). "Design and technology programme of study: ks3". Full text available at: http://curriculum.qca.org.uk/subjects accessed on 17.10.07.

Royal Academy of Engineering (2000). "The Universe of Engineering - A UK perspective". London: Royal Academy of Engineering.

Williams, J. (2002). "Processes of Science and Technology: A Rationale for Cooperation or Separation" Paper available from the Proceedings of the PATT 12 Conference 'Technology Education in the Curriculum: Relationship With Other Subjects'. Proceedings available at this URL: http://www.iteaconnect.org/Conference/PATT/PATT12/PATT12.pdf

Zuga, K. (1996) in Yager, R. (Ed.), "Science - technology - society as reform in Science". New York: New York Press.

Gender & pedagogy

Patricia Murphy

Patricia Murphy is professor in
Education (Pedagogy and
Assessment) in the Faculty
of Education and Language Studies
at the Open University, England.
She writes postgraduate courses and
supervises in the areas of curriculum,
learning and assessment generally
and science and technology
specifically. Patricia has a background
in research in assessment and
effective teaching and learning
particularly in relation to equity
and gender and has directed
numerous funded research projects
examining curriculum innovations
in science and technology education
in primary and secondary schools.
She has published widely
across these areas.

Gender & pedagogy
Patricia Murphy

Introduction

It is claimed that design & technology in the National Curriculum for England and Wales makes a unique contribution to the development of all young people by preparing them to participate in the rapidly changing technologies of the futures. The national curriculum made design & technology compulsory for all five - sixteen year olds; this extended access to primary children and to pupils, post fourteen. However, post fourteen pupil choices remained in terms of which aspect of the subject students could study. Look at the table below, which shows entry trends across design & technology subjects for boys and girls. Is this familiar to you and is it replicated in your educational context? Clearly the extent to which we prepare pupils to participate in future technologies varies considerably depending on whether they are a male or female.

Subject	2002		2003		2004	
	Male	Female	Male	Female	Male	Female
Electronics	18	2	17.8	1.5	17.1	1.4
Food technology	27	75	28.9	74.9	28.9	74.1
Graphics	61	47	59.5	45.9	57.5	44.4
Resistant materials	89	27	87.8	24	85.9	21.3
Systems control	13	1	13.5	1.1	12.5	1.1
Textiles technology	2	46	1.6	48.5	1.7	50.8
Other D&T	5	3	9	6.7	11.4	8.1

01   01 Entry by thousands of male and female students in design & technology GCSE subjects. (Source: www.dfes.gov.uk/rsgateway)

Yolande Brooks (2003) commenting on pupils' design & technology option choices observed that *'there are still many areas of life where boys will be boys and girls will be girls'* (p. 4). How you respond to this comment could be *'This is just what pupils are like'*. Or you might believe that pupils' choices reflect something about the subjects or something about how we, and others, represent the subjects to pupils. Sue Eaton (2003) observed that the use of CAD/CAM in textile product courses for 11-14 year olds encouraged boys to take the subject further as it showed that it *'was not a "posy" subject but one which uses machinery and precision to a strong degree'* (p. 2). Do you associate the use of machinery and precision with things that boys do particularly well

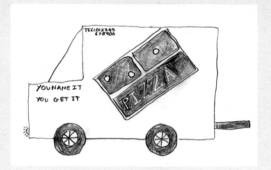

02   03

02 Examples of girls'
-    (aged 10 - 11)
03 vehicle designs.

and like, as opposed to girls? Sue also noted that pupils were aware that *'most famous dress designers are men'*, and the small number of boys choosing to study textiles were influenced by career aspirations.

There is significant gender stereotyping in students' career choices evident in the different vocational pathways taken by girls and boys. Angela Roger and Jill Duffield (2000) identified two influences underlying girls' persistent opting out of science and technology courses: students' view of themselves and future possibilities; and career awareness. They described the relationship between self-concept and career awareness as the *'interaction between the way pupils see themselves and the opportunities they perceive are open to them'* (p. 374). Self-concept shapes the attitudes to subjects of boys and girls alike and is a predictor of subject choices.

Do you in your choice of tasks and in talking about practices tend to reinforce traditional views of how technology is used in the workplace? In your mind's eye who are the successful pupils in your subject, are they typically boys or girls? Why do you think that might be?

Consider these quotes from teachers about their views of what girls and boys are like in relation to design & technology.
- *'Electronics in the end isn't a girls' thing.'*
- *'You have your high technological boy... he's a very technological kiddo and he is able to work at very high level, logical, technical, mathematics etc. The girls are more artistic in their approach. They're far more quality-conscious than the boys.'*
- *'The lads who are really good scientists, mathematicians, they tend to go for the electronics side of it.'*
- *'They're [girls] neat about what they do. Their attention to detail is often better than the boys, so the chances of their products working are great.'*
(Murphy, 2006, p. 225)

How did you react to the quotes? Are girls innately more artistic than boys and is this the case for all girls? Are boys logical and therefore does it follow that girls are illogical? If you think of any common myths about gender they typically treat all males and all females as the same. One teacher commenting about primary girls' and boys' designs observed, *'the boys will want to make it move and the girls will colour it'*. Have a look at the initial drawings of Y6 pupils in the illustrations above; what do you notice about them?

Look at the purposes the designs serve. The girls' examples are for transporting food, people and animals whereas the boys

04
05 06

04 Examples of boys'
- (aged 10 - 11)
06 vehicle designs.

Gender & pedagogy   Patricia Murphy

are for getting places fast, safely or for defence. Brunner, Bennett and Honey (2000) reported similar findings and described girls' vehicles as household helpers or improvements to technologies that solved real life problems. Boys' vehicles were characterised as having the capacity to take them wherever they wanted to go instantly. Are you aware of differences in girls' and boys' approaches to designing and making? How would you characterise these differences? How do you explain them? To begin to unpack why gender differences emerge in what teachers say, and what pupils do, you need to consider how thinking about gender and learning has developed.

Understanding learning and gender

Talking about the way that 'boys' and 'girls' are reduces gender to biological sex, i.e. a fixed attribute of an individual. It implies that as groups, females and males experience the world in similar ways. However, any view that assumes meanings and experiences are stable across populations of people is inconsistent with thinking about how human understanding develops. Susan Greenfield, the neuroscientist, describes how understanding of the world develops through a process of associations between characteristics of objects, people and experience. These associations lead to objects and people gradually acquiring *'ever more eccentric and intense degrees of significance'*

(Greenfield, 2000, p. 52).
Several ideas follow from this:
• people and events acquire differential degrees of importance for individuals;
• the world as we experience it is personal; it is what we make of it;
• meaning is not pre-existing, rather being a human is to engage constantly in a process of negotiation of meaning.

If we think of learning as a process of meaning-making then teaching is not a simple process of transmission (input) and reception (output) mediated only by the innate characteristics of the pupils. The personal way of knowing described by Greenfield determines our interpretations of, and responses to, new situations. Teaching and learning is a dynamic process; meanings shift and evolve as activity develops and evolves. Think about some recent lessons, each represents a new situation where new meanings have to be created between you and your pupils as they engage in activity with the tools made available. These tools include the physical equipment and the ways of acting, talking and being, that are valued - in the subject. Your practices cue what it is appropriate to do, say and produce in the design & technology setting and therefore have a major influence on the meanings that pupils create. Similarly what pupils bring into learning situations influences what is available for them to learn. This includes how pupils see themselves in relation to the subject, both in the present and in the future.

Jean Lave and Etienne Wenger describe how, in this view, learning and knowing is better understood as relations among people in activity: *'in, with and arising from the socially and culturally structured world'* (Lave and Wenger, 1991, p. 51). Gender is central to the way life is organised and construed and is embedded in our thinking and routines. It is, therefore, a significant influence on the process of learning both in terms of how you represent your subject and who can do it and how pupils feel positioned in relation to it. So how does this influence operate? In trying to represent masculinity and femininity we tend to place them in opposition; what one is the other is not, and this becomes part of what we take to be 'normal', the common sense way of understanding the world.

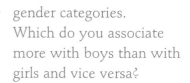

Look at the following words that teachers used in interviews to describe girls and boys:
- independent/dependent,
- conformist/risk-takers,
- diligent/slapdash,
- neat/careless,
- circumspect/opinionated,
- motivated/disaffected.

These too work on oppositions and represent gender categories. Which do you associate more with boys than with girls and vice versa?

Putting these words together creates identities that we extend to our pupils that are gendered and constrained. We all know opinionated girls and motivated boys so can challenge these stereotypes. How often though do we allow that girls can be risk-takers and what impact might that have on what they feel able to do in design & technology?

Through our language we talk into being the categorisations we use to identify what it is to be masculine and what it is to be feminine. These ways of representing gender change over time and continue to be influenced by the vestiges of previous world views. Gender is, therefore, better understood as a social construction, which sets up expectations of what it is to be identifiably masculine or feminine that are more or less stable factors of a culture. Children are aware of the need to be identifiably male or female and locate themselves within and through these social gender categories as they learn to make sense of the world and of themselves. Bronwyn Davies (2003) talks of children's need to *'get it right'* and to do this students have to know the ways in which cultural practices can be varied. Gender is not, therefore, a static identity but a learned capacity of pupils to provide and read depictions of masculinity and femininity

(McDermott, 1996, citing Goffman).

> Think of a girl and a boy as they engage in different aspects of design & technology that are typical of their experience from age 11-14. Imagine them entering a textiles classroom and then a resistant materials workshop. How might they read gender in these settings?
> In which setting would you anticipate they each would feel a greater sense of belonging and therefore a better chance of 'getting it right'?

Working with gender

Design & technology - a masculine domain?

The notion of the living 'female' universe to be nurtured and protected emerged in Greek and early pagan philosophies. In the nurturing organic framework those who mined mother earth were portrayed as uncivilised brutes. This imagery was no longer tenable when the industrial revolution in the 18th and 19th centuries necessitated unprecedented access to the earth's resources and the means to shape them. To sanction this change in societal behaviours and the right of 'man' to have dominion over the earth required a shift in the language. Joan Rothschild (1983) describes how the emerging discourse, which sanctioned technological activity, placed aesthetics in opposition to the technical and characterised femininity as passive and masculinity as dynamic. The female role was to stabilise by holding, protecting and preserving. Males were portrayed as the manipulators, the doers assaulting nature and *'the inventor, the user, the thinker about and reactor to technology'* was male (1983 xix). In this way ideas about gender and ideas about technology became associated in industrial society.

'They [society] all agreed that there was some natural and necessary connection between working with your hands, being skilled, being independent, and being a good man.'
(Schwartz Cowan, 1997, p. 218).

This construction of masculinity affected the practice of technology; men could invent machines and women and children could operate them. However, when there was a struggle to maintain control over access to machinery, men appropriated skilled work and 'women's work' was restricted to the unskilled and routinised (Wajcman, 1991). Consequently 'technical competence' was seen as integral to masculinities and women were positioned as the technically incompetent.

The design & technology curriculum specification for England and Wales drew together subjects that had deeply gendered histories, which reflected these practices. The two main contributors were craft, design and technology (CDT) and home economics (HE) which traditionally were taught to boys and girls as separate groups. HE was to train girls into the domestic roles they were destined for. CDT, which was a subject taught to boys, drew on the workshop skills traditionally associated with male working class occupations and crafts.

Both subjects tended to be aimed at non-academic students and were viewed as lower status than academic subjects like science and maths. This historical legacy is important as it can continue to influence how subjects are represented and how children relate to technical activity.

" Excerpt 1 - the boys only group

Teacher: The idea of joining materials together goes way back. Man held together spears, joined flint to doweling with twine. Now we use more sophisticated joins. If you want a bridge to go over a river you need joins that are strong and permanent, or the surface of a road, you can't have something temporary. Can you give some examples of joins that can be taken apart?
Boy 1: Nut and bolt.
Boy 2: Nail.
Boy 3: Staples.
Teacher: What about permanent?
Boy 4: Welding.
Teacher: Welding makes one piece, you can't unjoin it.
Boy 5: Glue

A boy started to talk about rafts and how they were joined.

Teacher: In the high seas you might want your raft to be springy and flexible so that it does not come to harm…That kind of join goes back possibly 3000 years.

The teacher explained that early man learned the technique of splitting logs to make wedges and sketched a 3D drawing of two wooden batons overlapping and bound and wrote string, leather, bark next to it. The boys copied the sketch into their books. One boy observed that the Tudors and Victorians probably would have used wedge joins.

Teacher: The Tudors probably would have, because most of their roofs were thatch, but by the time we get to the Victorians most of the roofs were not. They used nails. The teacher sketched a nail with a right angle in it.

Teacher: A blacksmith would have made that. Why was it shaped like that?
Boy: It's a tent peg?
Teacher: Right area. Think about the ground and a house.

The teacher referred to metal nails used in the Iron Age and the mass produced ones of today then drew a French nail.

Teacher: …could be bought in B&Q and a French nail is made of wire. Imagine a machine hits the top of the nail, it spreads out. The technique is called 'upsetting'.
Boy: Whacking
Teacher: Yes, it is basically whacking. We don't use much iron these days but an alloy of iron and carbon, steel, makes the metal harder.

The teacher went on to refer to several male inventors and inventions such as the Philips screw, etc., and discussed glue and how it was initially made from animal gut. He talked at length about the different chemicals used to make adhesives. "

Look at the excerpts and observations below, from the beginning of two resistant materials lessons to introduce pupils to a range of joins made from different materials. The teacher was trained as a CDT teacher and the pupils were in Y9 (aged 13-14) and taught in single-sex groups although the school was co-educational.

Gender & pedagogy Patricia Murphy

Excerpt 2 – the girls only group

Teacher: The posh name for glue is adhesive. Wood is a traditional material.
It is old-fashioned. There are two things to worry about with wood. There are frames and carcasses. An example of a frame is what you are resting on at the moment, a table. What do you think a carcass is?

He spelt out the word carcass on the board.

Girl 1: A box.
Teacher: Yes.
Girl 2: What about a chest?
Teacher: Yes a chest of drawers would be a very good example. Notice when I start my drawing I start a little further down from the top.

He sketched a 3D drawing of a table and a carcass.

Teacher: The trouble is you have to hold that together with something [points to a join in the drawing] What would you use?
Girl 3: Glue.
Teacher: Yes...I know you are not very happy with 3D drawings I suggest you do it lightly [to erase mistakes more readily].

As the lesson went on the teacher referred to other domestic items such as shelves, mirror frames and jewellery boxes. He talked of the girls doing something only if they 'couldn't persuade your husband to fix it'.

Another time in discussing a particular joint he commented:
Teacher: Have you seen your Dad doing that?

He continued to comment about the girls and their drawing skills:
Teacher: If you think you can handle the drawing...I would like to think you could draw...

He often took over the drawing for some pupils.

(See Ivinson and Murphy, 2007)

These two excerpts are very different. Notice how with the 'boys' group it is assumed that knowledge is shared; with the 'girls' the opposite is the case. Is there a possibility that this could happen in your practice or that of your colleagues?

The teacher covered a wider range of materials with the boys and assumed they could cope with scientific information, which he excluded from the girls' lesson. Look at the historical references, which gave the boys a context to understand the link between joins and structures over time. This along with the reference to male inventors gave them both a sense of history and an identity they could associate with. For the girls they are the passive users of technology not the doers. Their role was to look after home furnishings. The teacher saw his subject as troublesome for the girls. In his practice he acted as though drawing skills was something girls were not capable of achieving, i.e. an innate deficiency. Hence rather than seeing the need to open up practice to enable the girls' participation by modelling drawing he did the drawing for them or let them flounder.

Do you, in linking your lessons to technological action in the world, represent the achievements and roles of both males and females? Do you consider that girls or boys might feel a different sense of belonging in your subject and do you attempt to change your practice to give them access?

Does this seem an extreme example exacerbated by the separation of girls and boys and the teacher's background? Another teacher, in the same school teaching the same age pupils, who was more recently trained, made a point of situating resistant materials in the domestic realm for both boys and girls. He made a very successful change in his practice to engage girls with the machinery. The girls talked of being *'trusted to use the machinery'* and *'knowing how to work it [the machine]'*. This teacher opened up access to the tools of the subject, extending girls' agency, i.e. the realised capacity to act upon their world (Holland et al., 1998). However, this same teacher made no such change in the 'all boys' group, assuming boys were not only competent, but felt competent, to participate. Yet as one boy, who was anxious to drop the subject, commented: *'I am just afraid of hurting myself'*. The teacher's practice confronted this boy with an identity he did not share but to ask for help would reveal this.

Try observing how different pupils engage with activities and the equipment routinely used in your subject.

> What differences between boys and between girls did you notice and what insights does this give you into what they feel able to do?

Look at the table below and the pass rates for the GCSE subjects in 2005.

GCSE D&T subject	Entry in thousands		% achieving A*- C grades of students attempting the subject	
	Male	Female	Male	Female
Electronic products	15.9	1.1	58	73
Food technology	27.2	66.7	44	63
Graphic products	49.2	37.4	47	65
Resistant materials	80.4	18.0	49	65
Systems control	11.1	0.9	57	76
Textiles technology	1.6	46.6	37	69
Other D&T	13.3	8.5	51	68

07 % male and females at the end of KS4 gaining a pass or higher (A*- C) by subject in 2005.
(Source: www.dfes.gov.uk/rsgateway)

This table shows that many girls and boys achieve well across the subjects in design & technology, which challenges assumptions about incompetence or innate differences, attributed either to girls or to boys. Where there is a major imbalance between girls' and boys' entry the minority group is considered to be the more highly selected i.e. representing more able and committed pupils. It is, therefore, expected that their performance would be higher than the majority group. The figures indicate that this may be the case with girls but not for those boys choosing to study textiles and food technology.

What pupils pay attention to

Children learn what is important for them to pay attention to in managing a gender identity, and what is not, and from an early age are observed to engage in different activities and roles even when using the same resource. As they learn from what they do real differences emerge in what they become familiar with, and in what they understand is purposeful activity. For example when playing with construction kits young boys were observed to focus on making structures that moved whereas girls were more likely to use structures as part of their social play. These differences in what girls and boys tend to pay attention to influence what they focus on in design & technology tasks. Girls' concern with the social context dominates their designs and they are more likely than boys to consider aesthetics and user needs. Boys are more likely to include detail about mechanisms and structures focusing on the physical aspect of needs and wants. This can result in certain girls facing complex problems and solutions that teachers do not anticipate in the support and resources they make available.

In a study involving secondary pupils given the opportunity to generate authentic designs it tended to be girls who situated their response in the context of the person's needs and the circumstances in which the product would be used. Moisture sensors were used to create a bath alarm for a grandmother and housed in a water drop shape. A rain alarm for a mother's wash line was in a sock-shaped housing (Murphy 1999). If you reconsider the drawings on pages 238 and 239 you can see this concern with people and the social world in the girls' examples. Also if you remind yourself of the way technology became associated with gender (noted on page 238) notice how what boys and girls have learned to pay attention to reflects very closely the way that masculinity and femininity, in relation to technology, was characterised.

'Design and make' activities often start with a brainstorm of needs and wants. The needs and wants that pupils identify reflect their values and commitments, and this is influenced by gender. The needs and wants that emerge define the problem space

in which pupils work on their design and make skills. Pupils' commitments, therefore, influence the learning opportunities available to them. For example in a study that evaluated the Nuffield Primary Design & Technology resources for teachers (Barlex, 2001) one activity had children designing a bus. Most boys began their making task with the moving parts whereas girls generally focused on the interior features for the passengers and the exterior appearance. At the end many girls' buses looked like buses but lacked wheels or had rather inefficient wheels. Many boys' buses looked like moving cardboard boxes (Murphy and Davidson, 1997). Leonie Rennie (2003) working with elementary pupils making pirate boats also noted this effect referring to the different levels of construction skills as well as differences in how the boats were designed and furnished. Only boys made boats from wood and girls made all the boats that were less well constructed. It was perhaps not surprising that the national Assessment of Performance Unit's survey of 15 year olds in design & technology found that girls did better than boys as a group on tasks that involved identifying underlying issues and empathising with users' needs. Boys did somewhat better in generating ideas and in modelling working solutions (Kimbell et al., 1991).

Pupils and teachers are often unaware of how gender influences learning outcomes in design & technology.

> Why not look at initial design ideas to see what pupils appear to prioritise? Or use peer review at the initial design stage to engage pupils in reflecting on the nature of their priorities in relation to physical, social, and emotional and market needs before they commit to their design solution.

Product analysis tasks involving a range of products can also open up pupils' thinking about different emphases to meet different needs.

Pupils' perceptions of relevance

The tendency for girls to focus on appearance and boys to consider structures first is evident in the emphasis they give to design and to making in their design & technology activities. In a study with 13-14 year-old pupils (Ivinson and Murphy, 2007) one activity observed was to design and make a vehicle with four wheels to carry a kilogram weight five metres. All the boys worked first on the structure to meet the criteria of stability, strength and movement. Appearance was a secondary consideration: *'it's the capability of the designs that's key'*. The girls gave priority to presentation and appearance so one chose to

work with plastic and used vacuum-forming. Another girl, Julie, aware that the value she placed on design might prevent her meeting the brief was prepared to take the risk: *'I'm just hoping that the design mark is really good and it will make the five metres'*. Another pupil was well aware of the gendered nature of design & technology practices describing them as things *'girls don't normally do'* but had an interest in pursuing her study of resistant materials in spite of this.

'When they [girls] grow up they're just beauticians or working on computers and all things like that and when something goes wrong, like, my Mum, she can never do [fix] it...When I get older I just want to be able to do it all myself instead of relying on everyone else.'

For the teacher the skills acquired through the design and making of artefacts such as a model car have an obvious relevance to life. In interview he described how measurement in relation to where to drill the holes for the model car axles could be linked to the context of putting up a shelf and buying a microwave to fit a given space. Creating joins was another feature of the activity and for the teacher this knowledge would enable pupils to *'do those little jobs around the house'*. For Julie the importance of the making for her learning was not clear, as the teacher did not articulate it. Nor could the teacher know, unless he spoke with the girls, that their design decisions were constraining their opportunities to develop the making skills he valued. The teacher could

> **Girl:** How do you put the times?
> **Teacher:** Where would you put the three waits?
> **Girl:** Three waits?
> **Teacher:** Yes, there are three of them.
> **Girl:** What, large?
> **Teacher:** Well, one of the three ones will be determined, say, by road conditions or by the amount of traffic. You've pressed the button; this automatic would link; amber appears; so, wait there then.
>
> **Girl:** Where?
> **Teacher:** There's a timed wait. You put it in between the commands. So, you just put a little arrow there, and say: here we'll wait. We don't know how long the wait is at the moment, but there is a specific wait time band between you pressing the button and the system operating, and there are two more. It might be a wide road. Say, a wide road?
> **Girl:** Longer for an old person.

make quite inaccurate judgements about pupils' achievements and capabilities without access to what they prioritise.

The relevance of what it is possible to learn through design & technology activities cannot be assumed. I have pointed out how boys and girls become familiar with different aspects of their environment and what they consider relevant follows from these differences in experience. Pupils need teachers' explicit help to make bridges to what is unfamiliar to them in design & technology subjects so that they can understand their relevance. If this had happened with Julie and the other girls you could imagine that they might have made very different design decisions.

In many interventions to change participation for girls and boys products are selected that we know girls and/or boys find relevant and therefore engaging. For example, Yolande Brookes (2003) reported on a school that was encouraging girls in their study of systems & control by focusing on textile products such as children's play mats. An emphasis on industrial applications is often used to engage boys. This is a useful short-term strategy but can reinforce the influence of gender rather than challenging it in the long term. What is important is to use tasks that are authentic and relate to the real world but to provide bridges where you anticipate girls and boys may lack relevant experience. This may be more likely for boys in food

and textiles and for girls in systems & control and resistant materials. You can only find this out though if you ask pupils about what they perceive to be of interest and relevance in the activities you select or why they may lack this in their view.

In a study of electronics in schools a teacher who was very successful in engaging girls used a task of programming a pelican crossing with Y10 pupils. The design decisions involved giving thought to the context of use and to the users. The teacher in setting up the task made continual references to where PICs might have been experienced by pupils. Look at the excerpt above and how the teacher bridged between the task and the pupil's experience to create and maintain relevance in learning.

Ways of working

Pupils value having autonomy and responsibility for their own learning and this is an essential aspect of pedagogy that engages girls and boys. In many studies differences in how boys and girls work have, however, been noted. Girls state a preference for working together and boys for working alone.

Think about the way teachers characterised boys and girls as independent/dependent.

Teacher: Yes, for granny pushing a trolley, easy to hit.
Girl: We put that in there?
Teacher: OK, when the people are crossing. It goes, yes, there.
Girl: Wait's put in it or...?
Teacher: Yes, put a wait there. OK, we're stopping the traffic here...What are the people doing? They're going. The wait light is on, so you actually have to tell them to wait all the time...
(Murphy et al., 2004)

Notice how the teacher emphasises physical issues to do with traffic and road conditions as well as the people who might be using the crossing. Another important feature of his practice that pupils commented on was the support he gave them to be autonomous and make decisions for themselves.

Do you consider collaboration as indicating dependency? Do you associate independence in working with ability and intellectual flair? Some teachers discourage collaborative work in design & technology as they see it as an opportunity for students to 'freewheel'. Have you noticed which pupils tend to engage in discussion and which tend to work alone?

Girls are described as facilitators giving lots of support to others in discussing strengths and weaknesses in designs. Girls are more likely to do this than boys even when they are working on individual products as they often talk out loud their problems and potential solutions keeping track of their own and others' designs and product issues. We described how learning was a process of negotiating meaning. Collaboration with peers provides pupils with alternative ways of seeing the world and thinking about it. Successful collaboration involves verbally explicit planning, negotiation about alternatives, equitable involvement in shared decision-making and opportunities to resolve conflict through dialogue. The ability to negotiate the shared endeavour in activities is a fundamental prerequisite of participation and collaboration is key to this. Some boys may however struggle to see the value in collaborating and need support to engage in it effectively. One problem for girls is if their collaborative approach is interpreted as them being less able or deficit.

The "Young Foresight" (Barlex, 2002) approach to designing uses group work, as a means of engaging pupils in authentic practices and as a means for learning. It provides guidance about group tasks and support that enable collaboration. Both boys and girls in the evaluation of "Young Foresight" valued the opportunity to collaborate: *'It works better when we're in groups, more ideas than if you work as an individual. You can see things from different perspectives'*. Industrial mentors supported teachers in enabling collaboration: *'the other thing we teach them is to work as a team. At the end of the day it's not just one person sitting there with all the ideas. There is a huge team process going on and they have to learn to work with other projects, make decisions, sort problems, all those sort of things'*.

Another difference in ways of working is that girls appear more willing to consult the teacher whilst for some boys this is the last resort. However how teachers respond to girls seeking help can limit their learning.

For example some teachers, instead of modelling possible solutions and offering alternatives, identify the problem and solve it without discussion, removing girls' independence and undermining their agency. Some boys, as we have noted, who feel unable to ask for help, either from other boys or the teacher, struggle and often fail to progress. To encourage these boys there needs to be a shift in emphasis on to the learning process away from the product and value given to learning how things work *'even if you don't get it right'*.

Summary

Technological practices and design & technology subjects have a deeply gendered history and the discourses that relate gender and technological activity reflect this.
If we view gender as a social construction that emerges as pupils commit to meanings and positions as they participate in activities in subject contexts then we can change its influence on pupils. The difficulty is that much of its effects are invisible to both teachers and pupils. The discussion has shown how gender can emerge in teachers' practices and in pupils' expectations of themselves in relation to the subject. What teachers do can alter how pupils are positioned in relation to design & technology subjects and extend to them an identity of participation and belonging. To achieve this, attention has to be paid to:

- how we talk about subjects and who is included and excluded by this;
- the assumptions we hold about what girls and boys can do;
- what tasks are selected and how the relevance of what they offer pupils and their learning is made explicit;
- treating girls and boys as individuals and not homogeneous groups;
- what girls and boys bring to their design & technology lessons, i.e. their learned priorities and ways of working;
- strategies that make visible to pupils their commitments and the consequences of these for their design decisions and solutions and therefore what is available for them to learn;
- the support needed for pupils to develop new learning habits;
- extending subjects to include a broader view of technological practices which embrace a wider future-orientated conception of technological activity and careers.

References

Barlex, D. (2002). 'Young Foresight. Shaping things to Come', London: Software Production Enterprises. Included in the Key Stage 3 Strategy resources, see also this URL: www.youngforesight.org

Barlex, D. (2001), 'Primary Solutions in Design and Technology'. Nuffield/DATA, London, www.primarydandt.org.uk

Brooks, Y. (2003). 'Breaking with tradition'. In "Modus". 3, (pp. 4-5).

Brunner, C., Bennett, D. T. & Honey M. (2000). 'Girl games and technological desire'. In R. Pea (Ed.), "The Jossey-Bass Reader on Technology and Learning". San Francisco: Jossey-Bass Inc.

Davies, B. (2003). "Shards of Glass: Children Reading and Writing beyond Gendered Identities". Cresskill, NJ: Hampton Press Inc.

Eaton, S. (2003). 'Crossing the Barriers, Why do boys take GCSE textiles?'. "Modus". 3, 2-3.

Greenfield, S. (2000). "The private life of the brain". London: Penguin Books Ltd.

Holland, D., Lachicotte Jr, W., Skinner, D. & Cain, C. (1998). "Identity and Agency in Cultural Worlds". Cambridge, MA: Harvard University Press.

Ivinson, G. & Murphy, P. (2007). "Rethinking Single Sex Teaching". Buckingham: Open University.

Kimbell, R., Stables, K., Wheeler, T., Wosniak, A. & Kelly, V. (1991). "The assessment of performance in design and technology". London: Schools Examinations and Assessment Council.

Lave, J. and Wenger, E. (1991). "Situated learning: Legitimate peripheral participation". Cambridge: Cambridge University Press.

McDermott, R. P. (1996). 'The acquisition of a child by a learning disability'. In S. Chaiklin & J. Lave. (Eds.). "Understanding practice - Perspectives on activity and context". Cambridge: Cambridge University Press.

Murphy, P. (1999). 'Supporting collaborative learning: a gender dimension'. In P. Murphy (Ed.). "Learners, Learning and Assessment". London: Paul Chapman Publishing Ltd.

Murphy, P. (2006). 'Gender and Technology: Gender Mediation in School Knowledge Construction'. In J. Dakers, (Ed.). "Defining Technological Literacy Towards an epistemological framework". New York: Palgrave Macmillan.

Murphy, P. & Davidson M. (1997). "Evaluation: First phase, Nuffield Design and Technology in the primary curriculum". London: Nuffield Foundation and The Open University.

Murphy, P., McCormick, R., Lunn, S., Davidson, M. & Jones, H. (2004). "Evaluation of the Promotion of Electronics in Schools Regional Pilot: Final Report of the Evaluation". London: The Department of Trade and Industry and the Open University.

Rennie, L. J. (2003). 'Pirates can be male or female: investigating gender-inclusivity in a years 2/3 classroom'. "Research in Science Education". 33, 515-528.

Roger, A. & Duffield, J. (2000). 'Factors underlying persistent gendered option choices in school science and technology in Scotland'. "Gender and Education". 12. (3), 367-383.

Rothschild, J. (1983). "Machina Ex Dea", New York: Pergamon Press.

Schwartz Cowan, R. (1997). "A Social History of American Technology". Oxford: Oxford University Press.

Wajcman, J. (1991). "Feminism confronts technology". Pennsylvania: The Pennsylvania State University Press.

Implicit theories & pedagogy

Wendy Dow

Wendy Dow is a lecturer in Educational Studies at the University of Glasgow. Her main research interests are the effect of implicit theories on pedagogy and learning. She has worked collaboratively on a range of projects in design & technology education and has carried out research in a number of areas pertaining to the field. She has acted as a consultant to the European Commission on a project to increase interest in mathematics, science and technology across Europe.

Implicit theories & pedagogy

Wendy Dow

What are implicit theories?

In the cartoon above, Calvin has worked out an important aspect of life - that what people say and how they actually feel deep down doesn't always correspond. This is also reflected in many common sayings in our culture.

'Practise what you preach!' 'Actions speak louder than words.' 'He talks a good game.'

How many times have you heard this kind of thing said - or said it yourself? And there are many other similar sayings that you will be able to think of that suggest that very often what people do or say does not match what they actually think or feel at a deeper level. Why do you think this should be?

You might suggest that we are just hypocritical or that we often consciously hide our true feelings to protect ourselves or others. This may certainly be the case at times, but quite often people are quite *unaware* that what they *say* differs quite a lot from what they actually think and consequently how they actually act. The concept of implicit theories can offer some important insights into why this should be so.

02 Careful research can often be wildly at odds with the implicit theories that people hold to account for everyday things and events in their world.

Research (done mainly in psychology) suggests that we all hold what are called 'implicit theories'. These are sets of beliefs or assumptions that we are not necessarily fully conscious of and that we may even find hard to put into words. Nevertheless these theories or beliefs can have an enormous impact on how we act and react in everyday situations. They are different from the kind of theories that you will have learned about in teacher education courses or from textbooks about teaching and learning.

Researchers and academics develop theories based on the careful collection and investigation of evidence over time. These 'expert' theories that are the result of this careful research can, however, often be wildly at odds with the implicit theories that people hold to account for everyday things and events in their world. For example, experts may insist that research clearly demonstrates that we don't catch a cold through going out with wet hair, but try convincing your mother or grandmother of that!

To translate this into classroom practice, if you were to ask teachers what kind of teaching methods were best for effective learning in the classroom, it is most likely that they would talk about the kind of methods that they have been taught in initial teacher education courses, or have read about in books on education. These explicit or espoused theories are the expert or academic ones. They will also be able to give very good reasons why these methods are, indeed, currently considered the most effective. They will even genuinely believe that their teaching is closely informed by these very methods. But if you have the chance to observe these same teachers in action in a busy classroom situation, especially when the pace is frantic and things are happening very quickly, you may well find that many act in ways that are not in fact compatible with the academic theories they have just espoused. What is more, they are probably not even aware that this is happening. This is not hypocrisy! It is just that their *implicit* theories, rather than the expert, academic theories they have learned about, are the ones that are guiding how they act.

The 'implicit' nature of implicit theories

What exactly do we mean by implicit? Just as there are certain actions that we perform automatically without even thinking about them (like putting one foot in front of the other when we are walking or changing gear when driving) there are certain beliefs, attitudes, theories or assumptions that are automatic and which, without us thinking about them, or being particularly aware of them, can strongly influence how we act.

03 Oliver Sacks.
(Photograph ©
Nancy Crampton.)

In his book "**An Anthropologist on Mars**", the neurologist Oliver Sacks gives a good example of the implicit nature of these thoughts or beliefs (or in this case memories) that can have such an impact on our actions. Sacks describes a patient whose short-term memory had, because of a brain tumour, completely disappeared. Although he had no problem remembering events prior to the onset of his illness, present events left absolutely no trace in his memory. Each day Sacks would visit his patient, shake hands with him and introduce himself. Each day the patient, who had no recollection of who this visitor was, acted as if Sacks was a total stranger. On one occasion the neurologist, as an (admittedly rather cruel!) experiment, concealed a needle in his hand, and as the patient shook hands with him, he stuck the needle into the patient's palm with enough force to make him exclaim and draw his hand away in obvious distress and pain. After this incident, although the patient clearly continued to have no memory of who Sacks was when he entered the room each morning, as soon as Sacks held out his hand, the patient would draw his hand sharply away. When asked why he was reacting in this way, he was completely unable to give a reason. The explanation is that although he could not say *explicitly* what was causing him to act in this way, at some deeper level there was *implicit* memory of the pain that Sacks had caused and it was this implicit memory that was now influencing his actions.

In the same way, the implicit theories we hold can influence us in numerous important ways.

Where do our implicit theories come from?

Clearly the example given above is an extreme one. Nevertheless, even when our brains are totally healthy, we are quite often equally unaware of the influence of our implicit theories on our actions. Part of the reason for this is when and how our implicit theories are formed.

It is generally believed that our implicit theories are formed at a very early stage in our lives. We get our ideas about how the world operates, about such things as the relative importance of effort and ability in achieving success, about how important it is to be competitive or collaborative, and about what kind of personality qualities are desirable from the ideas parents and teachers pass on to us from a very early age. Primary school teachers in particular have an important part to play in the kinds of implicit theories children develop about such things as the nature of knowledge, whether or not everyone can succeed, how challenging tasks are interpreted and whether or not such things as ability and personality are fixed or can change over time.

Knowledge is absolute	Knowledge is tentative & uncertain
Exists outside the 'knower'	Cannot exist independently
Consists of isolated facts	Consists of integrated concepts
Is handed down by experts	Is constructed
Is acquired quickly by some	Is gradually acquired by all

04 Two ways of
- organizing a
05 classroom.
(Photograph 05
by MadMaven/
T.S.Heisele.)

06 Views of
knowledge.

Why are implicit theories important?

The implicit theories which we develop through these early interactions are important because they impact upon all aspects of our lives and in turn influence many aspects of our own teaching. This applies to general issues as well as to those specific to the design & technology classroom. The kind of implicit theories that we as teachers hold are particularly important because of the messages that we in turn can give to children.

Even such a simple thing as the way our classroom is laid out will give powerful messages about what we implicitly believe.

Think of a classroom you know well.
Where is the teacher's desk?
Is it clearly visible at the front of the classroom, or is it hardly discernible among the pupils' desks?
Is there even a separate desk and (more comfortable) chair that clearly belongs to the teacher?
Are the pupils' desks arranged to face the teacher's desk?

Are they arranged so that pupils are encouraged to work predominantly as individuals or as groups?

These things can tell a great deal about a teacher's implicit beliefs about how knowledge is constructed and evaluated, where knowledge resides and how it occurs as well as implicit theories about personality and motivation.

Views of knowledge

Classroom structures that emphasise teacher control suggest an implicit theory of knowledge as absolute, (i.e. there are right and wrong answers) that it is passed on by experts (the teacher) and that pupils learn best through listening, watching and absorbing this expert knowledge. It also suggests an implicit view of pupils who are lacking in motivation - unless kept under constant and strict surveillance - who are intrinsically lacking in curiosity or interest and who are unable to construct knowledge for themselves. Structures that emphasise pupil autonomy and interaction, on the other hand, suggest very different implicit theories - ones in which knowledge is uncertain and constructed through active interaction both with the environment and with others within social situations. It also suggests an implicit view of pupils as self-motivated, curious and interested in learning for its own sake.

Entity Theory	Incremental Theory
Intelligence is innate	Intelligence is acquired
Intelligence is fixed & stable	Intelligence is flexible
Intelligence is global	Intelligence is context specific
Intelligence can be measured by tests	Intelligence can be demonstrated in many ways

07

07 Entity and incremental theory.

You can also tell a lot about implicit theories by little things like the kinds of questions teachers ask.

> Think about the kind of questions you ask pupils. Are they predominantly questions to which you, the teacher, already know the answer? Is the role of pupils therefore to find out (usually in competition with each other) which particular answer you are looking for? Or are they predominantly questions to which there are several possible answers, with no one answer being 'correct'? In this case are pupils encouraged to discuss with their peers the various possibilities before making a contribution?

Again the first scenario suggests a very different set of implicit theories about both what knowledge is and how learning occurs from the second. Similarly, the kinds of tasks that pupils are asked to do and the degree of choice they have over what tasks are completed and in what order can give insights into the kinds of implicit theories held.

> Think about the kind of tasks you ask pupils to do. Are these open or prescribed? How much choice do pupils have either in which tasks they complete or the order in which things are done? What does this tell you about your implicit theories relating to knowledge and learning?

Entity and incremental theories

Carol Dweck and others have identified and explored the implicit theories that people hold about certain important personal attributes such as intelligence and morality. This research suggests that two distinct assumptions can be held. We may, on the one hand, implicitly believe that such attributes are fixed and unchangeable and that they affect all areas of our learning. Dweck calls this an entity theory. On the other hand we can implicitly assume that these are context dependent and can change and develop over time. This is called an incremental theory. Carol Dweck sums up the two theories as shown above.

08 Carol Dweck.

Whichever view we hold will have important implications for how we act. If we implicitly believe that intelligence is fixed and unchangeable, we are likely to react differently to pupils in a number of ways than if we have an implicit belief in the flexibility of intelligence - without necessarily realizing that we are doing this.

For example, our implicit theories about intelligence can subtly influence who is given praise - and for what.

Think about who and what you praise in your classroom. Is it the pupils who get the right answers and complete work correctly or those who take on challenging tasks and persevere in the face of difficulty despite making lots of mistakes? In other words do you encourage ability or effort? What do you think the implications of this will be?

If we hold an implicit entity view of intelligence, we will consider success to be a result of ability. This means we will automatically regard some pupils as intrinsically 'brighter' or 'smarter' than others and will see some as less capable of learning. Those who are considered able are more likely to feel encouraged and competent while those who are not are more likely to feel written off, overlooked or perceive themselves as failures. In turn, pupils who develop entity views of their own intelligence are more likely to avoid challenging tasks since failure at these will be interpreted as lack of ability. They are therefore less likely to persevere when the going gets tough. They will be concerned with how they perform compared to others rather than how much they are learning and improving in the subject. They will play safe and avoid risk in an attempt to appear competent at all costs. If we hold an incremental theory of intelligence, however, and encourage this in our pupils, we will more likely create an atmosphere where learning (rather than performance) is emphasized, where pupils will put success down to effort and where there is acceptance of challenge and perseverance in the face of difficulty.

The above table summarises the impact of emphasizing performance or learning goals in classroom situations.

Our implicit theories can even influence how we react to the way that pupils behave. When a pupil disobeys an order, for example, or acts in an apparently aggressive manner, our immediate reaction can give us some insight into the kind of implicit theories that we hold. If we immediately come to the conclusion that this is a disobedient

Performance goals encourage:	Learning goals encourage:
Competition	Self-improvement
Comparison with others	Personal growth
A focus on appearing competent	Knowledge and skill acquisition
Avoidance of challenge	Acceptance of challenge
A focus on ability	Acknowledgement of effort
External control (e.g. by rewards)	Self-control
Helplessness in the face of difficulty	Optimism in the face of difficulty
Low self-expectations	Constructive self-criticism
Low persistence	Persistence

09

09 The impact of emphasizing performance or learning goals in classroom situations.

or aggressive person, we are implying that these are personality traits that are global and fixed - i.e., an entity theory of personality. We will be more likely to keep an eye on the pupil, expecting him or her to be disobedient and aggressive in other situations. If our immediate response is that the pupil didn't obey because s/he didn't understand the request or wasn't listening, or was acting in an aggressive manner because s/he was frustrated or some other reason related to the context in which the behaviour occurred, then this suggests a very different implicit view of personality - one that regards it not as fixed and global but flexible and context dependent - in other words, incremental. In this case we will have very different expectations for the future behaviour of the pupil. This in turn will influence how the pupil acts.

Think of some incidents from your own experience. What was your *immediate* reaction?
What does this tell you about your own implicit theories of intelligence and personality?

What areas of design and technology can our implicit beliefs impact upon?

Our implicit theories can influence all aspects of our classroom practice but there are some

aspects that are particularly relevant to the teaching of design & technology. For example, just as we can hold entity or incremental theories about intelligence and behaviour, we can hold similar theories in relation to creativity, a construct which is considered central to the teaching of design. We can implicitly regard creativity as something that someone has naturally, a personality quality that is global and fixed and which can be easily measured (just like intelligence). That is, we can implicitly hold the theory that there is such a thing as a creative person and that creativity will manifest itself naturally whatever the context. Or we can implicitly see it as something which can be acquired by all pupils, a quality that can be developed through practice and instruction within a supportive, collaborative context. Again, what we implicitly believe will subtly influence how we teach and how we react towards individual pupils in our class.

If we hold an implicit *entity* view of creativity we are more likely to control and structure tasks for all but those considered most 'creative'. We are more likely to be concerned with developing carefully structured time frames for completion of the work and with guiding pupils through a carefully structured, linear design process. Within this framework, the artifacts of pupils perceived as 'less creative' may be used for demonstration purposes in an effort to help them 'keep up' with the rest of the class whilst the artifacts of those regarded as naturally creative may be held up as examples of best practice which others will never aspire to meeting! The focus of the final evaluation is more likely to be the *product* rather than the *process* of design. Risk-taking will be subtly discouraged and challenge kept to a minimum while social comparison and competition will flourish. If we hold an incremental view of creativity, on the other hand, we will encourage all pupils to develop their own ideas at their own pace and within their own time frame. Design will be regarded as an idiosyncratic and messy activity and evaluation will more likely focus on the process and progress of each individual rather than comparison with others. Within this framework, the emphasis is on individual pupil choice, challenge and risk-taking. Within this ethos, social comparison and competition will be discouraged.

Think about your own design & technology classroom. How does it compare to the two different scenarios described? If some of your teaching is based on a rotational circus so that you get a group for only a limited period of time before the pupils leave and you begin teaching another group, what effect will

that have on the way you teach? Over such a sequence of lessons do some pupils produce a product quickly and then need to be found additional activities whilst others just never finish? Is there a way of using time so that both product and process can be given appropriate emphasis in ways that encourage creativity, autonomy and risk-taking for all?

The very nature and purpose of design & technology education and its place and role in the curriculum is another area where implicit theories will exert a subtle but important influence. For example, if design & technology education is implicitly seen as a haven for less academic pupils, or a means of producing a future work force with manual skills, it will be presented very differently than if it is implicitly regarded as an entitlement for all.

How do you think these different implicit beliefs might influence the way that design & technology is regarded and presented?

> Read through the examination specifications for the focus areas you teach. Are there any clues as to the implicit theories adopted by the examining body? If so how might these influence the classroom?

Design & technology is a complex subject involving a wide range of activities chosen to meet the particular learning criteria. Some will develop making skills, some designing skills, some technical or aesthetic understanding, some appreciation of the relationship between technology and society. Achieving breadth and balance across this range within the context of national curriculum requirements or the demands of an examination specification is no easy task. Some of the decisions you make will be as a result of your implicit beliefs, but others will be made for you by others. These others will in turn be influenced by their own implicit beliefs. If design & technology education is regarded as essentially vocational, or suitable mainly for less academic pupils, for example, there is likely to be a greater emphasis placed on practical tasks, on skill development and on the production of 'well made' artifacts at the expense of other possible aspects. However, if design & technology is seen as an entitlement for all, there will be a clearer recognition that all young people live in a technologically mediated world and that one of the functions of design & technology lessons is to enable them to engage in informed debate about the nature of this world and how it influences their lives. There will also be the recognition that the act of designing and making is primarily a powerful means of cognitive growth for all as opposed to an activity preparing some young people for a career in the manual trades. These differing positions will almost certainly influence teaching methods. A practical, vocational model, for example, automatically lends itself more to methods involving teacher demonstration and transmission of facts and skills, with pupils following similar carefully prescribed learning outcomes. An entitlement model, on the other hand, lends itself more to methods which encourage active participation through collaboration, reflection and debate.

How can we tell what our own implicit theories are?

If, as I suggested at the beginning of this chapter, our implicit theories are difficult to express and may not even be within our conscious awareness, you may well be wondering how we can possibly know just what implicit theories we hold. There are a number of ways that can help us become more aware of our own implicit theories, although it must be stressed that this can sometimes be difficult to achieve.

10 | 11 | 12

Metaphors often
used when talking
about education.
10 A lion tamer.
11 A gardener.
12 A coach in a race.

Uncovering our own implicit theories can also be uncomfortable - especially if we really did believe that we were indeed 'practicing what we preached'. It is probably only through attempting to explore these, however, that we have any real hope of fully controlling what governs our actions in the classroom.

Since implicit theories appear to develop at an early age, one way of making implicit theories more explicit can come from exploring early memories of our own educational experience.

Think about your earliest classroom experiences. Think about how the classroom was set out, what qualities were encouraged by the teacher, what kinds of things attracted praise, and how you were made to feel about learning. This can help to give you clues about the kind of implicit theories that you now hold. Talk to a friend or write in detail about these early experiences. This can go some way to helping you determine what kinds of implicit theories you absorbed from your earliest classroom experiences. You can do this with both general classroom experience and your early experiences of design & technology classrooms.

Another way is to explore the kind of *language* that you use when talking about your experiences of school, both as a pupil and a teacher. When we talk naturally we tend to use metaphors without really being aware that we are doing this. An exploration of the metaphors we use in ordinary everyday conversation when talking about such topics as teaching and learning, schools and pupils, can often give us important insights into the implicit theories we hold.

The pictures above suggest some of the more common metaphors that are often used when talking about processes pertaining to education. It is not that we explicitly think about teaching being like becoming a lion tamer in a circus or a gardener or the coach in a race, but the kind of language we use can help us see what implicit theories lie behind the pictures that the language conjures up.

 Think about all the words and images relating to gardening that are used in describing schools or the processes of teaching and learning. Write these down.

You probably thought of things like ideas 'taking root', 'budding' and 'flowering'. You have probably remembered that we talk of early schools as 'nurseries' or 'kindergartens'. Metaphors of growth and nurturing abound as children 'blossom and grow'; and ideas either 'bear fruit' or 'wither on the vine'. However, if you think about this more deeply, a number of different implicit assumptions also come to mind. If we extend the metaphor we can learn a lot more about the possible implicit assumptions underlying the discourse. Gardens, for example, can differ dramatically in how formally they are laid out and where the focus of control for growth lies. Are all the plants that are of the same type grouped together? Are plants laid out in neat rows? In either case what happens to the weeds, or those plants which for whatever reason don't seem to fit in? Are some plants more highly prized than others, and therefore more carefully nourished? Where does the control over growth reside? Are plants carefully watered, pruned, fed and weeded or left to flourish in a more wild and natural state? Are plants allowed to support each other symbiotically, with intervention from the gardener only when necessary? What are the implications of these different types of garden for when there is no gardener constantly present to nourish and tend? In the former scenario, does growth stop and do the plants wither and die helplessly because all nourishment has come from a source outside them? By a detailed unpicking of this kind of extended metaphor, we can begin to get a clearer idea of the different implicit theories underlying them.

Quite often we use metaphors that give us a powerful insight into our view of knowledge and education without even being aware that we are actually using metaphor. Listen to the kind of language that you use (or that others use) in the classroom or in casual conversation in the staff room. Do you, for example, talk about children having to try hard to *'catch up'* or describe them as *'falling behind'*? When talking about learning do you think that some children can *'pick things up easily'* or *'catch on quickly'*? These may demonstrate implicit theories of learning as a competitive race and knowledge as something which is factual, concrete and 'out there' rather than learning as collaborative and knowledge as socially constructed, uncertain and contested. The kinds of metaphors we adopt can therefore powerfully define all areas of our teaching including how we structure our classes, how we view knowledge, how we define and structure instruction and the kinds of pupil-teacher interactions we encourage.

Think of the different metaphors that are used when describing schools (e.g., a factory; a zoo;

a prison). What implications do these different metaphors have for how learning and teaching is viewed? Reflect on the kind of metaphors that you use automatically, when talking about your pupils or your classroom, and consider what these tell you about your own implicit theories.

Can we change our implicit theories and if so how?

Becoming aware of our implicit theories is clearly not an easy task. It can take a lot of hard reflection on our own actions and careful analysis of our own discourse to begin to become aware of the implicit theories we hold. But what if we do begin to have an insight into our implicit theories? Can we then control them, or even change them to bring them into line with the theories we espouse?

Implicit theories *can* be difficult to change, partly because we have generally held them for so long and partly because once established they form frameworks within which new information and experiences are constructed and evaluated. New information which backs up our implicit theories is therefore much more easily noticed and remembered than

information which appears to challenge or contradict them. This type of information is more likely to be automatically rejected or ignored. This doesn't mean, however, that we are at the helpless mercy of our implicit theories. As they are evident in action, a careful and reflective analysis of our actions can help determine how great a mismatch there is between what we actually do and what we think we do in classroom situations. The greater the mismatch between the two, the greater is the need for a conscious attempt to change. If, for example, you really believe that you adopt an active, constructivist approach to learning but actually spend much of your time making sure that you know everything there is to know about a topic before you feel confident to teach it, then your implicit theory of learning may be rooted in an expert transmission model which is very different from the one you espouse. The evidence will be in the way you teach. Do you use your expert knowledge to guide pupil conversations so that they construct for themselves an improved understanding or do you use your expert knowledge to provide correction? Being aware of this can help you to consciously act in a different way, a way that is more consistent with the kind of teacher you would really like to be.

Ask a colleague whom you trust completely to observe you in the classroom. Ask them to note down details of the content of your lesson, the teaching methods you use, the kinds of questions you ask, what you give praise for, the kind of help you give, the language you use etc. (If possible a video tape of your lessons can be a powerful vehicle for this type of analysis). Give some really deep and careful thought to how much your actual actions reflect the theories you espouse as opposed to those you hold implicitly.

Of course even when we become aware of our own implicit theories and how they are influencing our actions, that may not be the whole story. Things will still be complicated by the fact that the people who are responsible for writing policy documents, and for running schools and design & technology departments, will all have their own implicit theories and these may well be in conflict with the implicit theories which you hold. Although this can clearly cause enormous problems, unless you are first of all aware of what your *own* implicit theories are, you are unlikely to be able to even begin to address this particular problem.

An important first step, therefore, is to attempt to become familiar with the implicit theories which influence your own actions in the classroom. Only then will you be in a position to determine to what extent they are in accord or in conflict with the implicit theories underlying policy and the organization of particular schools and departments. With reflection and through practice over time, you will therefore, hopefully, become more confident that, unlike Calvin's mom and dad, you are taking the first steps towards ensuring that you do indeed 'practice what you preach'.

Further reading

If you want to explore the idea of implicit theories in more detail (and find out more about what your own implicit theories might be), then I would recommend the following books. These are very accessible and interesting as well as being highly informative.

Dweck, C. (2000). "Self Theories: Their Role in Motivation, Personality and Development". Columbia: Columbia University Psychology Press.

Yero, J. (2002). "Teaching in Mind: How Teacher Thinking Shapes Education". Hamilton, Montana: MindFlight Publishing.

Design & technology: seeing both the wood & the tress

Peter Toft

Dr Peter Toft HMI is Ofsted's specialist subject adviser for design & technology. He oversees its inspection in English schools and from this formulates accounts, for government and practitioners, of the standards pupils achieve and how effectively it is taught, managed and resourced. He has had various assignments in HMI, prior to which he held teaching, management and research posts in secondary, further and higher education and was an author and chief examiner.

Design & technology: seeing both the wood & the trees

Peter Toft

Introduction

Design & technology became compulsory in the English National Curriculum for maintained schools in 1992. It was the product of a sustained period of innovation in various parts of the country's education system which gathered momentum after the mid 1960's but began much earlier. Various strands of this evolution were discerned by Don Porter HMI (1), writing in 1967:

'The present situation may be seen…as the outcome of almost a hundred years of evolution.
The workshop (and domestic) crafts began as a pastime, but as changes inside and outside the schools influenced educational policy, they were regarded as pre-vocational, scientific, aesthetic or simply as a necessary ingredient in general education. Recent developments naturally draw attention to the scientific and technical possibilities of craftwork. It is, however, essential to keep in mind the recreative and aesthetic value. A study of the history of the crafts in schools suggests that they might serve several purposes simultaneously…'
'The story of technical education in secondary schools has similarly veered from course to course. It was first regarded as a means of passing on skill and technical knowledge to future artisans, bolstering to some extent a dying apprenticeship system. Later, its importance for the future employers and officers in the armed services led to interesting schemes being introduced, especially in certain of the independent schools. Then came a long period of relative neglect until gradually the significance of what was called "the practical approach" was realised. This principle underlies many of the recommendations of official reports, from Hadow (1926) to Crowther (1959) and Newsom (1963), but at first it presupposed the identification and segregation of those who could best learn in a practical way into particular schools. The significant feature of recent developments is that we now have, for first time since 1895, substantial support for the idea that some form of technical education must become a part of the general preparation for life which the secondary schools provide, that it is not something to be reserved for the artisan, the manager or the designer, but an essential part of secondary education for all.'

Don Porter thus identified two significant themes which have influenced the recent development of design & technology and which are very much alive today. These are that:
• the subject is taught to achieve a number of differing and sometimes conflicting objectives; and
• it has evolved into a widely accepted part of general education for all pupils in maintained schools.

The subjects' evolution after Don Porter's seminal report was fed by various initiatives in schools, teacher training establishments, examination boards, local authorities and HMI. Some of this took place in major national projects. The Schools Council Project Technology, directed by Geoffrey Harrison, was set up in 1966:

*'to encourage technological activities in schools
and thereby develop a range of abilities and
provide motives which are often overlooked
by more traditional approaches.'* (2)

Scientific, engineering and design dimensions
were added to the craft activities then
common in schools. A wide range of new
teaching materials and procedures extended
craft teaching. It was complemented by the
Schools Council Design and Craft Project.
This ran from 1974 under John Eggleston's
leadership to increase the relevance of craft
subjects to students growing up at that time,
to modernise provision and to develop
designing. Other major projects followed
both before and after the establishment
of the National Curriculum. The Gatsby
charity funded the Technology Enhancement
Programme which has taken, for example,
modern industrial technology and presented
it so that teachers have been able
to incorporate it effectively in their teaching
of design & technology.

More broadly, the Royal Society for Arts,
Manufactures and Commerce was influential
in raising the profile of practical capability
in the country at large through its
"Education for Capability" manifesto towards
the end of the last century. Through this,
the view was widely publicised that:
*'There exists in its own right a culture which
is concerned with doing, making and organising
and the creative arts. This culture emphasises the
day to day management of affairs, the formulation*

*and solution of problems and the design,
manufacture and marketing of goods and services.
Educators should spend more time preparing people
in this way for a life outside the education system.
The country would benefit significantly in economic
terms from…Education for Capability.'*

Much influenced by these and other
initiatives, design & technology was given
a major role to play within the National
Curriculum. Initially, it was called 'technology'
and it brought together aspects of the teaching
of five contributory subjects: art & design;
business education; craft, design & technology;
home economics and information technology.
After a decade and a half of evolution and
consolidation within the subject, the nation's
needs are changing, and with them the
curriculum. Design & technology has now
become optional within the 14 - 16 age range.
Vocational courses are being developed
for those in the 14 - 19 age range.
The Department for Education and Skills and
the Qualifications and Curriculum Authority
are reviewing various aspects of the National
Curriculum and a policy of personalising the
curriculum is being implemented. It is very
timely, therefore, for teachers to take stock
of design & technology in this changing
context, to examine its underlying principles
and to attempt to distinguish 'the wood from
the trees'.

This publication for teachers should contribute
significantly to such a stock taking. It should
also lead to a deeper understanding of the

subject and the complex issues with which teachers, managers and policy makers need to grapple when making decisions about its further development. As the scope for teachers to engage in curriculum development increases now that the National Curriculum is becoming more flexible and new dimensions such as the vocational are added, the publication should provide teachers with material to stimulate their critical thinking and capacity to innovate, to improve classroom practice and to keep under review, in a knowledgeable way, the case for general education to have a substantial technological dimension.

The wider context of design & technology

David Barlex starts the book off by considering how design & technology has been justified in the curriculum in recent years. The architects of this subject in the National Curriculum were originally charged by ministers to view technology as that area of the curriculum in which pupils design and make useful objects and systems with a range of materials and technologies, including those in use in modern industry. Students were to learn effective methods of working, including the use of ICT and also to work within realistic financial and technical constraints. The subject subsequently developed the aim of enabling pupils to learn to live effectively and creatively in the made world and contribute to the shaping of this world.

Most subjects have something valuable to add to this wide focus on the made world, so what is distinctive about design & technology? A key characteristic is that, within the realm of technology, it helps students to 'know how' as well as to 'know that'. They should develop design & technological capability by learning and applying knowledge and skills, both from technology and other disciplines, through a series of progressively demanding technological projects in which they design, make and evaluate functioning products or systems. The subject is essentially practical and creative, and is more concerned with shaping the world we live in than with understanding it.

Technological capability has increasingly been seen as useful for life in a knowledge economy. David Barlex shows how it encourages students to isolate key issues in complex situations; seek out and apply relevant knowledge; make decisions and value judgements; think creatively in developing new proposals and learn something of the art of project management and how to make things happen. Beyond this, other commentators argue that students should develop a critical understanding of the moral and political context of technology, for example in how finite resources are exploited or how market forces influence the ways in which technology is used to create wealth and support our way of life. In such a view design & technology should focus more on students learning to judge the validity of human purposes as well as on realising these purposes by using technology to develop functioning products.

In the daily life of a secondary school, with its busy routines, crowded curriculum and the need to provide effectively for learners of all abilities, what are teachers to make of this range of aims for the subject? Is there a danger of overloading design & technology? How could other subjects be encouraged to contribute, especially in developing critical awareness of technology? How could smarter planning of the curriculum help to secure this?

The curriculum and its subjects evolve as times and conditions change. Whilst in the throes of change, it helps practitioners whether they are teachers, examiners, curriculum developers or inspectors to have a clear view of the distinctive features of subjects at any one point in time: without this, it is difficult to convey a coherent picture to students or to teach them effectively.

Within Ofsted, when drawing up our evaluation programmes for this subject, we currently make a number of assumptions about design & technology. Readers are invited to consider these as a workable means of developing a framework which is clear, coherent and manageable and within which effective schemes of work can be prepared. These assumptions are:

- Technological capability, along with other characteristics such as language and scientific enquiry, separates us from other species. As Bronowski wrote: 'Man…has a set of gifts which make him unique among animals so that, unlike them, he is not a figure in the landscape - he is a shaper of the landscape'. (3)
- Design and technology was developed to teach technological capability in general education. The compound noun 'design & technology' was carefully chosen by the subject's architects. It shows students that, within this subject, the act of designing takes place within technological contexts.
- Designing is an intellectual process. It brings into being ideas intended to be made real and which meet our needs or purposes. The ideas will have the potential to be created in practice otherwise they would be little more than fantasy.
- Designing is more than planning, problem-solving and invention. It generally involves the solving of problems, often a number at a time. It goes beyond this, however, as the student considers values and attitudes and how to meet human needs.

Designing will usually require planning, as the immediate driving force for action, and this will take place at various parts of a project. Usually, designing builds on that which already exists. Occasionally, however, it exploits the invention of something new. Even when an invention has been conceived and patented, as in James Dyson's cyclone technology, designing has to take place thereafter to translate the invention into a functioning product, such as the carpet cleaning machine which some people might need and buy. Designing is rarely a linear activity. It is often tentative and iterative and it progresses, usually, through a series of approximations until an acceptable product is developed.

- Technology is a collection of powerful forces which help us maintain and improve our life support systems, especially when practised through industry. We assume that design & technology is an important part of general education for students growing up in our culture. It can help them to develop technological awareness, understanding and capability. These should help them to live effectively in, and help to shape, the made world and also prepare them for a productive career. In the words of John Mattick HMI, writing in 1988 (4): *'I suggest that to be a cultured person today means having some perception of technology, some awareness, understanding and capability.'*

- In England today, design & technology education is intended to reflect these points. It is also influenced by the inheritance from decades of practical education in this country. This includes the specialist teacher skills, resources and accommodation which are an embedded feature of English schools. These form powerful opportunities for the subject, as well as constraints, not least in the emphasis we put on developing practical capability within the focus areas of food technology, resistant materials, textiles and systems and control.

Marc de Vries begins his careful analysis of the nature of design & technology by showing that though technology is regarded as benign to humans, it can also be malign. This complex issue is rarely featured in the teaching which we observe in design & technology lessons. For some, this is an opportunity missed to engage students in speculating about future possibilities, since creating things for future use lies at the heart of the subject. It also sidesteps reflection about the extent to which technology is a neutral force or whether, in itself, it encourages humans to behave well or badly towards each other.

Marc de Vries gives valuable leads to those who are developing or evaluating curricula for the teaching of design & technology. He identifies four perceptions of technology, each of which is embodied within our subject. These are:

- technology as artefacts, each having a structure which is related to its function, with function sometimes having unintended features;

- technological knowledge which, though having similarities with other bodies of knowledge, has the distinctive features of being concerned with effectiveness, with how things should or could be and with 'knowing how' as well as 'knowing that';
- technical processes, through which we design, make and test things. These are complex and variable and there is no universal 'design process' for all technological activities, although formally structured processes are useful at stages in students' learning;
- technology as a means to achieve human purposes. These are, again, complex and subject to differing and often conflicting values which can be easily distorted through the use of false premises in arguments.

Various practical issues flow from this. There was a period in the early phase of National Curriculum design & technology when inspectors and others became very concerned about how technology was being interpreted. Some courses were based on the assumption that students should only be taught technological knowledge and skills as and when they needed them to complete a project. This subverted standards of design & technology capability in two ways: firstly, it discouraged teachers from using sequence and progression to promote rigorous learning and application of technological knowledge and skills; and secondly,

it underestimated the very significant practical difficulties of teaching a potentially different set of knowledge and skills to each student in a class when they were developing different designs. Some of the early and open ended schemes for National Curriculum design & technology floundered because of this and other misconceptions about the nature of technology, leading to a significant loss of technological rigour in students' learning.

One theme which has run through design & technology course development has been how to deal with two types of knowledge:

1. contextual knowledge which relates to the design need being tackled and which could involve studies across a range of subjects; and
2. core technological knowledge which relates to the specific technologies being used for the solutions.

A control system for a greenhouse, for example, needs contextual knowledge about horticulture as well as core technological knowledge about control systems. How well do you think each of these types of knowledge would be promoted by (1) students learning and researching independently, and (2) students being taught the same content in class groups?

In 2006, after a survey of how food technology was being taught within the National Curriculum for design & technology in English secondary schools, Ofsted reported (5) on a fundamental clash in teachers' minds between teaching about:

1. healthy eating and effective cooking on the one hand; and
2. developing food products to be marketed to meet consumer demand and make profits for a company's shareholders.

Given what Marc de Vries has written about the nature of technology, you might like to consider your views of the inspectors' conclusions:

'In essence, a tension exists between teaching about food to develop skills for living and using food as a means to teach the objectives of design and technology which needs to be resolved to remove many teachers' confusion.'

Continuing to examine the wider context of design & technology education, Stephen Petrina's polemic on the politics of technology paints a thought provoking if dystopian picture of the near future. The collision of corporate and individual interests in the control of technology lead him to argue forcefully that technology is not neutral but that it serves the interests of the powerful. This links with and goes beyond Marc de Vries' explanation of how technology is a device to advance human purpose. Stephen Petrina argues that human purpose, however, like the control of technology is currently very much under the influence of corporate bodies which are not necessarily working in the interests of individuals. He believes that students should be made aware of this and be encouraged to discuss its implications for them and society. He argues strongly that more open sources and open access technology, for example software, should be widely used in schools, and also that, ultimately, the technological choices made now will have profound implications for our descendents.

Inspections of the teaching of graphic products within design and technology in the secondary phase often highlight courses in which students are asked to promote a given product by developing packaging and a 'point-of-sale display'. Some teachers are concerned that this kind of work encourages students tacitly to accept advertising and marketing as essential activities in our consumer society. What are your views on this, in the light of Stephen Petrina's paper?

How should students in secondary schools be taught about who controls technology and the choices made as this control is exercised? Which subjects might be best placed to contribute to this?

Steve Keirl continues with this consideration of the wider context of design & technology. He examines the complex relationships between teaching and technology in a political democracy. Touching upon aspects of globalisation, the market economy and the knowledge society he highlights how many competing interests influence design & technology. He explains that these change in time and that the context is complex. He argues that we can all, as participants in design & technology education, help shape its future, though some will have more power and more self awareness than others to do so. Like Marc de Vries, he explains how design & technology has a coherence based upon the teaching of a series of linked skill areas, an understanding of the impact of designing and making, and the development in students of the will to act and create. He believes that the subject's contribution to education is all the stronger when these aspects are combined within a collective professional vision of the subject. Such a vision is a necessary basis for the subject community to hold and argue for a coherent philosophy and place in the curriculum. Whilst not all teachers may want to be visionaries he makes a strong case for them to develop this aspect of their professionalism.

This point is increasingly being recognised among design & technology teachers now that the National Curriculum requirements are being reduced and schools are given increasing scope to innovate and personalise the curriculum for their students. He argues further that teachers intending to innovate need to make time for professional development which, arguably, would include considering the many issues raised in this book. Interestingly, our own recent inspection evidence has shown a number of design & technology departments in which such professional development has gone well beyond what Steve Keirl calls results-driven *'performance training sects'*. In such departments, teams of teachers are forging ahead in the provision of modern design & technology and students are achieving high standards. Our evidence suggests that such departments are as successful as they are for two main reasons. These are: the high calibre and efforts of the design & technology specialists; and the effectiveness of senior managers in creating school climates in which the students are well motivated and can see clear value in learning what is taught, both overall and within the technological domain.

Sustainability and design & technology

One increasingly important part of Government policy in England is to develop education for sustainable development (ESD) in the curriculum. This concept touches upon various subjects, not least geography, and its importance for design & technology is discussed by Margarita Pavlova and James Pitt. They make the telling point that if all of mankind lived as we do in the UK, we would need the resources of three planets. Various remedies are given such as population reduction, reducing use of resources, improving the efficiency of our uses of resources. All add up to the concept of sustainable development both for present and future generations, about which much has been expressed across the globe.

They consider the contribution which design & technology might make to ESD. They outline the Department for Education and Skills policy for sustainability in education, noting that design & technology should contribute significantly in five of its eight 'doorways' to sustainability:
1. food and drink;
2. energy and water;
3. travel and traffic;
4. purchasing and waste;
5. buildings and grounds.
Our inspections show that such areas are sometimes considered in design & technology project work, though there is much to do to make such work consistently thorough across the country.

They outline a distinction. On the one hand, ESD is a policy in which pupils are invited to consider sustainability issues in some projects.

On the other hand, ESD is a frame of mind in which students might routinely be expected to consider the deeper causes and motives which underlie our wasteful use of planetary resources. They propose conducting product life cycle analyses in depth as a way of encouraging students to think deeply about sustainability. They argue that students need to be involved in the analysis of our underlying motives for acquiring products and consuming resources.

Concern over the use of resources, and whose purposes are served best by it, are related to a broader issue covered in the parable "The Tragedy of the Commons" (6). This seminal work was first published in 1833 but its basic premise - that things which are held in common to the most people are the least well cared for - was originally coined by Aristotle. The parable shows that when specific resources are freely available they became over exploited and depleted because individuals doing this maximise their own benefit with little heed to the cost of over exploitation which is borne by the majority.

Encouraging students to consider these matters is very important. This will not be simple however. We know from our inspection evidence that design & technology is highly popular among students because of its active, practical nature and the scope it gives them to develop and realise their own ideas. We also know that many head teachers regard its well managed practical learning

as a stabilising force in their schools. It would be most unwise to lose the motivation and involvement created by the activity of designing, making and testing functional products. This implies that, often, teachers will need to encourage their older students, especially those in the 14 - 19 age range, to consider sustainability within their designing, making and evaluating. For younger students in the 11 - 14 age range, who generally follow courses which are more tightly controlled by their teachers, the actual projects set will need to refer specifically to sustainability to ensure that it is effectively covered. Many students, as the authors acknowledge, may be resistant to this and effective methods will need to be developed. Some teachers have succeeded in capturing the imagination and youthful zeal of their students to grapple with sustainability in design and make projects, but this does require careful planning and persuasion, and for teachers to be well informed.

How might you develop your design & technology curriculum to incorporate rigorous thinking about sustainability without losing the intrinsic interest pupils have in their current designing and making? How might you do this in conjunction with the teachers of other subjects?

Vocational education and design & technology

Like ESD, education for vocational development is a growing and increasingly justified force in design & technology. During much of the fifteen year history of design & technology in the National Curriculum, the subject has been taught as a confirmed aspect of general education. As such, it is popular among students. It covers technological 'know how' which might form a basis for further vocational or specialist study. In the wake of the National Curriculum, many vocational or specialist courses in fields such as catering, construction, control technology or motor vehicle technology have disappeared but in recent years they have begun to reappear. This is as part of government policy to improve the skills of students entering the workforce in an increasingly competitive, globalised economy. Vocational education has been brought back to prominence whether in the form of specialist GCSE courses or diplomas in areas such as engineering or hospitality and catering, or in a broader swathe of 'work-related learning' activities.

John Dakers casts a critical eye on the emerging vocational situation and its implications for design & technology.

He has a particular concern about the traditional role played by its craft-based antecedents in providing largely for less capable pupils. There is, of course, no necessary reason for vocational courses to be provided only or mainly for less capable students. If this were the case, how would universities be able to justify teaching such highly vocational subjects as law or medicine? Nevertheless, he is concerned about past experiences in schools where often vocational education has been reserved for the least able students. He asks searching questions about how limiting certain kinds of vocational courses to less capable students might reduce the opportunities for advancement which might be afforded by studying the more highly prized academic courses. He also notes in an historical analysis that there may be a correlation between the social status of students and the extent to which they veer towards general, academic courses or those of a specialist, vocational nature.

Whatever the correlation, the current government policy is to develop vocational education for some students in the 14 - 19 age range and, by 2013, that 90% of school leavers will be expected to have a vocational qualification by the age of 16. The aim is to equip them to survive in and contribute to the workforce, through which we create national and personal wealth. One particular facet of this is the current concern in some industrial sectors about the difficulty of recruiting staff to work at craft and technician levels. We will all have heard of recent shortages of crucial specialists such as plumbers. We may also appreciate how these shortages are to an extent being filled with staff from overseas and that some argue this is because we have not trained enough British people to do them. The Sector Skills Council for Science, Engineering and Manufacturing Technologies (SEMTA) has invested much time in helping to develop the vocational GCSE course in engineering with the clear aim of encouraging up to ten thousand additional students per year to enter craft and technician level engineering employment. This might be seen by some as encouraging premature specialisation. It is clear from our inspection evidence, however, that many secondary students find vocational provision increasingly attractive because of its relevance to their future economic well being.

John Dakers makes a strong case for design & technology to be seen as part of general education and not as a vocational activity. Its continuing place in the National Curriculum for pupils in the 5 - 14 age range, and its continuing popularity as a GCSE subject, reflects the view that design & technology is a general subject. In Ofsted, we routinely observe the subject being taught in this generalist way whilst helping students learn about modern industrial production and its use of resources, together with aspects of consumerism. This links closely with vocational education. In addition, though, design & technology does provide a basis

for further specialisation in activities requiring 'know how' as well as 'knowing that' within a range of vocational fields. In our view, it would be most unwise to sever the clear connections between generalist design & technology and specialist vocational courses: we do not see them as mutually exclusive. It would be equally unwise for teachers of design & technology to ignore the connections that exist between our subject and the many related aspects of the fourteen vocational diplomas currently being developed.

> How can the broad educational aims of design & technology (promoting, for example, investigating, solving problems, creativity, critical evaluation, project management) be brought into vocational provision for 14 - 19 year old students in such a way as to help develop their capability in the chosen vocational areas?

Creativity, designing and problem solving in design & technology

Over the years, Ofsted's reports on school design & technology have highlighted problems in the teaching of designing. In 1999 (7) we reported that:

'Pupils generally understand the main stages of the analytical and linear approach to designing used in design & technology by most schools. Pupils use a design brief, usually provided by the teacher, to guide their thinking as they design products to fulfil an identified need. In many schools, however, attainment is limited because pupils spend too much time on superficial work associated with the presentation of their design portfolios at the expense of the main core of designing and making activities. At best, pupils use their knowledge and understanding to develop a design specification and plan the stages in production of the products they have designed. They are then able to evaluate the quality and effectiveness of their solutions rigorously against this, sometimes showing highly innovative ideas.

A higher, but decreasing, proportion of pupils design in more superficial ways so that, for example, having copied from textbooks or worksheets, they fail to demonstrate understanding of the materials, components and processes they will use. These pupils have to rely heavily on step-by-step instructions from their teachers and the evaluation of their work is less objective, expressing personal opinions rather than making an objective analysis of their work against design criteria.'

For 2006 (8), we were able to report, for some schools, an improvement in this state of affairs:

'More generally, capable and enthusiastic teachers develop and follow schemes of work based on a range of modern and interesting "design and make" projects. They use a range of methods to stimulate students to think and to include all class members, including, for example, brainstorming, structured group discussions, reference to the work of professional designers, makers, chefs and engineers, and to previous design & technology work completed by former students. Teachers are responsive to individual student's reactions in lessons and are quick to incorporate their preferred ideas in class discussions. By direct and focused questioning, they ensure that all members of classes participate and they value their contributions. In all of this, good behaviour, and a well controlled school are important in establishing very inclusive conditions within design & technology.'*

Some of this improvement in the teaching of designing, and its link to making, has been influenced by the National Strategies Key Stage 3 initiative for design & technology; this emphasised ways to improve the teaching of designing. Nevertheless, our inspection evidence shows a continuing need to improve the teaching of designing in many schools, as well as a need to improve the way it is externally examined. The contributions by Malcolm Welch on the practice of designing and how pupils learn to design are thus very topical. They are thought provoking in showing the sheer breadth of creative activity which we call designing and how this draws upon a wide range of considerations and contributes to our quality of life and profoundly influences our culture.

Over a century ago, one of the key ingredients in the successful teaching of crafts in classes in schools was the development of systematic method. The one-to-one method of instruction followed by individual practice had worked well in apprenticeship and domestic learning. It was clearly impractical in schools given their student: teacher ratios. To make craft teaching more systematic, De La Vos in Moscow analysed tool processes and constructional techniques. He reduced workshop operations to fundamental sub-processes and arranged them in a sequential order of difficulty for pupils to learn skills progressively. To achieve this he had to analyse the knowledge and skills needed for specific tasks, to be fully aware of essential procedural steps, decide what knowledge would effectively reinforce skill acquisition and which teaching methods would be most appropriate. The series of exercises produced made it possible for one person to teach many pupils in a short time, with some degree of confidence in what might be learned and with the ability to assess and offer necessary remedial help. To facilitate this each pupil had his own kit of tools and work-station. This method was developed further by Professor Woodward in Chicago, from where it filtered into England (9).

The design & technology community has inched forwards in recent years towards similarly systematic methods for the teaching of designing. In doing so, it has recognised that the methods of designing are more complex, iterative and unpredictable than those for making. This requires more caution in developing systematic teaching methods than it did for making. Malcolm Welch's considered analysis of where we stand now will be of great interest to teachers who are striving to improve the effectiveness of pupils' learning to design. He tackles complex issues including dealing with ill-defined problems, constructive thinking, the modelling of ideas and relevance to students, before moving on to an exploration of what pupils need to learn in designing.

How confident are you in the effectiveness of your methods of teaching pupils the skills of creative designing? Is there a case for you to be more systematic? If so, how would you avoid dampening among your students any flash of inspiration? Such inspiration, rare though it may be, is unpredictable and may challenge conventional thinking. This was seen when Sony's designer of the Walkman was initially castigated for producing a 'tape recorder' without a recording function or a loudspeaker.

How should teachers deal
with such an eventuality
in their own classes?

One of the aims of design & technology in
the National Curriculum is to prepare students
to be able to use and understand changing
technologies. The use of computers is well
established in the subject, for example, in
information retrieval, data analysis, controlling
systems and computer aided designing and
manufacturing. In fact, inspection evidence
continues to show that design & technology
is a highly prolific user of computers
compared with other subjects. Increasingly,
many students are becoming proficient
in the use of powerful software programs
for designing. Some of the product and
engineering designing carried out in the 14 - 19
age range is very sophisticated and, to an
outside observer, seems extremely impressive.
Such computer-aided design (CAD) does much
to raise the apparent productivity of students.
This is hardly surprising since CAD
programmes are now in widespread use in
industry to raise the productivity of designers.
We need to be careful here, however, and to
ask searching questions about the real impact
of CAD on students' actual design
& technology capability.

What do teachers and
examiners need to do
when assessing students'

attainment in computer-aided
designing to distinguish their
real designing capability from
that which merely reflects
the capability of the
hardware and software?

Creativity is inextricably linked to designing.
It also lies at the heart of students' capability
in making. It is a competence which the
government currently aims to promote in
schools, not least because of the importance
to the national economy of the creative
industries. In a very useful analysis, David
Spendlove and Marion Rutland identify four
areas in which creativity should be expected
in design and technology. These are:
concept, aesthetics, technical and construction.
They helpfully stress that creativity requires
self motivation, skills of creative thinking,
skills within the area of practice and an
acceptance that pupils need help to develop
in these three ways. As with Malcolm Welch's
contribution, they outline a range of strategies
to promote creative thinking. Amongst these,
they recognise a critical issue. Unfortunately
many of our teachers do not because they feel
impelled to teach their students to pass
examinations by following sequences in
projects in such a way as to maximise their
marks. For the writers, however, this critical
issue is that students need time to think, make
associations and reflect. Our evidence shows
that the importance of gestation time is barely

recognised in the short modules common in the design & technology curriculum for students in the 11 - 14 age range. They are rarely given the chance to think ahead in such courses by being given an introduction to the next task before the current task has been completed. Creative thinking is rarely neat and though it can be aided by good structure in teaching it is not formulaic. David Spendlove and Marion Rutland stress this, as well as the need for good classroom management.

Ofsted's evidence shows very clearly the importance of structure in projects, good classroom management and high expectations of students to think creatively. Creativity tends not to thrive in chaotic classrooms. Thus:
'Pupils in a highly performing suburban school studying GCSE food technology worked from design briefs through product development to quality control. Design briefs were appropriately challenging and provided realistic context for product development which motivated pupils. They were encouraged to pursue individual lines of enquiry and think creatively: this developed their skills and confidence as independent learners. Research was tightly tailored to the project specifications and supported by the use of templates to keep it purposeful and analytical. All pupils understood nutrition well and could link some of what they were doing to what they had learned about food materials in science. They also had a good general understanding of healthy eating and felt confident to make their choices in their practical work. All carried out detailed computer-based nutritional analyses of their products,

using appropriate software. They modelled other industrial practices effectively, for example, in using digital images of their work recorded by web cam on the food labels for their products.' (10)

Moshe Barak makes a similar point in his examination of strategies, schemes and heuristics to promote problem-solving in technology education. He stresses that problem-solving occurs within a context and will depend on a student's past experiences, and that constraints, rather than a loose and random flow of thinking, encourage creative problem solving.

This is well illustrated in a recent review by Ron Rigby of the control technology course developed in Doncaster and Manchester schools for students aged 14 - 16, prior to the National Curriculum. (11) This practical course was taught by pairs of staff from craft, design & technology and science departments. Students worked at their own pace through a series of investigative assignments covering a range of fields such as structures, gears, electricity, rectification and pneumatics. Each assignment had its own follow up sheet, which the students could use to check their work. Designing and making projects, initiated by teachers and pupils, were central to the course. Students were presented with tightly defined problem solving exercises throughout.

As an example of the ingenuity a single design brief could generate in the classroom, a local authority inspector, on a routine visit to observe control technology in a high school, was invited by a student to set him a problem. He stated that tropical fish were kept at his home and as he was to be away for two weeks and was in need of a gadget which would automatically deposit a measured amount of fish food into the tank each morning at day break. The student who had requested a design problem subsequently informed him that the problem was solved and he could collect the 'fish feeder' at any time. This student, very troublesome in other subjects and with difficult home circumstances, was later employed in the electronics industry and after a few years set up a successful technology business in Canada. He had clearly found the realism, technological rigour and the tight, problem-solving structure within which control technology was taught very helpful in his own creative development.

As Moshe Barak notes both convergent and divergent thinking are required at various times as students solve problems. He outlines a number of very interesting strategies in which students can be encouraged to solve problems effectively and he argues convincingly that such strategies need to be taught systematically.

The similarities between the chapters of this book on designing, creativity and problem-solving need to be stressed. Each is written from a specific angle and each is packed with insight from which teachers would profit through deeper study. When teaching you may find it profitable to combine practice from each area if you are to maximise the effectiveness of learning to design.

> What are the implications for teaching which the chapters on designing, creativity and problem solving have in common? How might you build these into your schemes of work?

Before moving on, another perspective on these matters needs to be considered. Various pieces of research carried out by Richard Kimbell and his colleagues have been very helpful in enabling us to clarify how designers think and make decisions in, for example, dealing with complex tasks, modelling possible ideas and thinking as a client might do. Their work has made a fundamental contribution to our understanding of how students might think whilst designing and how we might reliably assess their designing capability. Those interested in these fields, may find Richard Kimbell's seminal work of 1997 of interest. (12)

Making skills and technological knowledge in design & technology

As design & technology evolved from the previous craft subjects, students were increasingly expected to design as well as to make products. This combination has made the subject more complex to learn, not just because there is more to learn, but mainly because when students design products they tend quite rightly to generate designs which are unique to themselves in one way or another. In a class of twenty students, each wanting to make something different yet each needing to learn new making techniques and technological knowledge before they do so, it is easy to lose sight of the value of pre-planned class teaching to cover knowledge and skills efficiently and to make the most efficient use of scarce time. This becomes an issue of classroom management. Teachers resolve it by balancing the aim for pupils to design individually with the need for the techniques being used to be restricted to what a class and teacher can cope with safely and effectively. Without such management, an inverse relationship creeps in between the quality of making and the range of design ideas generated: the broader this range, all other things being equal, the less sophisticated will be the making techniques and the quality of finished products.

Frank Banks and Gwyneth Owen-Jackson look at this difficult issue from a number of directions. Do students always have to make their designs? Does this limit their creativity? Do they always have to design what they make? How can students be supported through designing, and also through making? Are there solutions in CAD CAM?

The compound noun 'design & technology' was selected to name this subject in the National Curriculum in order to emphasise that design and technology capability included a rounded capacity to design and make products within various technological fields. In some countries the emphasis is put on 'technological literacy' often developed by academic studies of the scope and effects of technology. In our country we have striven to combine 'knowing that' with 'knowing how' to develop practical and technological capability. We aim for students to learn by doing to be 'design & technologists' rather than simply to learn about this subject by observing, drawing and writing about it.

Inspection of design & technology in schools over the years points to an indispensable role for making. The subject is very popular among pupils in the compulsory school age, largely because it is active, practical and enables them to develop their own ideas into functioning products. However, it is expensive to teach given the costs of materials and equipment, and the fact that class sizes need to be small to secure the health and safety of students. In some schools, the teaching of making is undermined by shortages of specialist teachers, especially in food technology and systems and control. Moves to downplay the importance of making or to reduce the technological challenge of making with difficult materials or complex equipment, would no doubt be attractive to those struggling to recruit specialist teachers or working to reduce the costs, but this would seriously undermine design & technology education.

More fundamentally, however, to sideline the making of functioning products would destroy the coherence of the subject. To design without making or by making only concept models have places, as suggested, at times in a course. To do this universally, however, would be like teaching students to compose music without allowing them to play it and judge how good their compositions were. Students would not be able to judge the quality of their design ideas with any reliability if no functioning product or system had been created to test. Furthermore, to be able to design but not make, like being able to make but not design, would render it difficult to achieve the aim of enabling students to develop all-round design and technology capability, and in doing so, become able to operate effectively in, and to help to shape, the made world.

Another key aspect of comprehensive design & technology capability is the way in which it is reinforced when students learn technological knowledge effectively and apply it appropriately as they design, make and evaluate products and systems. Our starting point within Ofsted is quite simple: design & technology without the requisite technological context and knowledge does not readily justify its place in the curriculum. In the early days of the National Curriculum, we observed lessons with depressing regularity in which classes were working on such a wide range of tasks within widely open-ended themes that technical content became trite. Alan Smithers and Pamela Robinson, in a research paper (13), hit the nail on the head in declaring that:

' (the main) reason why technology in schools seems so elusive is that it embodies the aspirations of a number of different interest groups which have been kept together only by pitching its objectives and content at such a high level of generality that it can include almost anything. If it is to be given shape and substance as a subject then agreement will have to be reached at the much more difficult level of detail.'

Defining technological knowledge and determining the most effective ways of learning it and appropriate ways of applying it are not straightforward, however, and the paper by Gwyneth Owen-Jackson and Torben Steeg considers the ramifications of this.

They make a number of telling points:
1. work in this subject relies on 'tacit knowledge' of the kind pupils absorb when for example handling materials or modelling ideas;
2. technical knowledge is wide in scope and often draws upon content from other subjects, especially mathematics and science;
3. that we need to distinguish between knowledge about the design problem and the knowledge required to create solutions;

4. that students need to be guided to discover the appropriate technical knowledge;
5. teachers have a clear duty to bring this about;
6. that pupils learn best when they interact with the knowledge and construct their own meanings from this interaction;
7. that learning, according to some, takes place in a specific context and for pupils it becomes bound to this context, making transfer of learning, for example, between subjects or projects difficult.

These points are critical for teachers and you will need to consider them carefully as you plan courses, despite the fact that external examinations will determine, to an extent, the content you expect your students to learn. Design & technology has evolved partly through the amalgamation of subjects and partly through the addition of modern and 'hi-tec' content. As a subject community, we have during this evolution, encountered a problem which has recurred generally as the curriculum expands, namely that as subject content becomes broader, and time available and the efficiency of teaching remain stable, there is a tendency to lose depth. The review of control technology courses in the period before the National Curriculum already noted gives a clear picture of the depth of technological knowledge which was learned and applied and which was, arguably, deeper than that which is achieved in some current GCSE courses.

This is partly why it is so important for Gwyneth Owen-Jackson and Torben Steeg to emphasise, as they do, that technical knowledge is important not just so that pupils can design and make effectively but also so that they gain a better insight into how our technological world works and how they can contribute to this.

One oft mentioned way of strengthening the technological rigour of design & technology is to develop its connections within the curriculum to mathematics and science. Various projects and schemes have contributed widely to this very difficult matter in recent years, not least the Technology Enhancement Programme, the Engineering Education Scheme and the Young Engineers competition. Students participating in such schemes have had significant opportunities to work on real design & technology projects, often under the guidance of specialists from industry and sometimes drawing in depth on knowledge from mathematics and science. Within STEM (science, technology, engineering and mathematics), a wide range of activities currently runs throughout the country to help schools to strengthen such interdisciplinary activities.

Dov Kipperman and Mark Sanders carefully examine the case for such activities and in doing so they note that:
1. there are various ways in which the school curriculum can be organised partly to reflect the interdisciplinary nature of the real world;

2. that much research and theory indicates that learning can be enhanced when cross-curricular links are carefully planned and reference is made to the learning in other subjects;
3. that various development projects here and overseas have shown how this can be achieved; and
4. that such plans require teachers to be aware of what is being taught in the related subjects in order to promote successful learning for their students.

Activities linking design & technology with mathematics and science are such a good idea, they beg the question of why they are not more prevalent in schools already.
The writers consider this and outline how schools use subject disciplines as a convenient way of planning and timetabling teachers.
In secondary schools, the barriers to cross-curricular planning created by subject organisation can be formidable. Our inspection evidence indicates that even where teaching in design & technology is very good, and teachers are well aware of, for example, the science underlying what they teach, that collaboration with science departments can be very difficult. Thus in a recent report (5), on Food Technology Ofsted noted:
'Even in the very best courses seen, there was very little evidence of effective joint curriculum planning between food, science and business studies teachers, to enable pupils to apply in food technology what they had learned in science, mathematics and business studies. Schools missed opportunities

to increase pupils' insight and sense of connection between subjects by synchronising the teaching of the theory, in science or business studies, with practical applications in food technology. This was reflected in the following example from a mixed ability Year 10 class.

The lesson dealt with gels, suspensions and foams as colloids. References were made to some of the chemical properties of eggs. Pupils at one stage perked up when volunteers were called to use different whisking techniques to create foams and compare characteristics. The lively question and answer session which followed showed reasonable gains in pupils' knowledge. All the pupils were studying science, yet no attempt was made in planning or teaching this lesson to link colloids with what they had learned in science about elements, molecules, compounds and mixtures and how colloids, as examples of mixtures, related to the basic chemistry.'

At a deeper level, a very well researched, if deeply depressing, account of the political influences on, and in-fighting between pressure groups within, science and technology education in England after 1945 was published in 1985. (14) Gary McCulloch et al showed just how difficult it can be to bring about change. This is especially so when pressure groups from subject areas, and within subject areas, have very different perspectives on what constitutes high status knowledge and who should teach what. They were shown to put the interests of their pressure groups above those of students as they ploughed their own partisan furrows rather than collaborating with others for the good of all.

Kipperman's and Sanders' paper should help teachers and planners to develop equally effective ways of overcoming barriers and they quite rightly stress that this will only happen if someone takes the initiative and ensures that managers and potential collaborators from the other subjects are persuaded to participate with enthusiasm. Given the essentially interdisciplinary nature of technology in the world at large, it would seem to be well worth the effort to forge such developments and the writers' advice on how to do so is very sound. Despite the difficulties revealed by Gary McCulloch's research, there is plenty of evidence that success can be achieved in forging effective collaboration between subjects: it does require additional effort, however.

Gender in design & technology

Another fundamental issue for design & technology teachers, which is deeply influenced by different perspectives, is that of gender. Great strides have been made since the era when girls' and boys' crafts were separate entities. This has been supported by the feminist movement, legislation on equal opportunities, specific curriculum projects in the 1980's designed to make technology education appealing to girls,

and the subsequent development of design & technology as a subject for both girls and boys. Although entries to GCSE continue to show that most candidates for electronics are boys and most for textiles are girls, significant numbers of girls and boys respectively choose resistant materials and food technology and in graphics the situation is close to even. This represents a large shift since the 1970's when home economics was almost exclusively restricted to girls and technical studies to boys in secondary schools.

Patricia Murphy's paper on gender and pedagogy takes us some way forwards from the simple concerns of recent years to make design & technology attractive to pupils of both sexes. She focuses sharply on the differing perceptions which both teachers and pupils have of the subject, how it should be taught and how boys and girls expect to behave when they study it, and on how gender differences emerge in teaching and learning. Drawing upon research findings from neuroscience, she refers to the subtle ways in which children learn and develop meaning based on the collection of their own experiences and their interactions with others. In this context, gender is better understood as socially constructed. Teachers can be observed, depending on their sensitivity to pupils' needs and their intention to help them personalise their learning, both reinforcing gender stereotyping or teaching in such a way as to help both boys and girls to progress through activities with which they may be unfamiliar or uncomfortable because of their own perceptions of what constitutes masculine or feminine behaviour.

There are, of course, other important aspects of gender. A recent American publication (15), drawing on current research in genetics and brain-imaging, indicates that, almost from conception, the brains of boys and girls differ. These are ground breaking ideas and they do encourage us to exercise caution when we assume that gender differences in our pupils are very largely a function of learning and cultural pressure: there may well be biological differences which would cause us to question some of the assumptions which we currently make about gender stereotyping.

Also, the difference in performance between boys and girls in design & technology, especially in the GCSE examination, is very marked. Within Ofsted we are concerned about this. Our reports have referred to this regularly over recent years. Girls out perform boys significantly in attaining the higher grades of A* to C and the gap between them has been around 16 - 17 percentage points in England for some years. A recent reduction in this gap is encouraging but there is much for students, teachers and examiners to do to improve the performance of boys. Our inspection evidence is clear on this: the lower achievement is not just caused by a few disaffected boys with socially deprived backgrounds who are demotivated by some design & technology provision but a wider

group of boys. This, together with the more general educational and social reasons for the underachievement of boys needs addressing. Many less able pupils, and many boys, find the desk-bound and paper-based investigative, design and evaluation work required by GCSE boring. Many girls, in contrast, find it appealing. Does this mean that, to an extent, we have feminised the design & technology curriculum? Some boys tell inspectors they would prefer a greater emphasis on practical and technological skills. For them, these are seen as relevant to the craft and technician level careers, and occasionally to professional careers in engineering, to which they aspire as well as to the prospect of applying such skills in their future home lives.

> Given the current drive to promote personalisation and choice in students' learning, especially in the 14 - 19 age range, are we doing enough for the development of that significant minority of pupils, including some boys, who are currently not well motivated by design & technology?

The design & technology teacher's role in assessing students' work is complex, partly because of the variety of activities which learners engage in and also the breadth of the subject content. Recent years have seen much development in the ways in which teachers are advised to assess their students' work, not least in the activity of formative assessment within the wider context of "Assessment for Learning" (AfL). Stephanie Atkinson and Paul Black give a lucid account of how current AfL practice, which is based on research evidence, can be effectively used by teachers. They draw out very clearly the aspects which are of particular importance in design & technology. Teachers will find that the advice contained in such a chapter will have implications for their teaching and for the involvement of students which are at least as significant as those for gauging students' progress. They conclude with a cautionary note, which is well backed up by the evidence from inspections: developing this approach to assessment can have a profound and positive impact on learning but it requires much thought and management and is probably best carried out by teachers working in a team rather than as individuals.

In a chapter which touches upon all of the others in this book, Wendy Dow outlines how our professional beliefs and actions can be shaped by 'implicit theories' which we hold but do not fully recognise. The consequence can sometimes be that our actions, especially when we are under stress, do not always match our expressed beliefs: we don't necessarily practice what we preach. This has important implications for the way teachers perceive and relate to students or to one another as well as for how they view the subjects they teach and the kind of learning activities they set.

As your read the chapters in this book, including this one, try to identify signs of implicit theories held by the authors. A good start would be to look at the various sections on designing: is there evidence of an implicit theory that designing, being related more to the intellectual, professional and 'white collar' world of industry is more valuable to our subject than making, which is related more to the practical, manual and 'blue collar' world of industry? If so, what are the implications for inclusion: how well might this implicit theory serve the interests of all kinds of pupils, including those who struggle with intellectual designing but excel in practical making?

Another useful exercise would be to look at mixed ability teaching which is common in design & technology for a variety of reasons and, according to our evidence, generally accepted by teachers of the subject. Try working on this with a colleague. Where mixed ability teaching is espoused by this colleague and he or she believes differentiation by outcome is effective, attempt to gauge how well in his/her lessons, teaching and learning are actually differentiated in practice?

The possibilities of critical evaluation of your own performance or for other aspects of the design & technology department in which you work are very considerable and I would recommend a review of implicit theories as part of any rigorous subject self-evaluation. As Wendy Dow indicates, however, recognising implicit theories, and dealing with them once identified, are difficult tasks: this is a good reason for carrying out such self-evaluation with colleagues who might more clearly recognise your theories once they are put under the spotlight.

Making it happen

Teaching in a secondary school is a demanding business. Design & technology, with its wide subject breadth and the crucial requirement to manage diverse activity and complicated equipment whilst securing the safety of students, makes it even moreso. In such a situation, you are more likely to turn your intentions into reality and make an impact as a new teacher if you manage your contribution effectively.

Nick Baldwin and David Barlex deal with this aspect of management to make things happen in their paper on developing your own curriculum. They outline the main conditions which are generally met when design & technology provision is effective, note the crucial importance of team work and stress the need to campaign among students, parents and senior managers to demonstrate the educational value of studying our subject. They make it clear that the most successful teachers of design & technology are likely to be those who, having mastered the basics of teaching the subject, are willing to develop wide professional interests and a willingness to see vistas beyond the confines of their own classrooms.

Conclusion

This book contains a collection of carefully considered papers covering our evolving subject. Each paper has raised a number of important issues, some which have actual or emerging solutions and some which are as yet unresolved. Some of these will require action at a national level but many are within the scope of thoughtful design & technology teachers refining practice in their own schools.

I would like to conclude this commentary on the content of the book by highlighting some key issues which our inspection evidence indicates need dealing with, both by teachers and those with wider responsibility for the development of design & technology.

Sustainability

There are differing opinions about how we should best deal with emerging problems associated with climate change, the pressures put upon our planet's natural resources by industrialisation in developing countries and the continuing rise in the population. They range from reducing consumption at one end of the spectrum to developing new technologies which make better use of resources at the other end.

- What role can the teaching of design & technology play in helping students to contribute to the various potential ways of solving these problems?

Globalisation

In the National Curriculum, design & technology is related in part to ways in which manufacturing industry supports our way of life. Manufacturing is changing, however, and much of the mass production of basic products has moved overseas. Despite this, there continues to be an advanced manufacturing base in this country, though it continues to shrink, and also a great deal of wealth produced through design and creative activities.

- How should design & technology evolve to remain relevant to the needs of students preparing to be adults in this evolving economic context?

Technological Change

The National Curriculum "Importance of Design and Technology" statement (16) declares that *Design and technology prepares pupils to participate in tomorrow's rapidly changing technologies'*. Advances, for example, in robotics and nanotechnology are routinely referred to in the media, including those publications read by some teenage students.

- What should be done to enable the subject community of design & technology teachers to keep abreast of technological developments and draw them into their teaching? Who should do this and how should the priorities be decided?

Technological Rigour

As the subject has broadened in scope since its antecedents before the National Curriculum it has not generally been given extra teaching time to cope with this.

One of the consequences, in many schools according to our inspections, has been a decline in technological rigour and often a loss of some of the more challenging making processes such as those associated with high precision engineering.

- How can teachers preserve and restore technological rigour within this very broad subject?

Differentiation and inclusion in teaching

The majority of design & technology courses are taught to classes of mixed ability. Often this is because schools or teachers believe this to be the most effective method of organising the teaching of the subject. Generally, in the 14 - 16 age range, when schools provide a wide range of design & technology courses, it is difficult to organise effective ability grouping. However, our inspections have pointed out that often teaching is not well differentiated in such classes and does not challenge the least and, especially, the most able students sufficiently. For some students, this is insufficiently inclusive. Also, the performance of boys lags significantly behind that of boys, especially in the GCSE examination. This is a general problem among a number of subjects but it is particularly marked in design & technology.

- What can teachers and schools do to strengthen differentiation and personalisation in design & technology courses, and in doing so, help to further the inclusion of students and the aims of the government policy "**Every Child Matters**"?

- What can be done to raise the performance and levels of motivation of those boys who are not achieving what they are capable of in design & technology?

Education for 14 - 19 year old students

Major changes are being planned for the courses being offered to students in this age range, including the provision of more vocational learning.

- What practical steps can design & technology teachers take to ensure that the subject evolves, whilst retaining its basic integrity, to remain relevant to students as they have an increasing range of vocational courses to follow?

These issues, together with the many issues raised by all of the contributors to this book need resolution. However, they will not all be resolved overnight. The introduction to this book emphasised that the collection of papers is meant to be dipped into and revisited in response to your needs as a teacher. So it is with the issues raised: you will find it most useful to consider which appear most relevant to your work in hand. Furthermore, and again as stressed in the introduction, the place of subjects in the curriculum is always contested. As a design & technology practitioner, you will be better prepared to teach courses which are valuable and relevant to your students, and to defend these courses when they are contested, the more you are able to consider the issues raised in this book. This will be effective to the extent that you can grasp the various and sometimes conflicting objectives which design & technology is intended to meet. In doing this, you will need carefully to separate the wood from the trees. I wish you well in this important endeavour.

Peter Toft HMI is Ofsted's specialist subject adviser for design & technology. He has written this chapter in a personal capacity.

ACKNOWLEDGEMENT

I am deeply indebted to my former HMI colleagues Mike Ive OBE and John Mattick for their very helpful suggestions on the content of this chapter.